ECO-SOLUTIONS

ECO-SOLUTIONS:
A CASEBOOK
FOR THE ENVIRONMENTAL CRISIS

Edited with Introductions
by Barbara Woods

SCHENKMAN PUBLISHING COMPANY

Cambridge, Massachusetts

Distributed by General Learning Press

Schenkman books are distributed by
General Learning Press
250 James Street
Morristown, New Jersey

Library of Congress Catalog Card Number: 78-183952
Printed in the United States of America

The American problem (of pollution and environmentalism) is enormous, but it is absolutely tailored to the American genius. To solve it needs energy, resource, invention, and a certain ruthlessness. I shall have been a very bad observer and a worse prophet, if America is not only of comparison less polluted in ten years' time (than now).

C. P. Snow, 1971

To My Parents

Acknowledgments

The preparation of a book of readings has its tedious side. The editor's life is not all gaiety and excitement. Helping in the more onerous aspects of this undertaking were Nancy Thompson and Polly Ferraina, crackerjack typists, Michael Murphy, talented draftsman and Maureen Osolnik and Mary Klatt, keen-eyed readers. Finally, special thanks are due to Neil Kleinman, editor and publishing expert.

CONTENTS

INTRODUCTION

There are cycles to the frenzies of public concern that strike America. Sometimes they center on foreign threats, sometimes on domestic threats to the nation's welfare. During the latter part of 1969 the United States allowed itself to be caught up in a new kind of public alarm. This latest crisis concerned man's destruction of his environment. What might be called the Year of Ecology (1969–1970) saw the public become sensitive to the way we have used this country's natural resources. This awareness culminated in the nationwide celebration of Earth Day, first held in April, 1970, and again in April, 1971.

Yet the sudden urgency of this concern does not reflect a new and imminent destruction of the environment; in many areas conditions have improved rather than deteriorated in the past decade.[1] Rather this concern represents a change in perceptions. We no longer accept pollution as an inevitable concomitant of progress. We see that we do not have an unlimited amount of natural resources. Most of all we are alarmed by the growing danger to basic elements which sustain life: air and water.[2] Perhaps part of this new-found impatience with environmental squalor can be ascribed to envy. Horizons have broadened. Trips to Europe and to new communities such as Reston in Virginia have begun to have an impact on public sentiment. Returning home from a healthier or more pleasing environment, one is more tempted to ask: "If they can do it, why can't we, here? now?"

The present broad support for immediate environmental action represents perhaps a typically American response to an identified but not as yet well understood problem. Historically we try to solve problems quickly rather than give in to passive, fatalistic suffering. Moreover, there is a growing suspicion that despite tight budgets, unemployment and stock market slumps, this nation is at last rich enough and knowledgeable enough to make an appreciable dent in our environmental problems. Certainly broad segments of the population, particularly the more affluent, have shown some willingness to pay higher taxes for less squalor. In past years the well-off have, in fact, paid the cost in lengthy commuting to increasingly distant suburban oases. Now they may be ready, if shown the way, to quit running and take on the surrounding mess.

The sense of impending crisis has been fed by a seemingly endless stream of apocalyptic literature on the perils of uncontrolled pollution, beginning in 1962 with the publication of Rachel Carson's *Silent Spring*.[3] In innumerable publications vivid examples of this alarmism can be found, each more frightening than its predecessor, covering every aspect of environmental pollution. Two of the most vivid are "Eco-Catastrophe!" by Paul R. Ehrlich,[4] and a terrifying playlet entitled "Last Gasps" by Terrence McNally.[5] Both extrapolate current trends into the not-so-distant future to dramatize what could happen to our world if we continue on our present course. McNally's drama is a series of brief scenes. Each begins at 11:59 and at the stroke of 12:00, when the air reaches a level of pollution incapable of supporting life, the actors give one last gasp for breathable air and failing, they expire.[6]

Paul Ehrlich, a biologist who has cancelled his long term insurance, provides a chilling preview of future environmental destruction: The end of the ocean came late in the summer of 1979.

By 1977 the annual yield of fish from the sea was down to 30 million metric tons, less than one-half the per capita catch of a decade earlier. This helped malnutrition to escalate sharply in a world where an estimated 50 million people per year were already dying of starvation.

Air pollution continued to be the most obvious manifestation of environmental deterioration. It was, by 1972, quite literally in the eyes of all Americans. The year 1973 saw not only the New York and Los Angeles smog disasters, but also the publication of the surgeon general's massive report on air pollution and health . . . suddenly our citizens were faced with nearly 200,000 corpses and massive documentation that they could be the next to die from respiratory disease.

And 1973 was also the year in which most people finally comprehended the indirect threat . . . Insect populations boomed because they were resistent to most pesticides and had been freed, by the incompetent use of these pesticides, from most of their natural enemies. Rodents swarmed over crops, multiplying rapidly in the absence of predatory birds. The effect of pests on the wheat crop was especially disastrous in the summer of 1973, since that was also the year of the great drought. Most of us can remember the shock which greeted the announcement by atmospheric physicists that the shift of the jet stream which had caused the drought was probably permanent. It signalled the birth of the Midwestern desert.[7]

All of us would feel better if Ehrlich could be regarded as a solitary crank preaching doom on street corners. After all, Rachel Carson was decried as an alarmist when *Silent Spring* appeared. But, unfortunately, Ehrlich has many gloomy colleagues. Virtually every major publication, and many technical and professional ones as well, has contributed scare articles, many of them written by reputable scientists, forecasting imminent environmental suicide by the inhabitants of Spaceship Earth. The most panicky suggest that no solution is viable short of an immediate rejection of our present life style and reversion to lower living standards. One author calls for banning the automobile, as well as trucks and buses, because the internal combustion engine is responsible for approximately 60 percent of the nation's air pollution.[8] The argument against the internal combustion engine as a dangerous anachronism[9] has been extended beyond the automobile's contribution to the pollution problem to include, among other things, its extensive consumption of land for highways, both destroying valuable open space and converting our urban areas into paved jungles, and its responsibility for 1.75 million American deaths since 1900—far more than perished in all the nation's wars—with an annual death rate presently nearing 60,000.[10] Some argue that the end of the gasoline engine would also mitigate the danger to sea life, which in spite of its apparent limitless expanse can easily be destroyed by continuing oil spills.[11]

The same type of drastic action is urged on the pesticide front. Recent research into the effects of DDT and other persistent "hard" pesticides indicates the probability, as Rachel Carson warned in 1962, that these poisons are already affecting wildlife and human beings in a number of potentially serious and almost unimaginable ways: genetic effects through chromosomal changes; tumors of the liver and lungs in mice; liver cancer, leukemia, high blood pressure, and carcinoma in humans with unusually high residues of DDT and related pesticides stored in body tissues.[12] In fact, most of the DDT ever used is still active in the atmosphere or locked in the soils ready to be removed by evaporation or by run-off into the sea—over 1 billion pounds of DDT are still in the biosphere. With a 10–50 year half-life remaining, the effects may well be horrendous.[13] One recommended solution: Ban *all* hard pesticides immediately.

Population is another area of major concern. Although present annual rates of increase in population have fallen to under one percent in the United States and much of Europe, growth is continuing at the rate of three and four percent annually in Latin America, the Philippines and other underdeveloped areas. The growth rate for the world as a whole has been accelerating in recent years from 1.1 percent in the 1920's to two percent in 1963 and an estimated three percent in 1970.[14] At the present world rate some demographers predict that by the year 2100 every acre of the earth's surface would be as densely crowded as New York City is today—except that we can probably count on horrible famines, foreseen by the late 1970's, to keep the population spiral down.[15] It was the crowded streets of New Delhi that started Ehrlich on his prophetic career, previewing the doom he foresees for all of mankind.[16] Drastic solution: Zero population growth with governmental intervention everywhere through tax incentives, bonuses, licensing procedures and other measures to limit procreation to two children per two adults.

If one grants the reality of the crisis that Ehrlich and so many others have described, the question is whether the kinds of visionary solutions proposed to date are really helpful. Certainly it is infeasible to call for banning the automobile and the elimination of all use of hydrocarbon pesticides until satisfactory alternatives have been developed. And government regulation of family size is presently unacceptable; even dictatorships have been unable to legislate births (although many have been expert at increasing death rates). Since much of the available literature dealing with these problems would have readers believe that only in drastic measures lie mankind's salvation, the public is understandably frustrated. The situation may be critical, but the public has not been persuaded to adopt extreme remedies; proposals for selling the family car and submitting to mass vasectomies have not yet caught on.

Perhaps one reason why this flood of environmental publications has not been wholly convincing lies in the strange failure to concentrate on developing sound financial data. Many scattered statistics are bruited about but there is little solid information on the benefits and costs of pollution control and on the financial side of remedial and preventive programs. The hard pressed taxpayer is simply warned that cleaning up the environment and preventing further deterioration of our natural resources will require vast sums of money with the certainty of higher taxes on his strained family budget and the implicit threat that other urgent social needs such as public education, health and welfare may thereupon be neglected. The worst of it is that the cost menace may be partly illusory. Proper bookkeeping would make vigorous environmental action much more saleable since the taxpayer is already paying a high, albeit difficult to measure, price to maintain a satisfactory quality of life in a heavily polluted world. The effects of pollution might be called disproducts: the loss of health and working effectiveness due to the strain of living under conditions of high noise levels and polluted air, the costly problem of disposing of some 3.5 billion tons of waste [17]—about five pounds for each man, woman and child in the United States each day—the stress on mind and body resulting from overcrowding and commuting in heavy traffic, all can be assigned dollar values. But at the same time, there are hidden costs: the destruction of natural resources and the loss of open space, the general ugliness of the landscape from uncontrolled development and the proliferation of high tension and telephone wires. These costs are harder to measure; nevertheless, the decrease in property values in areas with a deteriorating environment, when compared with rising property values in more attractive neighborhoods, is a financial reality. And while not problems of immediate survival, they do take their toll and cut deep into the public consciousness.[18] In short, good cost accounting which weighs disproducts against the price of effective preventive action might prove to the taxpayer that the cure is less expensive—in actual tax dollars—than living with the disease.

This collection of readings is based on a simple premise: the time for panic and visionary schemes is past. Given the circumstances of general unawareness and skepticism in which the initial scare literature was produced, it is understandable that many writers concentrated on catching the attention of an apathetic public by shock tactics. They focused on the most extreme and alarming examples of environmental deterioration—and God knows there are enough of them. We must acknowledge our debt to these pioneers since it is due in large part to their efforts that the nation has been aroused to the dangers inherent in its life style. But now it is time to go beyond consciousness-raising to practical action. If the United States is going to deal with its environmental problems quickly and rationally, it is imperative that all levels of government and every member of society begin thinking in terms of practical solutions—both short and long range—rather than indulging in an orgy of self-flagellation followed by confusion and apathy when drastic recommendations not surprisingly fall victim to resistance and inertia.

A more logical approach begins with a calm assessment of the nature and extent of the problems requiring urgent attention. These hard facts lead to three considerations:

(1) The current concern over environmental quality is more likely to lead to lasting accomplishment if the costs as well as the benefits of pollution control are made clear.

(2) An absolutely "pure" environment—with every river a mountain brook, every city blessed with desert-fresh air, and every species of animal protected against any possible ecological damage—is unachievable, except at a cost so monumental as to destroy most other aspects of our high living standards. As in other areas of human life, we must weigh benefits against costs and select the level of environmental quality that most nearly balances what we gain with what we lose. To view every use of pesticide or every emission of pollution as an absolute evil is neither realistic nor helpful.

(3) Because the costs of reducing pollution are so high, the efficiency as well as the effectiveness of pollution control programs must be given attention. The more efficient the program, the more pollution control we buy for each dollar spent.[19] Information has already been assembled in a number of areas and it is now possible to identify on-the-ground, field-tested solutions to environmental problems developed in the United States, Europe and elsewhere.

A review of the literature reveals, however, that while practical solutions exist for many environmental problems, a great many areas still demand extensive study, research and planning before we can be confident that we have enough definitive answers to deal effectively with these problems. Furthermore, new technological advances seem to breed new problems and new sources of pollution; current solutions may simply be inadequate for tomorrow's needs. Still, there are exciting technological possibilities that should provide us with new, and perhaps less expensive, ways of dealing with environmental problems. To begin, we can try to identify the approaches that have worked, while identifying the further research that is needed.

The present feeling of urgency has finally brought together the traditional conservationists and a large segment of the population. But now, before the current interest in environmental quality dwindles, government at every level and a concerned citizenry must not only commit itself to a policy of preserving a satisfactory environment but must assume a genuine responsibility for leadership in mobilizing the nation's skills and resources to solve these problems. In spite of the currently fashionable rhetoric of concern, the present administration—following the time honored tradition of its predecessors—has not matched its impressive rhetoric with the substantial programs and funding levels needed to reverse disastrous environmental trends.

The major focus of government is, of course, on the military which absorbed about 44 percent of the federal outlays in 1969 and 37.5 percent in the 1971 budget, still the largest single expense, although a significant reduction has begun to be made.[20] Until this imbalance can be altered, the United States will probably continue to be short of funds to effect sweeping environmental improvements. State and local governments are chronically short of cash, and private enterprise will not act responsibly without very large direct or indirect federal incentives.

Furthermore, however much it can be demonstrated that effective environmental action tends to repay its investment, and, however much it may be argued that environmental programs are necessary for sheer human survival, it must be recognized that proponents of housing, mental health, transportation, education, and poverty programs can each make an equally valid case for a larger share of the federal budget. It is not surprising to find that charges have been leveled to the effect that ecology is a suburban "cop-out," marking a gross neglect of the poor, their employment and other needs. So, at the very least, many are worried that shifting the nation's resources in a new direction will starve vitally important programs. The trouble, of course, is that the pot of money never grows fast enough to satisfy legitimate demands for federal funds.

The low priority accorded to environmental problems, by deed if not by word, is not a recent development; it reflects a situation which has existed for decades. A number of articulate groups—the National Audubon Society, the Sierra Club, and the League of Women Voters, to name a few—have put pressure on legislative and governmental agencies to gain recognition of environmental problems and the need to deal with them. Usually well-educated and well-connected, such groups cannot be ignored. But because they did not represent a sufficiently large voting constituency in themselves, and because they ultimately failed to mobilize the broad base of public support to compel forceful government action, the usual government response was limited all too often to the devices available to supple statesmanship—setting up prestigious study commissions and making thoughtful speeches indicating deep concern. Unfortunately only rarely has this kind of simulated action been followed by any substantially funded programs, particularly because action is confronted by a combination of inertia, red tape and outright resistance to regulations, to change, and to higher taxes—each in their own way deadly enemies of reform.

As long as environmental concern is limited to small segments of the population, government has been able to postpone significant action for long periods of time. Examples of these delaying tactics can be found probably in every area of the country. A typical instance and one of considerable national concern can be found in the long and fruitless efforts to clean up the Potomac River. In 1970, after 30 years of meetings, studies and resonant calls for action, a federal health official warned that the Potomac was "a severe threat to the health of anyone coming in contact with it."[21]

The dismal chronology of "The Great Potomac Cleanup" is a clear warning. The Potomac was one of the first targets selected for swift action after Congress in 1956 gave the United States Public Health Service the authority to proceed against interstate water pollution. At a federal interstate abatement hearing in August, 1957 representatives of the District of Columbia, Maryland and the federal government—Virginia refused to attend—agreed the Potomac's condition was deplorable. A follow-up conference was held in February, 1958, with Virginia participating, at which agreement was reached on major goals: 80 percent pollutant removal efficiency from the major sewage treatment plant that year and a major expansion of the plant to be completed in 1965. There were supposed to be progress report meetings every six months, but during the next eleven years clean-up efforts were submerged in a series of comprehensive studies on the Potomac River Basin. Federal and state agencies argued over jurisdiction while responsibility for water pollution was transferred from the Public Health Service in the Department of Health, Education, and Welfare to the Department of the Interior.

In 1968 Secretary of the Interior Stewart L. Udall produced a report which claimed to encompass all the previous proposals. Just before leaving office in January, 1969, Mr. Udall called for the reconvening in April of the Potomac pollution abatement conclave that was recessed eleven years earlier. In addressing the April, 1969, session, the new Interior Secretary, Walter J. Hickel, said:

> We are here today, to put it quite simply, because the recommendations for collective action approved by the conferees in 1957 and 1958 have not been fulfilled. The lower Potomac River is grossly polluted. It is a shocking example of man's mistreatment of a natural resource—a national disgrace.[22]

As long as ecology engages the interest of a small minority, the Potomac pattern is likely to remain a prototype rather than a mutant: speeches, studies, calls for action and programs quickly bog down in a quagmire of jurisdictional squabbles and financial starvation. But by 1969 for the first time a genuine, broad base of popular support for ecological action seemed to be emerging. The lonely pioneers who have fought almost alone now have the backing needed for substantive action. But one must add somewhat pessimistically that, while the job can be done, it must be turned to quickly before public attention shifts to other crises.

The readings selected here have been chosen because they present a concrete set of directions to be taken. They present solutions and approaches which can serve as models to government officials responsible for dealing with the nation's environmental problems. To the extent that models could be found, specific short or long term actions are described in these essays and demonstrate by their achievements that some approaches to environmental problems have achieved noteworthy success. The case studies can guide officials in determining what steps could be taken to best meet their needs and encourage concerned citizens whose enthusiasm has begun to wane in the face of protracted and frustrating delay. In short, the readings should provide incentives and examples to inspire action. The public, now pretty much sensitized to the environmental crisis, must be given assurance that possible solutions to these problems are available. The alert, knowledgeable citizen, by making known the extent of his understanding of the problem can bring forceful, sustained pressure to bear on officials responsible for pollution control and thus make it much more difficult for government to ignore, evade or postpone action.

It would be useful and encouraging if we could identify a long list of success stories in coping with environmental problems in the United States, the most affluent nation and presumably the one most capable of solving any problem demanding heavy expenditures. Unfortunately, it has been necessary to look to Europe and other areas of the world in which, although the standard of living is lower, greater progress has been made in solving—or avoiding—many of the problems Americans have created largely through a combination of profligacy, neglect, callousness and self-imposed paralysis. This state of affairs is due—most noticeably in those countries which have had the greatest technological and economic growth—to the almost complete lack of interest in and concern for the environment. Whenever a conflict existed between production and profit on the one hand and protection of the environment on the other, environmental considerations were callously, almost casually, sacrificed as part of the "small" charge paid for progress.

The readings focus on areas vitally important to the quality of the environment. Although it is difficult to treat them separately, it seemed more effective to concentrate on each area individually with the understanding that each depends upon and relates to the whole. The sections include: (1) population, (2) air pollution, (3) water pollution, (4) noise pollution, (5) land use, (6) new towns, (7) solid waste disposal, (8) aesthetics, and (9) management and finance.

This book must be considered only a beginning. In many of the topics covered very few examples of successful field-tested programs seemed to be available; more models are desperately needed. Possibly they are already in existence but descriptions of them could not be located. Politicians and citizens alike need to become familiar with more information of this type and government agencies should distribute information of successful programs as it becomes available. It is hoped that future publications will continue to emphasize this positive aspect of the environmental crisis by adding to and expanding upon the material included in this work.

NOTES

[1] As Milton Friedman pointed out in a recent interview in the Chicago Tribune, pollution in Gary and Pittsburgh was considerably worse at the turn of the century than it is now. "Pollution," *Chicago Tribune*, April 12, 1970, p. 71.

[2] H. P. and Blanche L. Van Grikel, "The Phenomenon of Pollution," in *The Pollution Reader*, compiled by Anthony DeVos, *et al.* (Montreal: Harvest House, 1968), pp. 13–18.

[3] Rachel Carson, *Silent Spring* (Greenwich, Connecticut: Crest Books, Fawcett, 1962).

[4] Paul R. Ehrlich, "Eco-Catastrophe!" in *The Environmental Handbook*, ed. by Garrett De Bell (New York: Ballantine Books, Inc., 1970), pp. 161–176.

[5] Terrence McNally, " 'Last Gasps'—A New Play of Tomorrow?", *The New York Times*, October 26, 1968, pp. D1, D15.

[6] *Loc. cit.*

[7] Paul R. Ehrlich, "Eco-Catastrophe!", *The Environmental Handbook, op. cit.*, pp. 161, 167–169.

[8] "Man and His Environment: Some Basic Facts About a Growing Nation-wide Problem," *The New York Times*, April 20, 1970, p. 33.

[9] Agis Salpukas, "Pollution Foes Stepping Up Attacks on Auto Engine," *The New York Times*, July 11, 1970, p. 1.

[10] Editorial, *The New York Times*, July 7, 1970, p. 36. See also Kenneth P. Cantor, "Warning: The Automobile is Dangerous to Earth, Air, Fire, Water, Mind and Body," in *The Environmental Handbook, op. cit.*, pp. 197, 200–201.

[11] *Ibid.*, pp. 207–209.

[12] Steven H. Wodka, "Pesticides Since Silent Spring," *The Environmental Handbook, op. cit.*, pp. 76–91.

[13] *Ibid.*, p. 79.

[14] "Earth Day Special," *The Boston Globe*, April 22, 1970, p. 8.

[15] *Loc. cit.*

[16] Paul R. Ehrlich, *The Population Bomb* (New York: Ballantine Books, Inc., 1968), pp. 15–16.

[17] "Man and His Environment: Some Basic Facts About a Growing Nation-wide Problem," *op. cit.*, p. 33.

[18] Sanford Rose, "The Economics of Environmental Quality," in *The Environment: A National Mission for the Seventies* by the Editors of Fortune (New York: Harper & Row, 1970) p. 73.

[19] Charles L. Schultze, with Edward K. Hamilton and Allen Schick, *Setting National Priorities: The 1971 Budget*, (Washington, D. C.: The Brookings Institution, 1970) pp. 120–121.

[20] Charles L. Schultze, *Setting National Priorities: The 1971 Budget, op. cit.*, Table 1.1, p. 12.

[21] Gladwin Hill, "The Polluted Potomac: Sewage and Politics Create Acute Capital Problem," *The New York Times*, July 12, 1970, p. 46.

[22] *Loc. cit.*

I

POPULATION

Historically, population patterns and trends have been cause for worry on two counts—too little or too much. Between the mid-19th century and the mid-20th century, the French were fearful of being overwhelmed by populous Germany while many of the recurrent nightmares over the Russian and Yellow Menaces were linked to the threat of huge, mobilized populations overwhelming the West by sheer force of numbers.

Beyond these primarily political and national fears, there has been general concern throughout the world about overpopulation. Malthus' warning in his famous work of 1798 that wars and famines would thin out surplus population remains very much alive a century and a half later in some parts of the world.[1] Although population growth has slowed in economically advanced nations, largely through voluntary contraception, there is still a grim Malthusian threat of recurring famines in areas of Asia, Africa and Latin America.

The fact that the United States produces food surpluses not only for itself but for much of the world has not completely altered apprehensive forecasts of future disaster, even in a nation which has grown at less than one percent annually in recent years. There is still a widespread belief that the population growth of the United States, particularly in urban areas, will far outrun our ability to clothe it, water it, house it, educate it, provide it with adequate medical care, and find enough space for its automobiles and its waste products. Historically our answer to larger numbers of people using large numbers of goods and occupying large amounts of land has been advances in science and technology. Predicted shortages of oil, food, water and other commodities have not materialized because of the application of technological advances, and although costs of new materials have risen, worker productivity has increased even faster. Fortunately, in view of the expected decline in the birth rate in the 1970's, the United States may be able to remain a viable and even comfortable nation with a population stabilized in the 300 million range, provided that some way can be found to prevent most of the nation's population from crowding into a few score urban centers which represent only a tiny fraction of the nation's land area.

In much of the world, the prospects are not as disturbing as they were five or ten years ago. Population growth in most of the West and Japan now seems to be levelling off, and there are indications that some degree of decentralized settlement on the outer rings of metropolitan areas is taking place and that more is on its way. (See discussion of new towns in Chapters 17 and 18.) However, the rapid rise in population shows no strong evidence of tapering off in the underdeveloped parts of the world, a fact which will exert a great impact on this country. It seems probable that by the end of the 1970's explosive population growth in the United States may be regarded as yesterday's crisis; instead, we may hear warnings of biological suicide (and underpopulation) as was the case in Poland in the early 1970's and France and Sweden in the 1930's.

Meanwhile, birth rates remain relatively high among the poor. One thrust in population planning will continue to be toward improved health and child care for low income families. Part of this help will undoubtedly include family planning. Despite charges of "genocide" connected with family planning services to low income families (especially blacks), it is likely that the birth rates among the poor will continue to diminish largely as a matter of conscious choice, very much like the decline in birth rates among the more affluent classes. For example, both the white and the black birth rates decreased by a fourth between 1960 and 1968.

Population redistribution seems to be a more difficult problem. Complex tradeoffs between allocation of economic resources, improving the quality of life, and the freedom of citizens to live where they choose are involved in arriving at a national posture on population redistribution. Experience in Europe suggests that even totalitarian countries find it hard to counter the basic forces enticing people and economic development into large urban centers. Programs aimed at helping rural people to stay on the farms and people in distressed areas to find local jobs have had little success. The United States may find that a policy based on the Swedish model of combining and reallocating federal contracts, new towns, and family relocation allowances is more successful in guiding population growth into desirable patterns.

The readings in this section include discussions of population policy in the United States and descriptions of family planning programs in several countries where population control is a matter of public policy.

Both the essay by Judith Blake entitled "Population Policy for America: Is the Government Being Misled?" and the "Interim Report of the Commission on Population Growth and the American Future," address themselves to the question of establishing a population policy in the United States. The Commission states that it "views population policy not as an end in itself but as a means to facilitate the achievement of other social goals desirable in their own rights." Having made this point clear, the Commission suggests that initial efforts at population control in the United States should concentrate on preventing the birth of unwanted children. To accomplish this objective, however, vastly expanded efforts at education and the improvement of birth control methods must be undertaken.

Judith Blake concludes that if the rate of population growth in the United States is to be lowered, we must first recognize that our society has a "pronatalist" policy already in existence. Our society stresses that parenthood is a goal to which every normal person strives. Women especially suffer from stereotyped sex roles by the pervasive indoctrination which forces them into being mothers and housewives when they might wish instead to pursue a career. An "antinatalist" policy would reverse these attitudes and permit greater individual freedom to choose suitable roles or careers. Many educated women prefer smaller families and find that combining family and career is possible. If this trend continues the one or two child family will be the rule rather than the exception.

Few countries in the world have what can be called successful family planning programs. In fact, most if not all are still in the experimental stages; although early results may seem encouraging, it is still too soon to make an evaluation of them. "Population Crisis" from senate hearings on the population problem summarizes seven of the oldest and most promising public programs. These and other newer efforts deserve careful watching in coming years. In some nations strong government family planning programs and a higher standard of living is helping to bring this situation under control.

The United States has faced the prospects of a greatly enlarged population and the resulting demands this would place on its resources by realizing that a choice must ultimately be made between quality and quantity: if people want a higher standard of living they must have fewer children. Americans have decided to regulate their rate of growth without the major intervention of the federal govern-

ment, and it seems they will continue to do so. The role of the federal government can be limited to: (1) making birth control information available, or at least not preventing it from being distributed, to all those who want it in this country and abroad (including non-inter-ference with and possibly subsidies for low cost abortion facilities), and (2) sponsoring research into new and better birth control tech-niques.

NOTES

[1] Thomas Malthus, *Population: The First Essay* (Ann Arbor, Michigan: Ann Arbor Paperbacks, 1959).

1. Population Policy for Americans: Is the Government Being Misled?

JUDITH BLAKE

It seems clear that the suggested policy of poverty-oriented birth-control programs does not make sense as a welfare measure. It is also true that, as an inhibitor of population growth, it is inconsequential and trivial. It does not touch the principal cause of such growth in the United States—namely, the reproductive behavior of the majority of Americans who, under present conditions, want families of more than three children and thereby generate a growth rate far in excess of that required for population stability. Indeed, for most Americans the "family planning" approach, concentrating as it does on the distribution of contraceptive materials and services, is irrelevant, because they already know about efficient contraception and are already "planning" their families. It is thus apparent that any policy designed to influence reproductive behavior must not only concern itself with all fecund Americans (rather than just the poor) but must, as well, relate to family-size goals (rather than just to contraceptive means). In addition, such a policy cannot be limited to matters affecting contraception (or even to matters affecting gestation and parturition, such as abortion), but must additionally, take into account influences on the formation and dissolution of heterosexual unions.[1]

What kinds of reproductive policies can be pursued in an effort to reduce long-term population growth? The most important step toward developing such new policies is to recognize and understand the existing ones, for we already have influential and coercive policies regarding reproductive behavior. Furthermore, these existing policies

"Population Policy for Americans: Is the Government Being Misled?" by Judith Blake (Reprinted from the May 2, 1969, issue of "Science" Magazine)

relate not merely to proscriptions (legal or informal) regarding certain means of birth control (like abortion) but also to a definition of reproduction as a primary societal end and to an organization of social roles that draws most of the population into reproductive unions.

The existence of such pronatalist policies becomes apparent when we recall that, among human beings, population replacement would not occur at all were it not for the complex social organization and system of incentives that encourage mating, pregnancy, and the care, support, and rearing of children. These institutional mechanisms are the pronatalist "policies" evolved unconsciously over millennia to give societies a fertility sufficient to offset high mortality. The formation and implementation of antinatalist policies must be based, therefore, on an analysis and modification of the existing pronatalist policies. It follows, as well, that antinatalist policies will not necessarily involve the introduction of coercive measures. In fact, just the opposite is the case. Many of these new policies will entail a lifting of pressures to reproduce, rather than an imposition of pressures not to do so. In order to understand this point let us consider briefly our present-day pronatalism.

It is convenient to start with the family, because pronatalism finds its most obvious expression in this social institution. The pronatalism of the family has many manifestations, but among the most influential and universal are two: the standardization of both the male and the female sexual roles in terms of reproductive functions, obligations, and activities, and the standardization of the occupational role of women—half of the population—in terms of childbearing, child-rearing, and complementary activities. These two "policies" insure that just about everyone will be propelled into reproductive unions, and that half of the population will enter such unions as a "career"— a life's work. Each of the two "policies" is worth considering.

With regard to sex roles, it is generally recognized that potential human variability is greater than is normally permitted within each sex category. Existing societies have tended to suppress and extinguish such variability and to standardize sexual roles in ways that imply that all "normal" persons will attain the status of parents. This coercion takes many forms, including one-sided indoctrination in schools, legal barriers and penalties for deviation, and the threats of loneliness, ostracism, and ridicule that are implied in the unavailability of alternatives. Individuals who—by temperament, health, or constitution—do not fit the ideal sex-role pattern are nevertheless coerced into attempting to achieve it, and many of them do achieve it, at least to the extent of having demographic impact by becoming parents.

Therefore, a policy that sought out the ways in which coercion regarding sex roles is at present manifesting itself could find numerous avenues for relieving the coercion and for allowing life styles different from marriage and parenthood to find free and legitimized expression. Such a policy would have an effect on the content of expectations regarding sex roles as presented and enforced in schools, on laws concerning sexual activity between consenting adults, on taxation with respect to marital status and number of children, on residential building policies, ar.d on just about every facet of existence that is now organized so as exclusively to favor and reward a pattern of sex roles based on marriage and parenthood.

As for the occupational roles of women, existing pressures still attempt to make the reproductive and occupational roles coterminus for all women who elect to marry and have children. This rigid structuring of the wife-mother position builds into the entire motivational pattern of women's lives a tendency to want at least a moderate-size family. To understand this point one must recognize that the desired number of children relates not simply to the wish for a family of a particular size but relates as well to a need for more than one or two children if one is going to enjoy "family life" over a significant portion of one's lifetime. This need is increased rather than lessened by improved life expectancy. Insofar as women focus their energies and emotions on their families, one cannot expect that they will be satisfied to play their only important role for a diminishing fraction of their lives, or that they will readily regard make-work and dead-end jobs as a substitute for "mothering."

The notion that most women will "see the error of their ways" and decide to have two-child families is naive, since few healthy and energetic women will be so misguided as to deprive themselves of most of the rewards society has to offer them and choose a situation that allows them neither a life's work outside the home nor one within it. Those who do deprive themselves in this fashion are, in effect, taking the brunt of the still existing maladjustment between the roles of women and the reproductive needs of society. In a society oriented around achievement and accomplishment, such women are exceptionally vulnerable to depression, frustration, and a sense of futility, because they are being blocked from a sense of fulfillment both at home and abroad.

In sum, the problem of inhibiting population growth in the United States cannot be dealt with in terms of "family-planning needs" because this country is well beyond the point of "needing" birth control methods. Indeed, even the poor seem not to be a last outpost for family-planning attention. If we wish to limit our growth, such a desire implies basic changes in the social organization of reproduction that will make nonmarriage, childlessness, and small (two-child) families far more prevalent than they are now. A new policy, to achieve such ends, can take advantage of the antinatalist tendencies that our present institutions have suppressed. This will involve the lifting of penalties for antinatalist behavior rather than the "creation" of new ways of life. This behavior already exists among us as part of our convert and deviant culture, on the one hand, and our elite and artistic culture, on the other. Such antinatalist tendencies have also found expression in feminism, which has been stifled in the United States by means of systematic legal, educational, and social pressures concerned with women's "obligations" to create and care for children. A fertility-control policy that does not take into account the need to alter the present structure of reproduction in these and other ways merely trivializes the problem of population control and misleads those who have the power to guide our country toward completing the vital revolution.

NOTES

[1] K. Davis and J. Blake, Econ. Develop. Cult. Change 4,211 (1956)

2. Population Growth and America's Future

The Commission is devoting its second year to a detailed examination of the probable course of population growth and distribution and their environmental, economic, political and social implications. The aim is to determine what population prospects inevitably must be accommodated in the short run, and what kind of national population policy is desirable now for the long run. The concerns of overriding importance are whether population stabilization and redistribution of the population are desirable.

The Commission views population policy not as an end in itself but as a means to facilitate the achievement of other social goals desirable in their own right. Such goals would include improvements in the status of women, in the socioeconomic conditions of disadvantaged minorities, and in the health and opportunities of children born because they were wanted, as well as the easing of pressures on our resources and physical environment, health and educational facilities, and the problems of our cities.

The content of a population policy would not be immutable, but would need to be adjusted over time in the light of emerging developments, increased knowledge, and changing attitudes of both policy-makers and the general public. Thus, the Commission sees national population policy as an evolving rather than a static instrumentality.

... freely to choose ...

A key consideration for population policy is the current level of unwanted childbearing. This information is necessary to determine how much movement toward the cessation of population growth might ultimately result simply from preventing unwanted births. The sum of individuals' real preferences may in fact coincide with the welfare of society as a whole. There is some evidence (from the 1965 National Fertility Study) that the elimination of unwanted births would result in fertility levels ultimately commensurate with near-zero

Population Growth & America's Future, An Interim Report prepared by the Commission on Population Growth and the American Future. Washington, D.C.: Government Printing Office, 1970, pp. 25–31.

HOW MANY BIRTHS ARE UNWANTED?
ONE FIFTH OF ALL U.S. BIRTHS, 1960-65, WERE UNWANTED.

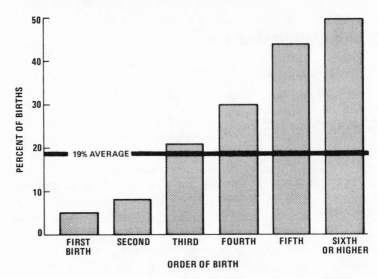

growth. If this conclusion is valid for 1970 (the 1970 National Fertility Study now underway will provide the basis for such a judgment), the policy implications can hardly be overestimated because the national objective could be attained by enabling individuals to achieve their own preferences.

Estimates made in 1965, based on married women's own reports about their childbearing experience, indicated that one-third of the married couples who did not intend to have any more children already had at least one unwanted child. In the period 1960–65 nearly 20 percent of all live births were reported as unwanted by their parents. Only one-fourth of all parents claimed to have been completely successful in preventing both unwanted and unplanned pregnancies.

The 20 percent of births reported as unwanted by their parents represent nearly five million children born between 1960 and 1965 who theoretically would never have been born if their parents' desires had prevailed. Fortunately many of these unwanted pregnancies and births become wanted children. But many do not.

Over and above the demographic significance of current levels of unwanted births, are the serious costs for both individuals and society. For many, it means poor prospects for employment and limited opportunities for themselves and their children. For others, the costs are measured in increased family stress and unhappiness, altered life plans, and less time and attention for each child. Unwanted pregnancy sets off a chain of events which acutely forecloses the life-chances of some young people; it leads to dropping out of school, precipitous marriage or an out-of-wedlock birth. Unwanted childbearing is associated with serious health consequences such as increased incidence of prematurity, mental retardation, infant and maternal mortality, and physical and emotional neglect and abuse.

While the incidence—and the consequences—of unwanted births are especially acute among low-income couples, it would be erroneous to regard the problem as one associated only with poverty. Couples in all socioeconomic groups have unwanted pregnancies and experience its costs.

Fortunately, unwanted childbearing is a problem we can do something about. Voluntary family planning has become a prevailing pattern in American life, practiced in some fashion at some time by almost all couples, regardless of income, class, religion, or color. Whether Americans are able freely to choose if and when to have children depends largely on the priority which we as a society are willing to devote to policies, and research and educational programs, to reduce unwanted pregnancy.

In 1970, the Congress, by overwhelming majorities of both House and Senate, adopted the Family Planning Services and Population Research Act of 1970 (P.L. 91-572), a measure signed into law by President Nixon this past December. The Act encourages the birth of wanted children and assists couples in preventing unwanted conception. The Commission endorses this significant advance toward the reduction of unwanted childbearing, and believes that this policy should be implemented promptly.

We shall return to this question in our final report, to estimate the level of governmental and private resources—financial, manpower and institutional—which would be necessary for a comprehensive national effort. We are also examining State laws still in force which impede the dissemination of family planning services to certain classes of individuals, and the impact of other policies and programs on the opportunity for couples to secure modern family planning services.

...not an easy task...

If it turns out that the prevention of unwanted births should be the main target of a growth policy, the goal would be to maximize popular information and understanding about how to control fertility, and to accelerate the development of more effective techniques and facilities for limiting childbearing. This will involve the Commission in further considerations of family planning services and education, contraceptive technology, adoption and abortion. These all pose moral and ethical complexities which the Commission is considering.

On the other hand, if population stabilization is desirable and its achievement would require more than eliminating unwanted child-bearing, then additional measures can be considered, such as changes in tax laws, the elimination of pro-natalist laws and programs, and educational programs. Some of the policy issues that would then be involved are much more difficult and potentially more controversial than those related to the prevention of unwanted childbearing. It would not be an easy task to develop acceptable measures that would lead to a slowing and eventual end of population growth. The best kind of national population policy would be one that serves the general welfare by promoting informed individual choice.

One obvious and fundamental change desirable in its own right, quite aside from its demographic impact, is to increase the opportunities for women to pursue activities other than exclusively domestic and childbearing roles. As the experience of other countries indicates, when women are able to work, birth rates decline.

As we have seen, population growth is also affected significantly by immigration. Should the volume of immigration be reduced? The historical role played by immigration in the growth of this country and our tradition as an open society make this question especially disturbing.

The issues with regard to the distribution of the population arise from the transition of the United States from an agrarian to an industrial and service economy and from a rural to a metropolitan way of life. The Commission seeks to identify the major stress points in this transition—stresses generated in the process of regional redistribution, metropolitan growth, the rapid expansion of suburbs and the depopulation of large areas of the country.

If it appears desirable to redirect growth, it will be important to know how this might be done. The Commission is studying internal migration and the characteristics of migrants, to find out at what stages in their career and life-cycle people might be responsive to incentives to move or stay.

A principal question is the role that Federal and State governments play in population affairs. Although the Federal government does not have an explicit, comprehensive population distribution policy, many of its policies, programs and statutes seem to have an impact on population distribution incidental to their main objectives. This inadvertent impact may be seen, for example, not only in the Federal Interstate Highway System, but also in the Federal Housing Administration program and federal procurement policies. Others, such as the Economic Development Administration, the New Communities Act and the urban renewal program, are designed in part to redirect growth.

We also have many laws directly or indirectly affecting the growth of population, such as those governing immigration, marriage, divorce, contraception and abortion, which require examination.

Basic to all population policy questions are the underlying legal, ethical and political issues. Constitutionality does not guarantee ethical acceptability, and Americans support a broad variety of ethical views that must be taken into account in any formulation of policy.

This, then, is the way the Commission views its task. We do not take future population trends as inevitable. We believe that there are short-run population trends already in process that simply must be accommodated, but that the longer-run future hangs in the balance. And it is not simply population growth itself that is the issue, but rather the quality of life that can be influenced so fundamentally by population. We have the challenge, and indeed the responsibility, to prepare for the future of coming generations of Americans.

3. Population Crisis

The following selections from the Population Crisis, *hearings conducted in 1968, summarize the essential information about the oldest and presumably most successful family planning programs yet undertaken in the world to date. The efforts of these and more recent programs deserve careful analysis for possible application in other underdeveloped nations. [Ed.]*

INDIA: Demographic Information

Date of last national census .	1961	Number of years to double	
Population (Jan. 1, 1968,		population at present rate ..	28
estimate)	517,525,000	Infant deaths per 1,000 live	
Births per 1,000 population		births	NA
(1966)[1]	43	Literacy rate	28
Deaths per 1,000 population		Labor force in agriculture	
(1966)[1]	18	(1951)	70
Rate of natural increase		Per capita gross national	
(percent of total population)[1]	· 2.5	product (1966)	$74

[1] Based on *An Analysis of the Population of India*, a paper prepared for A.I.D. July 1967 by George J. Stolnitz.

INDIA

Population and family planning programs

India's population—over 517 million—is almost one-seventh of the world total. At the current rate of rise (2.5 percent per year), it is increasing by more than 1 million each month.

Although the family planning movement in India was begun nearly 50 years ago, its development was slow until recent years. Initial stimulation was given by voluntary leaders, international organizations, and scattered but growing support from Indian universities and the medical profession.

U.S. Senate Subcommittee on Foreign Aid Expenditures of the Committees on Government Operations. *Population Crisis.* 91st Congress, 2nd Session, February 1, 1968, Part 3, pp. 556–558, 561–562, 580–581, 590–592, 593–594.

Increasing official interest led to the emergence of a national family planning policy in 1951, leading to program action on a limited scale. Relatively little progress was made in the first decade because funds were limited and the methods of contraception available were inadequate.

However, during the past 5 years a number of changes have occurred. The family planning budget has been increased substantially, and expenditures in 1966–67 have jumped to the rupee equivalent of $20 million, or approximately 70 percent of total expenditures during the previous 5 years. During the 5-year period 1966–71, India has budgeted $306 million (rupee equivalent) for family planning, and there are provisions for exceeding this amount if necessary. The goal is to reduce the birth rate from its present level to 22 births per thousand population by 1979.

Administrative changes have been made strengthening the organization structure of the program. Approximately 28,000 family planning centers have been established, including 20,000 subcenters in rural areas.

Most of all contraceptive methods are now offered, with emphasis on IUDs, sterilization, and condoms. The Government has recently approved the use of oral contraceptives in the national program, and pilot testing programs are being conducted. The Government is planning substantial expansion in production and distribution of condoms. In fiscal year 1968, the Family Planning Department reported over 1.8 million sterilizations and over 660,000 IUD insertions. The cumulative totals through March 1968 were 2,410,413 IUD insertions and 4,300,011 sterilizations.

A.I.D. assistance

Active U.S. interest in family planning began early in 1965, when an A.I.D.-sponsored team carried out an intensive study of India's program. A technical assistance project was then developed and a team of technical consultants recruited.

During fiscal 1968 A.I.D. provided a total of $7.7 million to finance a comprehensive program including technical assistance, organizational help, advanced training in the United States, contraceptives, program equipment and research. In addition, approximately $3 million in local currency generated under P.L. 480 sales programs was approved for family planning activities. Currently, the A.I.D. family planning assistance team includes eleven technical specialists serving as advisers to the Indian Ministry of Health and Family Planning.

The above assistance includes a number of noteworthy components:

In response to Government of India requests, A.I.D. has made available approximately $220,000 to finance the purchase of oral contraceptives for use in demonstration programs to determine their acceptability. About $2.9 million has been granted for purchase of condoms to be distributed through commercial channels on a demonstration basis.

A $2.7-million loan and $20 million in local currencies that help provide imported components for, and to finance the Indian manufacture of 6,000 family planning vehicles. Part of this vehicle loan and an additional $400,000 in local currency are being used to finance the manufacture of 85 audiovisual vehicles for a comprehensive new communications program.

A.I.D. is supporting several other family planning programs sponsored by the Indian Government: a direct mailing system for family planning materials, an "intensive district" program, the training of village midwives, services at Maternal and Child Health Centers, biomedical research, and the Demographic and Research Centre at Chembur, Bombay.

Other assistance

Private and international groups have assisted the development of family planning in India for many years. Prominent among these organizations is the Ford Foundation, which has spent over $9 million since 1959 in help to a wide range of India's family planning activities. The Foundation's program includes support to eleven medical and biological research laboratories for work in reproductive biology, and laboratory testing of new contraceptives. The Foundation has underwritten urban and rural family planning clinics and training programs for family planning workers. It has supported centers for testing motivational factors and communication techniques and pilot projects that incorporate family planning into public health services. A Ford grant to the Ministry of Health in 1964 assisted in establishing the National Institute of Health Administration and Education and the Central Family Planning Institute. Other Ford Foundation grants have supported costs of consultants, training, books and equipment purchases, and architectural services.

The Population Council provided guidance for setting up India's IUD production unit and has contributed equipment in the form of loops and inserters. It is supporting a 2-year study on the effect of IUD insertions. The Council has also supported the Chembur Demographic Teaching and Research Centre in Bombay since 1957, and has provided numerous fellowships. It has also assisted the establishment and operation of a Demographic Research Centre at Benares Hindu University. The Safdarjung Hospital in New Delhi and the S.A.T. Hospital in Trivandrum, Kerala, are participating in the Council's post partum program. In June 1968 under another A.I.D.-financed grant, the Council agreed to assist the Indian Government in establishing a national post partum program in family planning in 150 Indian maternity hospitals and clinics.

The Rockefeller Foundation is giving financial assistance to a comprehensive Rural Health Service project near Delhi that includes intensive demographic and family planning studies and services. The Foundation has made grants to Indian scholars for population research.

Assistance from the Pathfinder Fund began in 1952 and in 1953, Pathfinder financed a test of simple methods of contraception. Funds were also provided for a 2-year study by Indian physicians of oral contraceptives and to the Christian Medical Association of India for IUD-insertion incentives. In fiscal 1968 the Pathfinder Fund under an A.I.D.-financed grant assisted private Indian organizations in the family planning field to expand their activities in the urban and rural areas of India.

Some 108 Peace Corps volunteers are currently serving in India. Trained at the Universities of Chicago, North Carolina, Wisconsin, and Kentucky, the volunteers are involved in all nonsurgical aspects of the program: record keeping, program planning and promotion, supplies, establishment of new family planning centers, counseling, and demonstration of effective teaching skills. In the State of Bihar volunteers work at the block, State and District levels. In addition, all Peace Corps volunteers are given auxiliary instruction in family planning methods.

The Japanese Government sent five nurses to India in September 1966 for a 2-year period to engage in family planning guidance service at various hospitals.

INDONESIA: Demographic Information

Date of last national census .	1961	Number of years to double population at present rate ..	30
Population (Jan. 1, 1968, estimate)	111,427,000	Infant deaths per 1,000 live births (1962)	125
Births per 1,000 population (1962)	43	Literacy rate	43
Deaths per 1,000 population (1962)	21	Labor force in agriculture .. Per capita gross national	NA
Rate of natural increase (percent of total population)[1]	2.4	product (1966)	$100

[1] This is official figure; indications are that growth rate may be higher.

INDONESIA

Population and family planning programs

Advice on birth spacing has been provided by leading physicians in Indonesia since 1957. The Indonesian Family Planning Association— now the Indonesian Planned Parenthood Association (IPPA) and an associate member of the International Planned Parenthood Federation —has been active in recent years in providing information, training, and services. In October 1967 it was sponsoring approximately 70 clinics, most of them in Java and Bali.

The National and Provincial Governments sanction the use of their health personnel and facilities to provide family planning information and services.

In 1967 the Acting President of Indonesia signed the World Leaders' Declaration on Population, which has now been signed by Heads of State of 30 countries.

In April 1967 the Governor of Djakarta inaugurated a pilot program in the city under the administration of the Municipal Department of Health and sponsorship of the IPPA. Approximately 30 clinics are now in operation.

Data from a recent study among 2,000 families on knowledge, attitudes, and practices of family planning are now being analyzed. Another such study, sponsored by the Association, was made in 1967 in Bekasi county, a predominantly rural area immediately east of Djakarta.

Reportedly, there are some 4,000 maternal and child health centers in the country. Of these, some 2,500 are on Java, Bali, and Madura, where some 75 million of the country's population of 111 million live. The IPPA, at the request of the Ministry of People's Welfare, has prepared a proposed policy statement on family planning.

A.I.D. assistance

An A.I.D. consultant and Ford Foundation representative worked with the IPPA and Ministry of Health in Indonesia in September and October 1967 on details of an expanded program. This includes establishment of training centers, expansion of clinic facilities, identifying training needs, inventorying resources, defining program goals and objectives, exploring methods of operation, and establishment of an adequate system of records and evaluation.

A.I.D. is assisting IPPA in fiscal 1968 with a grant of $270,000 which includes commodity support and staff training in the United States.

Other assistance

The Ford Foundation made a 2-year grant in 1967 for $180,000 to IPPA for support of pilot programs. The Foundation has supplied a headquarters for the Association and is providing technical assistance through a full-time representative and some short-term consultants. The Foundation has also purchased three vehicles and provided some money for training.

The International Planned Parenthood Federation provided a $20,000 grant for general program support for calendar 1967, in addition to costs of training 40 Indonesians at the IPPF Family Planning Training Institute in Singapore. In 1968 IPPF is providing $236,000 to support the program and to institute and operate a training center.

The Population Council has made a grant to the IPPA covering some 250,000 intrauterine contraceptive devices and a few vehicles. A $26,000 grant was made in 1967 to help organize the family planning program. The Pathfinder Fund has furnished condoms and vaginal tablets for the program.

PAKISTAN: Demographic Information

Date of last national census .	1961	Number of years to double population at present rate ..	21
Population (Jan. 1, 1968, estimate)[1, 2] 127,773,000		Infant deaths per 1,000 live births	NA
Births per 1,000 population (1962–63)	54	Literacy rate	20
Deaths per 1,000 population (1962–63)	19	Labor force in agriculture ..	NA
Rate of natural increase (percent of total population)[2]	3.5	Per capita gross national product (1966)	$113

[1] U.S. Bureau of the Census, *Projections of the Population of Pakistan, by Age and Sex: 1965–66. A Measure of the Potential Impact of a Family Planning Program;* by James W. Brackett and Donald S. Akers, 1965.

[2] The Pakistan Planning Commission has published a series of population estimates, from which can be derived a population figure of 121.8 million on Jan. 1, 1968, based on a growth rate of 2.6 percent. The 3.5-percent growth rate above is based on the Population Growth Estimation project using data on births and deaths collected on a sample basis.

PAKISTAN

Population and family planning programs

The Pakistan family planning program, with vigorous official backing, strong financial support and sound management, has made significant progress in the last few years. It appears from available statistics that the program is largely meeting interim goals, and if it continues at its present pace, should meet its 1970 target of reducing Pakistan's birth rate from 50 per thousand to 40 per thousand.

A voluntary Family Planning Association was active as early as 1952 and in 1958 the Government issued a statement endorsing family planning. The program entered an initial phase in 1960 with demonstration programs in family planning, conducted by the Government of Pakistan with the aid of the Ford Foundation, The Population Council, A.I.D., the Swedish and U.K. Governments, the University of California, and Johns Hopkins University. Some 3,000 family planning clinics were established by 1965.

After more than 5 years of demonstration programs, Pakistan developed a Family Planning Scheme as part of its third Five-Year Plan. The program began in July 1965, with a 5-year development budget of $59.7 million (Pakistan rupee equivalent). It will be extended to all of Pakistan's districts by 1970. As of June 1967, the program had been activated in 36 of these districts.

By March 1968 the Pakistan Family Planning Council reported more than 1.3 million IUD insertions and over 200,000 sterilizations. (There were about 70,000 IUD insertions in the month of February alone.) Approximately 240 million conventional contraceptives had been sold by the end of February. By 1968 about 40,000 couples were using oral contraceptives and 1.4 million were using conventional contraceptives.

At this level of participation, the expected reduction of births by 1970 will be around 5 million. Incentive payments by the Government to organizers and acceptors have been a key factor in the success of the Pakistan program. One important operating problem facing the program is the limited number of lady doctors and lady family planning visitors available for IUD insertions. To meet this shortage of female personnel, a training program for lady family planning visitors has been established. These women, who are high school graduates, are being taught how to insert IUDs. Some 1,500 lady family planning visitors are in the field or under training. The family planning staff includes over 30,000 village family planning organizers and about 50,000 village agents (commercial distributors).

A.I.D. assistance

Since 1964, A.I.D. has provided technical assistance and participant training to Pakistan's family planning program. In 1965, a full-time demographer was assigned to the A.I.D. staff in Pakistan. To take family planning services and information into rural areas, a commodity loan for $500,000 was made available in 1966 for jeeps in West Pakistan, and for motors and materials for boats to use on East Pakistan's extensive inland waterways system. In 1967 a Cooley loan for $168,000 in local currencies generated by P.L. 480 sales helped expand a factory for contraceptive pills and other products in Pakistan. In fiscal 1967 A.I.D. obligated about $1 million and about $4.5 million in local currency for family planning in Pakistan in support of a comprehensive program including advisory assistance, participant training, and commodity supplies. The A.I.D. staff is made up of two public health advisor physicians, a public health administration advisor, a medical officer, two nurse advisors, two health education advisors, and a demographic research and evaluation advisor. A.I.D. will continue to work closely with the Pakistan Government to determine what additional inputs will be required.

Other assistance

The Ford Foundation has contributed $2,746,000 for research and training, mostly through grants to The Population Council, Johns Hopkins University, and the University of California. UNICEF has provided 108 vehicles and Johns Hopkins University and the University of California are providing advisory support.

The Population Council has supported the work of the Pakistan Institute of Development Economics and provides the services of a demographer advisor. It has also supported pilot projects of the Ministry of Health, Labor, and Social Welfare and the development of the National Research Institute for Family Planning. The Council supplies assistance to the Population Growth Estimate Study and the Pakistan Academy for Rural Development in Comilla, support for demographic research at universities, and fellowships for study abroad. The Jinnah Central Hospital in Karachi is a member institute in the Council's post partum program.

The International Planned Parenthood Federation provides assistance to the Family Planning Association, which has a major role in the program. Contraceptive supplies have also been donated by The Pathfinder Fund.

The British Government has supplied $71,750 in contraceptives for use in large-scale trials.

Since 1961, the Pakistan Family Planning Scheme has been one of the two major focal points of Swedish assistance. Swedish objectives have been to establish and operate model clinics, participate in training family planning personnel, assist in educational programs, organize research, and provide equipment. In an agreement signed in early 1966, Sweden agreed to supply all condoms needed for the national program. Some 115 million condoms were supplied in 1967. Between 1962 and 1968 total Swedish expenditures for the Pakistan Family Planning Program amounted to $4,980,000.

SINGAPORE: Demographic Information

Date of last national census .	1957	Number of years to double population at present rate ..	30
Population (Jan. 1, 1968, estimate)	1,979,000	Infant deaths per 1,000 live births (1966)	26
Births per 1,000 population (1966)	30	Literacy rate	75
Deaths per 1,000 population (1966)	6	Labor force in agriculture ...	6
Rate of natural increase (percent of total population)	2.4	Per capita gross national product (1966)	$555

SINGAPORE

Population and family planning programs

As early as 1949 a maternal and child health physician and several social workers obtained permission to provide family planning advice in municipal infant welfare clinics. Their work coupled with growing interest resulted in the formation of the Singapore Family Planning Association during the same year. The SFPA received a financial grant from the Government soon after its founding.

Gradually additional clinics were opened so that by 1965 services were available in 13 urban and 17 rural centers. The Singapore Family Planning and Population Board was created by the Republic of Singapore on January 9, 1966, as the national family planning agency charged with the responsibility of implementing a 5-year plan on family planning. Target of the program is reduction of the birthrate to 20 per thousand by 1971 and extension of family planning to 300,000 married women between 15 and 44 years old.

In 1958 the birth, death, and natural population increase rates were 41, 7, and 34 per thousand population respectively. By 1966 these had fallen to 30, 6, and 24 per thousand.

A.I.D. assistance

A.I.D. has provided no assistance to the family planning program.

Other assistance

The Ford Foundation made a 3-year grant in 1964 for a total of $582,000 to the University of Singapore to establish a center for economic and demographic research.

The International Planned Parenthood Federation carried on a Family Planning Training Institute in Singapore designed to fill training needs of countries in Southeast Asia and Oceania Region. Since 1964, the Institute has trained 416 individuals, with the greatest number from Singapore. In 1968, the target is 375 persons with a support budget of $186,000, including costs for operation of a demonstration unit and programs in Oceania.

The Population Council has given $3,700 to the Singapore Ministry of Health to provide IUDs and inserters for the national family planning program. The Council also provided a grant to the Kandang Kerbau Hospital in Singapore for a post partum program. The Pathfinder Fund has provided contraceptives.

In 1967 the Rockefeller Foundation granted $10,000 to the London School of Hygiene and Tropical Medicine in support of a population program being conducted at the University of Singapore.

The Norwegian Agency for International Development has granted $15,000 to help purchase a mobile family planning station stationed at Sembawang rubber estate.

SOUTH KOREA: Demographic Information

Date of last national census .	1966	Number of years to double population at present rate ..	3
Population (Jan. 1, 1968, estimate)	30,141,408	Infant deaths per 1,000 live	
Births per 1,000 population	NA	births	NA
Deaths per 1,000 population	NA	Literacy rate	7
Rate of increase (percent of		Labor force in agriculture ..	5
total population)	2.4	Per capita gross national product (1966)	$13

SOUTH KOREA

Population and family planning programs

Family planning activities began in Korea in May 1961 when the Supreme Council for National Reconstruction established a Special Advisory Committee to the Minister for Health and Social Affairs. Work on the development of a National Family Planning Program began in February 1962 and during this period a long-standing law prohibiting the importation of contraceptives was repealed. Government funds were made available for the family planning program and it was integrated into Korea's First Five-Year Economic Development Plan.

Assisting the Korean movement almost from its inception were the International Planned Parenthood Federation, the Pathfinder Fund, and the Population Council. The Planned Parenthood Federation of Korea became an affiliate of the IPPF in 1961.

In June 1963 a special unit for family planning was established in the maternal and child health section of the Bureau of Public Health of the Ministry of Health and Social Affairs. Similar units were formed in each of the nine provincial health departments and the cities of Seoul and Pusan.

The original goal of the first Five-Year Plan was to reduce the annual rate of increase from 3 percent in 1961 to 2 percent by 1971.

With the recent plans for an accelerated program utilizing oral contraceptives for IUD dropouts, the goal is now to reduce the annual increase to 1.9 percent by the end of 1970.

To reach its objective the Government estimates that by 1971 almost 2 million couples will need to be practicing family planning, or about 45 percent of couples in the 20–44 year age group. At the end of 1966 about 725,000 loops had been inserted, of which some 390,000 were placed in 1966. Other contraceptive measures advocated include vasectomy, and use of condoms and traditional methods. An expanded program using oral contraceptives for IUD dropouts is now under way.

There are more than 2,200 field workers in the program. Eleven nurse-midwives are field supervisors in each of the nine provinces and the cities of Pusan and Seoul. Some 273 senior field workers, either nurses or nurse-midwives, are stationed in 189 country and city health centers. Some 270 college graduates, 270 nurse/nurse-midwives, and 930 high school graduates act as assistant field workers in the 1,473 townships or small towns. An equal number of physicians, who have received refresher training, are designated "Family Planning Doctors." More than 28,000 volunteers work in the program at the level of the city ward, city subward, and neighborhood unit.

In addition to 1,100 IUD clinics and 700 vasectomy clinics, there are 11 mobile teams spending 20 days per month, each covering an average of three counties.

The Korean program has demonstrated the importance of creative leadership to carry on program evaluation and research whose results can be utilized immediately to make activities more effective.

The quality of organization, administration, supervision, and consultation has a strong bearing on program effectiveness. In Korea for instance, the percentage of achievement of goal in 1966 ranged from 55 percent to 102 percent in the nine provinces.

A.I.D. assistance

In fiscal 1966 A.I.D. assisted in equipping eight ambulance-type vehicles for IUD insertions and vasectomy operations.

In fiscal 1967 some $99,000 was provided to assist in securing about 50 vehicles for more mobile teams; in strengthening and expanding the national and child health program and integrating family planning services with it; and in developing health center branch units. In fiscal 1968 $1,490,000 in additional technical assistance was obligated for the program.

Also, under the A.I.D. contract with the Population Council a grant has been approved for $234,850 to the Planned Parenthood Federation of Korea, acting as an agent of the Government, to employ 140 field workers, a three-man evaluation team, nine field interviewers and their supervisor, plus data processing personnel.

The Korean program will provide oral contraceptives to an estimated 900,000 women who are expected to be drop-outs from the IUD program by the end of 1969. Part of the activity will include working with mothers' clubs to determine their effectiveness in motivation.

Another grant of $40,000 under the Population Council project goes to Yongsei University in an effort to determine in Kyonggi Province the most feasible and efficient means of making contraceptive services available throughout the nation.

The A.I.D. Health Chief in Korea has devoted substantial time to working with Government officials and representatives of other agencies in the field of family planning.

Other assistance

The Population Council has been very active in Korea since the beginning of the national program. The amount of assistance for calendar 1966 totaled $418,238. This has included sponsoring training in demography; provision of resident technical consultants; development of a population research and training center; development of a census volume, support of biomedical and family planning studies; evaluation of a survey of vital statistics; and travel grants for health workers. In 1967, a grant of $564,561 aided continuance of services in addition to support to Korea's national family planning program (through

1969), and studies at such institutions as Kyung Buk University, Seoul National University, and Yongsei University.

The Pathfinder Fund was an early supporter of the Planned Parenthood Federation of Korea through grants for educational materials and demonstration studies of the IUD.

The Planned Parenthood Federation of Korea became an affiliate of the International Planned Parenthood Federation in June 1961. It has continued to receive support from IPPF for its educational and informational work, as well as for its direct assistance to the national program, particularly in the operation of the mobile units and in training. The organization runs 13 pilot clinics of its own and has a field staff in each province.

For 1968 IPPF has programmed over $400,000 for maintenance and expansion of the family planning clinics; for seminars; for expansion of the training and education program; and for commodities, including audiovisual and office equipment, and vehicles.

The Swedish International Development Authority has agreed to supply up to 5 million cycles of oral contraceptives in an expanded program for IUD dropouts. SIDA has budgeted $425,000 for 1967–68.

TAIWAN: Demographic Information

Date of last national census .	1966	Number of years to double population at present rate ..	27
Population (Jan. 1, 1968 estimate)	13,892,000	Infant deaths per 1,000 live births (1965)	22
Births per 1,000 population (1966)	33	Literacy rate	78
Deaths per 1,000 population (1966)	6	Labor force in agriculture ..	NA
Rate of natural increase percent of total population)[1]	2.7	Per capita gross national product (1966)	$234

Current rate of population growth estimated to be 2.8 percent.

TAIWAN

Population and family planning programs

In Taiwan, the birth rate has dropped steadily from its recorded high of 50 per thousand population in 1951. This downward trend is believed to have accelerated following initiation of an unofficial family planning program in 1964. The family planning program goal is to reduce the annual increase to 18.6 per thousand by 1973.

The Government announced an official national program for family planning in May 1968. Government health officials have responsibility for education and motivation of the public toward improved maternal and child health. A Committee on Family Planning functions within the Provincial Department of Health for policy formulation and promotion of the educational program.

A voluntary organization, the Maternal and Child Health Association, provides family planning services via an islandwide network of clinics.

Primary emphasis of the program has been on the IUD. The target has been insertion of 600,000 loops by 1969. At midpoint in 1967, some 260,000 had been inserted.

Loop insertions are done primarily by private physicians, some 640 of whom were inserting loops at the end of January 1967. The program was also utilizing 329 pre-pregnancy health workers and 72 village health education nurses.

The Taiwan Provincial Health Department and the Taiwan Population Studies Center have been jointly responsible for organizing a widescale family planning program throughout the island. The Population Council has acted as adviser. This has included training of both medical and paramedical personnel. There has been extensive training of the island's doctors in IUD insertion. Training is also given pre-pregnancy health workers and for village education nurses.

The Department of Sociology at the Taiwan Provincial Chieng-Hsing University runs a course on population problems.

Taiwan has expressed interest in expanding its population training capability. A.I.D. has worked with the Population Council and Taiwan officials in developing an agenda for a regional conference in family planning held in Taiwan in May 1968.

A.I.D. assistance

A.I.D.'s economic assistance program to Taiwan was terminated in 1965. Some funds for the family planning program are still being derived from local currency administered by Taiwan that has been repaid on earlier P.L. 480 sales. For 1965–70 the equivalent of $1.5 million has been reserved from this fund for the family planning program.

Other assistance

Population Council support has geen generous and for calendar years 1966 and 1967 totaled $593,117. The resident representative for East

Asia is stationed in Taichung. He and his colleagues have assisted in many aspects of the program, particularly in evaluation.

Council assistance in 1966 and 1967 included a substantial cash grant; support for preparation and publication of an annual Demographic Fact Book; evaluation and training by the Population Studies Center; support for a study of pathologic pregnancies at the National University; assistance to the building fund of the Maternal and Child Health Association; costs of a Health Education advisor at the Department of Health; support of the family planning program operation; continuation of medical followup studies of IUD cases; travel grants for a staff member of the Population Studies Center to visit another program; grants to the University of Michigan's Center for Population Studies for research on fertility and family planning in Taiwan; and support for a Workshop Conference on Population Programs in East Asia in 1968.

The Pathfinder Fund helped initiate the family planning program in 1953. Pathfinder continued for a number of years to contribute funds, along with the Joint Commission on Rural Reconstruction, the Brush Foundation, and the Asia Foundation.

TUNISIA: Demographic Information

Date of last national census .	1966	Number of years to double population at present rate ..	29
Population (Jan. 1, 1968, estimate)	4,625,000	Infant deaths per 1,000 live births	NA
Births per 1,000 population (1966)	45	Literacy rate	25–35
Deaths per 1,000 population	NA	Labor force in agriculture ..	60
Rate of natural increase (percent of total population)[1]	2.5	Per capita gross national product (1966)	$208

Inter-censal rate of growth 1956–1966 was 1.7 percent.

TUNISIA

Population and family planning programs

The Tunisian Government launched a nationwide family planning program in 1966. Previously, in 1960, family allowance had been restricted and polygamy outlawed. Legal restrictions against contraceptives were repealed in 1961, and legal abortion was authorized for women with five children.

President Habib Bourgiuba, concerned about the country's population growth, stated in 1960: "The people must become aware of the population problem . . . we must cut down the birth rate." He is among the world leaders who signed the United Nations proclamation on world population in 1966.

Discussions on family planning between the Tunisian Government, the Population Council, and the Ford Foundation began in 1962. At the Tunisian Government's request, the Population Council sent a high-level mission to study the country's population problems in depth and to make recommendations.

The preliminary phase (participant training and surveys) of an experimental national program was begun in 1963. The Government sent a Family Planning Program Director and other Tunisian officials to visit Japan, Pakistan, and the United States to become familiar with family planning developments elsewhere. A 4-week seminar trained gynecologists, demographers, sociologists and communications experts in population and family planning. This phase also included a Population Council survey in 1964 of knowledge, attitudes, and practices related to family planning in Tunisia.

The survey reported that a high percentage of Tunisian women of all classes favored family planning, but that only 15 percent had any knowledge of contraceptive methods. The average women desired fewer than five children. Nearly half wanted to bear no more children, and nearly two-thirds wanted to learn fertility control.

The operation of IUD clinics in hospitals and maternal and child health centers began in 1964 with 12 clinics in urban and semi-urban areas. Half the clinics offered the IUD, while others offered other methods, including some experimental use of the pill. A total of 27,817 women attended the family planning clinics, of whom 18,522 received first insertions of IUDs.

The goal of the expanded program, which began in 1966, is to provide family planning assistance to between 30 and 40 percent of Tunisia's women of child-bearing age during a 3-year period. To accomplish this goal, it is planned to integrate family planning into the national health services and to offer family planning services through clinics in all hospitals and maternal and child health centers. Fifty-nine hospitals and health centers are currently offering IUD services. IUDs and other contraceptives are offered at no charge.

A post partum family planning program is being developed. Other program plans include sending 13 mobile teams, each having a doctor, a midwife, and a nurse assistant, to perform IUD insertions in towns and villages. All gynecologists and surgeons in the country have now received training in IUD insertions, and the intention is to train most of the nation's other physicians in this technque.

An expanded educational program is planned to include family planning meetings throughout the country and production of a variety of informational materials.

The Ministry of Health has undertaken the expansion of its statistical services with the training of several demographers at the UNESCO-sponsored African Demographic Research Institute in Cairo. Two Tunisians are currently enrolled in the United Nations-sponsored National Institute of Statistics and Applied Economics in Rabat, Morocco.

A.I.D. assistance

A.I.D. has provided advisory and communications assistance for the family planning program. In late 1967, $249,500 in U.S.-owned local currency was allocated to the Tunisian Government for use in its population and family planning activities. This is local currency generated by U.S. food shipments to Tunisia under Public Law 480.

In April 1968 A.I.D. initiated support for a 5-year family planning project to assist the Government of Tunisia develop family planning capability. Under the project, the Government, Ford Foundation, Population Council, U.S. Public Health Service, A.I.D., and several other donors will work together to reduce the rate of population increase. The program involves the establishment of an institutional capacity for family planning through a National Family Planning Bureau, and the provision of family plannir.g service, utilizing all standard contraceptive techniques. The program also includes training, audiovisual material production for mass communication and training, clinical and demographic research and evaluation.

Other assistance

The Ford Foundation granted $200,000 in 1963 to supplement $60,000 allocated by the Tunisian Government. The Foundation has continued to support the national program in 1966 and 1967 with a second grant of $324,000. Resident advisor services are provided by the Foundation through the Population Council.

With Ford Foundation assistance, the Population Council has contributed $750,000 to the Ministry of Public Health and Social Affairs since 1963 for aid in establishing the national family planning program and providing medical and demographic advisors. In 1966, the Council granted $26,243 for the experimental demographic program and $39,000 for demographic advisors. In addition, it granted $92,138 for support of a resident advisor, a medical advisor, and a physician trainee. The Council provided $8,560 in 1966 to the University of Tunis Centre d'Etudes et de Recherches Economiques et Sociales for demographic training and research.

Expected to begin full-scale operation in 1968 is a Mother-Child Health Center constructed and supported by the Swedish Government under an agreement signed with Tunisia in 1963. A family planning clinic at the Center is to provide medical treatment, consultation, and training. The staff includes a gynecologist, pediatrician, two midwives and two nurses. Through 1968, Swedish assistance has totaled $474,000.

The Pathfinder Fund has donated some contraceptives.

The Economic Commission for Africa, a United Nations organization, provides fellowships for Tunisian students attending the Rabat statistical institute.

II

AIR POLLUTION

Air pollution is for the most part a phenomenon of urban living that occurs when the capacity of the air to dilute pollutants is overburdened. Population and industrial growth and a high degree of dependence on the motor vehicle have caused new gaseous and particulate emissions; these complement, interact with, and further complicate the traditional problems of dust and wind.

Although there has been a history of air pollution "disasters" in the United States—Donora, Los Angeles, New York City—federal legislation to control air pollution was not passed until 1955. Even at this late date there were no viable state air pollution control programs. Until that time the only legislative progress made in the United States had been at the municipal level, but here too the effects were not exactly heartening: Chicago and Cincinnati passed smoke control laws in 1881 and by 1912, 23 cities with populations over 200,000 had passed similar laws. However, these had little effect on the pollution problem. Visible improvement in the air of many industrial cities was finally achieved only because an outraged public forced enactment and enforcement of improved smoke control legislation during the 1930's, 1940's and 1950's.

Since 1955, Congress has enacted several pieces of legislation dealing exclusively with air pollution. Acts passed in 1963, 1965, 1967 and 1970 have concentrated on standard setting and the creation of air quality control regions within states and within interstate regions. By May, 1971, the Environmental Protection Agency (EPA) had set national maximum standards for pollution levels. Although EPA Administrator William D. Ruckelshaus was quoted as saying, "These are tough standards", many environmentalists seem to disagree. As Ralph Nader pointed out, these have been exceeded by standards already set in several of the air quality regions.

The quest for standards which are reasonable from an environmental as well as an economic standpoint is at the very least a difficult one. Azriel Teller, in his essay entitled "Air Pollution Abatement: Economic Rationality and Reality," discusses several aspects of this issue through a cost-benefit analysis of economic and social factors. Teller feels that since pollution problems differ from region to region, due to conditions of geography, industry, number of motor vehicles, etc., the choice of standards should be made at the local or regional level.

The problem of enforcement, based primarily on the provisions of the 1963 Clean Air Act, has taken a back seat to the efforts to devise workable standards. Nearly a dozen enforcement conferences have been held and a number of suits have been brought against pollutors. However, the procedures involved in enforcing the regulations allow the pollutor to continue operation for several years following the initiation of a suit. Witness the case of the notorious chicken rendering plant in Bishop, Maryland, a case in which five years of conferences, public hearings, suits, and appeals were required before the plant was finally forced into compliance.

The problems of enforcement are discussed by George H. Hagevik in "The Los Angeles Experience." Hagevik analyzes the experience of Los Angeles in facing up to its air pollution problem, notably the worst in the nation. Although there is disagreement on the degree of success which Los Angeles can be said to have achieved through its program, at the very least it is obvious that the city is better off than it would have been if these endeavors, however experimental and inadequate, had not been made.

The problems of standards and enforcement require extensive research. The federal Air Pollution Control office (APCO) supports a broad program of research and development programs, with a fiscal year 1970 budget of $59.3 million and requests for 1971 of $63.3 million. The two principal areas currently under study include the development of technology for the control of stationary sources and the development of new low-emission power systems for motor vehicles. Emphasis in the first of these areas has been on the problem of controlling sulfur oxides and nitrogen oxides. It is hoped that the automotive industry will be able to develop at least two unconventional vehicle prototypes and to demonstrate commercial feasibility by 1975, but this goal is regarded as unrealistic by many supporters as well as critics of the automotive industry.

Bleak though prospects for developing new automotive engines may seem, it is essential that progress be made in this area, if we are to prevent increased pollution of our air. Despite strict standards and improved enforcement procedures, air pollution will continue to *increase steadily as more people drive more cars and use more electric power. It is expected, for example, that Americans will more than triple their use of electricity in the next 20 years and that the production of automobiles could and probably will climb to 41,000 a day by 1980—well over the present rate of 22,000 cars per day. Hence, pollution from automobiles will continue virtually unabated, regardless of present and planned controls.*

The impact of these developments on the quality of our air will without doubt be significant. Therefore, the air pollution control program should give special consideration to (1) the development of alternatives to the internal combustion engine, and (2) finding non-polluting methods of burning fuel to produce power and heat homes. The degree to which these goals are achieved will depend largely on the amount of pressure brought to bear on legislators and administrators by the general public.

4. Air-Pollution Abatement:
Economic Rationality and Reality

AZRIEL TELLER

1

A staff Report to the Committee on Public Works of the United States Senate stated: "There is strong evidence that air pollution is associated with a number of respiratory ailments. These include: (1) nonspecific infectious upper respiratory disease, (2) chronic bronchitis, (3) chronic constrictive ventilatory disease, (4) pulmonary emphysema, (5) bronchial asthma, and (6) lung cancer." [1]

Air pollution affects vegetation and livestock and causes property damage. "Most common materials are adversely affected by pollution. Metals corrode, fabrics weaken and fade, leather weakens and becomes brittle, rubber cracks and loses its elasticity, paint discolors, concrete and building stone discolor and erode, glass is etched, and paper becomes brittle." [2]

Residents of such areas as Chicago, New York, Philadelphia, Los Angeles, Cleveland, Detroit, St. Louis, Pittsburgh, and Boston are demanding that something be done to reduce the level of air pollution. For most pollutants, the question is not how to control air pollution, but rather how much to control it. Pollutants like fly ash can be controlled to the 99.9 percentile, but is this necessary? One must ask this question because air-pollution abatement is not free. In fact, the cost of air-pollution abatement rises at an increasing rate as the level of abatement increases. Assume, for example, that there are three identical control devices, each with a rated efficiency of 90 per cent, in series with one another. This means that for every thousand particles in the gas stream, nine hundred will be removed by the first device, and one hundred will remain in the gas stream to enter the second device. Ninety particles will be removed by the second device, leaving ten to enter the third device, where nine will be removed.

This leaves one particle remaining in the gas stream to be emitted into the atmosphere. Thus, one control device removes 90 per cent of the particles; two control devices, 99 per cent; and three control devices, 99.9. A 100 per cent increase in expenditure, therefore, results in a 10 per cent increase in abatement. A 200 per cent increase in expenditure results in an 11 per cent increase in abatement. Is this extra expenditure worthwhile? At the present time, no one can prove that it is. Nevertheless, a number of people firmly believe that the extra expenditure is necessary. Dr. E. Cuyler Hammond of the American Cancer Society, for example, has cautioned: "While we do not yet know the importance of various components of general air pollution, it would appear to be wise to reduce general air pollution of all types insofar as possible." [3] It is such specious reasoning that compels me to present an economic rationale for air-pollution abatement.

2

Economic Rationale

Clean air is a scarce resource. So are land, trees, human beings, animals, petroleum, and water. Like water, air is essential to life; however, unlike most resources, there is no market place in which air is bought and sold. This situation is not due to the inherent role air plays in our daily lives. (Food is also a necessity, but it is bought and sold daily.) It results, rather, from the nature of the product: The services of air are demanded by all but owned by none. Air is a collective good, and, therefore, it is society's responsibility to see that it is allocated efficiently.

Economics has two main applications to the study of air pollution. It enables one to estimate either the extent of the damage resulting from air pollution (that is, the external diseconomies of production) so that it can be rectified, or the market structure for clean air so as to determine the necessary amount of abatement. Since there is no formal market for the services of air (approach two), firms are allowed to impute their cost of production to some members of society (approach one). Thus, the two approaches are not separate and independent. There is a difference, however, between the two implications. Th first approach implies that firms have not been "good citizens" of society and consequently must be prohibited from contaminating the atmosphere. It suggests that it is unjust for producers to transfer their costs of production to an innocent party, that such practices should be stopped, and that the damages be rectified. But this is an all-or-nothing proposition. If approach one is used and it is decided that these diseconomies should be eliminated, there is no halfway point in eliminating the costs to society.

But there is another side of the problem that is rarely discussed— the diseconomies of consumption on the part of human beings, plants, and animals. Because they demand the resource air to be of a certain quality, they are imposing a cost on industries that also use this resource. Firms that would normally not abate are forced to, but the consumer of clean air does not pay directly for any costs of abatement.

This inconsistency can be demonstrated by an analogy. Let us assume that two brothers jointly own a piece of property. One brother uses the air over the property for testing high-altitude jet airplanes. The other brother uses the property to make sound movies. Obviously, the airplanes can be tested while movies are being made, whereas the opposite is not possible. These two activities could operate simultaneously if the noise from the jet were muffled. Who should pay for these mufflers? The jet pilot argues that both his brother and he have the right to use the property as they please. The pilot contends that since the moviemaker has selected an endeavor requiring quiet, he should pay for the mufflers. The moviemaker argues that his brother should bear the full cost, since his planes are disturbing the natural state. Approach one implies that the moviemaker has a just argument.

Analogically, no individual has the endowed right to obtain clean air free, simply because it is a necessity. A person does have the right, however, to have the opportunity to purchase clean air. Similarly, a person does not obtain food free because it is a necessity. Just because it is a necessity, a person has the right to have an opportunity to purchase food. Nevertheless, there are differences in the opportunities to obtain food, which is a private good, and clean air, which is a collective good. With a private good, if an individual wants a resource of a certain quality, he can purchase it himself. But with a collective good, the individual may not be able to obtain the quality he desires in a particular resource. Society as a whole might not want it. Society must simulate the market structure for collective goods like clean air and attempt to allocate them efficiently. It can only do this if it can estimate the demand and supply schedules for clean air.

In attempting to simulate the market for air, it is important to realize that demand and supply schedules are different for those sectors of society that produce air pollution and those that are affected by it.[4] The sources of air pollution have a demand for "air," whereas receptors have a demand for "clean air." These are different commodities; as such, the "demands" cannot be aggregated. In reality, there is no schedule for either the supply of air or the demand for air. The supply is there and, from our point of view, is essentially infinite. It can also be assumed that a source's demand for the resource air is infinite, since it could not operate without air. This is equivalent to the normal assumption that an individual's demand for air is infinite, since without air a person dies. Thus, there is no market for the commodity air, and no possibility of simulating one. In contrast, the supply of clean air increases as the degree of pollution decreases. The supply schedule for clean air can, therefore, be determined by estimating how much it would cost sources to reduce pollution. The demand for clean air can be determined by estimating the cost of the physical and psychic damage that results from different levels of air pollution and assuming that receptors would be willing to pay up to this amount so as not to incur such damage. This is, of course, not to say that they actually pay this amount.[5] This procedure can be illustrated with an example.

Table I / Cost to Society from Air-Pollution Damage
Cost to Society for Air-Pollution Control

Level of Abatement (per cent)	Total Damage TD	Total Cost of Control TC	Total Cost to Society TD + TC
10	$370	$ 15	$385
20	270	25	295
30	200	35	235
40	140	50	190
50	90	70	160
60	60	105	165
70	45	145	190
80	30	210	240
90	20	320	340
100	0	430	430

Let us assume that Table 1 lists the costs of the annual total damage to society that results with no abatement and also to estimated damage that would occur after different degrees of abatement. With 100 per cent abatement, no damage occurs. Table 1 also lists a schedule of the total cost of abatement. Society desires to minimize the total cost from both types of expenditures, as both are costs to society. With no abatement, too many of society's resources are being used to offset the effects of air pollution. Conversely, with 100 per cent abatement, too many of society's resources are being used to control air pollution. The objective is to select a level of abatement that minimizes the total cost to society. In the example, the optimum point is 50 per cent abatement. At this level, the resources of society are being allocated efficiently.

One can also determine the optimum level of abatement by charting the benefits and costs of abatement. The benefits from abatement can be defined as the value of the damage that is averted by abatement. There are other benefits to society besides those from air-pollution abatement. These are the benefits from national defense, automobile safety, foreign aid, production, clean water, recreation, and so forth. In order to achieve each of these benefits, one must incur a cost. With respect to private goods, it is a private cost. With collective goods, it is a collective or social cost. The value of abatement to society is the difference between the benefits from abatement and the cost of abatement. If society simulates the market structure for collective goods and attempts to allocate them efficiently, it must choose that level of abatement with the greatest value to society.

A benefit-from-abatement schedule can be obtained from the cost-of-air-pollution schedule listed in Table 1. With no abatement, the damage resulting from air pollution is valued at $370. With 10 per cent abatement, the annual cost from pollution decreases to $270. Thus, the benefit to society from 10 per cent abatement is $100, the difference in damage between no abatement and 10 per cent abatement.[6] The resulting benefits-from-abatement schedule is listed in Table 2. The cost-of-abatement schedule is the same as in Table 1.

Table 2 / Benefit and Cost of Abatement

Level of Abatement (per cent)	Benefit TB ($)	Cost TC ($)	Value to Society TB–TC ($)
0	0	0	0
10	100	15	85
20	170	25	145
30	230	35	195
40	280	50	230
50	310	70	240
60	325	105	220
70	340	145	195
80	350	210	140
90	360	320	40
100	370	430	—60

It shows the total cost of achieving each degree of air-pollution abatement. The objective is to select the level of abatement that maximizes the value to society. From Table 2, the optimum level of abatement is at 50 per cent with the total value of $240. Any other level of abatement would not be efficient, as it would be of less value to society. Two other important points can be seen from this simple example. First, the level of abatement selected when the benefits and cost of abatement are compared is the same as the level selected when total costs to society are minimized. Second, simply knowing that the total benefits for any single level of abatement are greater than the total cost does not help society in deciding where to operate. It does not indicate to society whether to increase abatement, as is the case for 10–40 per cent abatement, or to decrease abatement, as is the case for 60–90 per cent abatement. People often justify erroneously a level of control on the basis of the benefits of abatement being greater than the costs. C. W. Griffin, Jr., for example, stated in the *Saturday Review:*

> Even if air pollution presented no human health hazard whatsoever, we could justify a tremendous strengthening of control on purely economic grounds. . . . The nation's total bill is estimated at $11 billion a year, about twenty times the most optimistic estimate of the total national expenditures by industry and by all levels of government for control devices, research and enforcement programs.[7]

Even though Mr. Griffin states otherwise, his dubious estimates do not justify the conclusion that more abatement is necessary.[8] In order for society to determine the desired level of abatement, both the total-benefit schedule and the total-cost schedule are needed.

3

Economic Rationality and Reality

The greatest impediment to applying the theoretical determination of the level of abatement is the difficulty of estimating the benefits from abatement. In order to make such a calculation, the first and most important requirement is that there be a knowledge of the effects of air pollution. The short-run effects of an increase in the concentration, as well as the long-run cumulative effects, must be known. At the present time, there is some evidence, but there is no proof. This fact was clearly illustrated in a paper recently presented by E. Cuyler Hammond.[9] The paper, entitled "Epidemiological Evidence on the Effects of Air Pollution," surveyed the present knowledge of the influences of occupational, personal (for example, tobacco smoke), and general air pollution on morbidity and mortality. With respect to general air pollution, his findings on some diseases are as follows:

Lung Cancer

I want to make it clear that I am not dismissing general air pollution as a possible contributing factor to the occurrence of lung cancer at some future date. I doubt that general air pollution will ever rise to such a level as to present a large risk of lung cancer to the non-smoker; if it should do so, then lung cancer would probably be the least of our worries. However, if general air pollution should continue to increase in the future as it has in the past, it may well result in a considerable increase in the risk of lung cancer among smokers and among persons exposed to certain types of occupational air pollution.[10]

Chronic Bronchitis

Goldsmith has reviewed the literature on chronic respiratory disease in relation to general air pollution. As he points out in this connection: "No excess mortality from chronic respiratory diseases has been documented." On the other hand, available evidence appears to me to indicate that at least in England an "urban factor" of some sort increases morbidity from such disease. Presumably, the "urban factor" is air pollution. . . . The evidence is overwhelming that personal air pollution, in the form of cigarette smoking, causes a very great increase in both mortality and morbidity from chronic bronchitis.[11]

Emphysema

Both among non-smokers with occupational exposure and among non-smokers without occupational exposure, the rural percentages were a little higher than the metropolitan percentages. . . . This was generally the case among cigarette smokers (age and amount of smoking being taken into consideration).[12]

Coronary Heart Disease

Extreme general air pollution also appears to lead to an increase in deaths from coronary artery disease. . . . So far as I know, there is little or no evidence concerning the possibility of an association between coronary artery disease and general air pollution not exceeding the levels ordinarily present in many large cities.[13]

While there is some evidence that air pollution influences morbidity and mortality, there is no substantiation to the statement that "it would appear to be wise to reduce general air pollution of all types insofar as possible."[14]

The paucity of data does not imply that nothing should be done while further research is conducted on the effects of air pollution on material property and plant, animal, and human life. Air-quality standards should be established with the understanding that they may be changed as more evidence is accumulated. In the future, they may be made either more restrictive or more lenient. Two rationales are used in establishing air-quality standards. Each calls for a different approach to abatement.

Rationale One

The air-quality standard is set at that concentration which, if exceeded, would be "harmful" to society. If it is possible to predict when the standard will be exceeded, then it is necessary to abate only when trouble is expected.

Tragically, there is too much evidence on the effects of high short-run concentrations of pollutants. In recent times, serious air-pollution episodes have resulted in numerous deaths. The most acute was in London in 1952 when an excess of four thousand deaths occurred in a five-day period. These episodes can be predicted and abated. One approach is the air-pollution warning system proposed by the New York-New Jersey Co-Operative Commission in Interstate Air Pollution.[15] The proposal is worthwhile, first of all, because it recognizes that acute air-pollution episodes occur sporadically and can be predicted. Secondly, the degree of abatement reflects the situation at that moment. If the situation worsens, a greater amount of abatement can be used. According to the proposal, an air-pollution watch would be called if the meteorologists forecasted stable weather conditions for

Table 3 / Standards for Air-Pollution Alerts

Alert Status	Air Concentrations SO₂ ppm	CO ppm	Smoke Level COHS	Duration Sustained Levels of Air Concentrations (Hours)		N.Y.-N.J. Metro. Area Meteorology High Air-Pollution Potential Forecast for Next Hours	Act Pl.
Air-Pollution							
Watch	.5	10+	5.0	1	and/or	36	
FIRST	.7+	10+	7.5	4	and	36	
SECOND	1.5+	20+	9.0	2	and	12	
THIRD	2.0+	30+	10.0	1	and	8	

the next thirty-six hours, or if the air-pollution concentrations for sulfur dioxide, carbon monoxide, and smoke exceeded the levels listed in Table 3 for one hour. If the air-pollution concentrations and meteorological conditions further deteriorated to the levels listed in Table 3, an air-pollution alert would be called. The standards and the control actions taken under each alert are discussed below.[16]

First Alert: When air-pollution measurements exceed the standards for a first alert and the meteorological forecast indicates that profound stable air conditions will exist for the period of time tabulated on Table [3] . . . the Interstate Sanitation Commission recommends a first alert. If the states declare an alert, the following control measures will be taken by co-operating governmental agencies:

1. Large consumers of fuel are notified that an emergency is pending and are asked to reduce voluntarily their total fuel consumption to a minimum and substitute low-pollution-potential fuel where possible.

2. Industries and operators of municipal and commercial incinerators are asked to limit their activities which contribute to air pollution, except in those cases that are considered exempt, such as hospitals and other institutions essential to public health, safety, and welfare.

3. Motor vehicle operators are asked to reduce their activities to a minimum.

4. The public and refuse disposal operators are asked to cease open burning.

Second Alert: A second alert is recommended by the Interstate Sanitation Commission to the state agencies when the concentrations of air pollutants have reached the values established as the standard for this alert, when the weather forecast is for continued stable air conditions, or if the first alert has been in operation for twenty-four hours without a reduction in pollution. If a state declares a second alert, the co-operating government agencies require that all measures for the first alert be continued, with more stringent limitations on the consumption of fuel other than natural gas or Grade No. 2 fuel oil. Limitations are also set on the heating of homes and buildings, the use of domestic incinerators, and industrial operations. Motor vehicle operators are asked to cease operation on a voluntary basis.

Third Alert: It should be noted that a third alert indicates a serious danger to public health. The Interstate Sanitation Commission recommends a third alert to the state agencies when the concentrations of pollutants have reached the standards established for this alert, when the weather forecast is for continued profound stable air conditions, or when the second alert has been in operation for twenty-four hours (that is, a total of forty-eight hours after the initiation of the first alert) without reduction of pollution. If a state declares a third alert, the following actions are taken by the co-operating agencies and organizations:

1. All control activities of the first and second alert are continued.

2. Stringent limitations are imposed on traffic throughout the metropolitan area except for emergency vehicles.

3. Action is taken to reduce to a minimum industrial and commercial activity and public transportation.

Consideration is being given to limiting pollution by the following ways:

1. Stringent restrictions on the use and delivery of fuel oil, diesel oil, and motor fuels

2. Stringent restrictions on the burning of fuels other than gas

3. A curfew on lighting and heating similar to the brownout and heating limits during wartime.

Since operating and maintenance costs are functions of the number of hours a piece of equipment is utilized, the use of a regional warning system suggests an economical approach to the selection and use of air-pollution-control equipment. Depending on a city's industry, topography, and climate, the frequency of air-pollution episodes may range from zero to 100 per cent of the time. When a problem day is forecasted, it may be decreed that companies utilize their control equipment. This does not mean that companies cannot use their equipment more than is required or install more efficient equipment than is necessary. It does imply, however, that companies need not operate their abatement equipment 100 per cent of the time in order to satisfy th air-quality standards established by the control authorities. They may, therefore, invest more economically in control equipment.

The value of any warning system depends on how well weather conditions can be predicted. Like most other subjects within the area of air pollution, there is very little information on the ability of meteorologists to forecast air-pollution potential. Lawrence E. Niemeyer found that the highest particulate matter concentrations occurred in those periods when the following criteria were met:

1. Surface winds less than 8 knots

2. Winds at no level below 500 millibars (approximately 18,000 feet) greater than 25 knots

3. Subsidence, the slow sinking or settling of air from aloft, below 600 millibars (approximately 14,000 feet)

4. Simultaneous occurrence of the above with the forecast continuance of these conditions for thirty-six hours or more.[17]

From August, 1960, to July, 1961, the criteria established by Niemeyer were tested in the area of the United States east of the Rockies.[18] Within this period of time, twelve stagnation cases occurred, ten of which were forecasted. Another eight cases were forecasted, but not verified. Thus, with a total of eighteen forecasts issued, 83 per cent of the stagnating cases were predicted. As the meteorologists gain experience in forecasting air-pollution potential, their ability to predict will presumably improve.

Rationale Two

There are short-run, single-dose effects and long-range cumulative effects from air pollution. Also, there is a known relationship between a single high concentration and the long-run average concentration. Thus, the air-quality standard can be set so as to reduce the single high concentrations. If society always abates to satisfy this standard, then the long-run average concentration will also be reduced to a desired level.

This appears to be the approach followed by most air-pollution-control authorities even though, as illustrated by Hammond's survey, there is little evidence on the cumulative effects of air pollution. It is sometimes argued that Rationale Two is necessary to forestall any acute build-up of air-pollution concentrations. This is equivalent to saying that a region must abate 100 per cent of the time since a serious air-pollution episode is expected to arise, without warning, one or two times a year. This reasoning underestimates the ability of meteorologists to forewarn control authorities.

In general, then, the choice is between constant abatement and forecasting abatement. Within each choice, a number of approaches may be utilized in determining the necessary degree and cost of abatement. The naïve approach, which incurs the greatest cost to society, guarantees that there will not be an air-pollution problem. Each variation on the naïve can be considered a refinement and is based on the extent of our knowledge of the state of the environment. As more modifications are made, however, the probability of satisfying the air-quality standard declines, whereas the probability of finding the least costly solution increases. There is a trade-off between achieving the desired air quality and the determination of the least costly method. The latter involves an associated probability that the standard will not be satisfied. But there is also a cost in not utilizing the minimum-cost solution. Thus, the extent to which each model is used is determined by the knowledge of the environment, the desire to satisfy the standard, the desire to achieve accuracy in the estimates, and the desire to find the least costly solution to the air-pollution problem.

Two possible approaches are equiproportional abatement and selective abatement.

The Naïve Approach—Equiproportional Abatement: **The** naïve approach is the simplest method to apply in determining the degree and the cost of abatement. The approach assumes that all sources will reduce their emissions in the same proportion as the desired reduction in air-pollution concentration. Many people believe that this is the most equitable procedure since a source that accounts for x per cent of the total emissions is thus responsible for x per cent of the reduction. In reality, however, a source that emits x per cent of the emissions may be responsible for less than, or more than, x per cent of the concentration.

Selective Abatement: Selective abatement aims to find the minimum cost combination of abatement while still satisfying the air-quality standards. The theory behind selective abatement is that the cost of a unit reduction of emission is not necessarily the same for all sources, and that the effect upon a particular receptor of a unit reduction of emissions is not necessarily the same for all sources. Thus, for each source it is necessary to know the cost of abatement, the amount of emissions, and the relationship between that source and any receptor. The latter is sometimes known as a meteorological diffusion model.[19]

City-wide or industry-wide emission standards are examples of equiproportional abatement. They generally state that all sources of pollution of a given magnitude must reduce their emissions to a certain level. Even if a source is located on the downwind side of an air-shed, it must control its emissions to the same degree as a similar source located upwind. The consequence of emission standards is that some sources do not control their emissions enough, while others must exercise too much control. Moreover, firms do not have an incentive to relocate in an effort to reduce their effect on the level of concentration. In some cases, relocation might be a more efficient method of control than abatement by equipment. Emission standards make relocation impotent. Nevertheless, emission standards are more efficient than selective abatement when the cost of implementing and supervising selective abatement is greater than the additional benefits that result from selective abatement. For most sources of air pollution, the cost of administering equiproportional abatement is equivalent to that of selective abatement. In those cases where the sources are small but numerous, however, the cost of administering selective abatement may be exorbitant. Examples of such sources are private residential units, small incinerators, back-yard burning of refuse, and automobiles. Moreover, because automobiles are mobile, the relationship between the emissions of any particular automobile and air quality cannot be accurately ascertained. In general, however, if society uses only equiproportional abatement, it has chosen an inefficient method of reducing air pollution.

In Table 4, the costs of different approaches to abatement are

Table 4 / Estimate of the Relative Cost of Sulfur-Dioxide Abatement
Through Fuel Substitution
1960 Estimate for Nashville Metropolitan Area [a]

	Air Quality Level [b]			
	1	2	3	4
	%	%	%	%
1. Constant Abatement				
a. Equiproportional	48.5	66.4	86.8	100.0
b. Selective	13.0	25.8	39.4	71.5
2. Forecasting Abatement				
a. Equiproportional				18.0
b. Selective				12.9

[a] Low-sulfur coal was substituted for high-sulfur coal
[b] Sulfur-Dioxide Air-Quality Standards:

Level	2-hour average concentration (ppm)	24-hour average concentration (ppm)
1	0.50	0.30
2	0.40	0.25
3	0.30	0.20
4	0.20	0.10

compared.[20] The relative cost of constant abatement and forecasting abatement differ substantially. To satisfy air-quality level 4 by constant abatement costs per year five and a half times as much as forecasting abatement. Within constant abatement, equiproportional abatement is relatively more expensive than selective abatement. Generally speaking, the more severe the air-pollution problem or the more restrictive the air-quality standard, the smaller is the difference between equiproportional abatement and selective abatement. Thus, each city or air-shed must determine, in light of its own air-pollution problems, the relative worth of equiproportional abatement and selective abatement.

IV

The Mayor's Task Force on Air Pollution in the City of New York reported: "If New York had the sheltered topography of Los Angeles, everyone in this city would long since have perished from the poisons in the air." [21] This is true, but the point is that New York City is not Los Angeles. Each city is different and has its unique problems. The sources of pollution, types of pollution, receptors of pollution, and meteorology vary among cities. What is good for Los Angeles may not be good for New York. What is good for New York may not be good for Chicago. There can be neither a national blueprint for solving the air-pollution problem nor national emission standards. Each city or air-shed must approach air-pollution abatement with respect to its own particular situation, determining for itself whether it needs constant abatement, forecasting abatement, or a combination of the two; and, within the alternative selected, whether it needs equiproportional abatement, selective abatement, or a combination. Each city must decide the air-quality standards it needs. This does not imply that every air-shed is unique, that one city cannot learn from another city. Nevertheless, one city should not follow another city's air-pollution program without questioning the reasons for a particular action. Such reasoning does not abrogate the role of the Federal Government. The Federal Government should concern itself with studying the short-run and long-run effects of air pollution. It should help to develop and improve methods of abatement, conduct research on more extensive meteorological diffusion models and better meteorological forecasting models, serve as a center for air-pollution information, and assist in organizing interstate air-pollution commissions. On the other hand, the Federal Government should not establish national air-quality standards and, more important, must not establish national emission standards.

NOTES

[1] U. S. Congress, Senate, "A Study of Pollution—Air," A Staff Report to the Committee on Public Works, 88th Congress, 1st Session, September, 1963, p. 14.

[2] Ibid., p. 20.

[3] E. Cuyler Hammond, "Epidemiological Evidence on the Effects of Air Pollution." A paper presented at the 60th Annual Meeting of the Air Pollution Control Association in Cleveland, Ohio, on June 14, 1967.

[4] Sources of air pollution include such things as automobiles, industry, and incinerators. Receptors encompass humans, plants, animals, and property.

[5] The demand for clean air can also be estimated by questioning everyone on how much they would be willing to pay for clean air (that is, how much

is clean air worth to them). Assuming that there is complete information on the damage resulting from air pollution, that the marginal disutility of damage can be measured in monetary terms, that everyone has the same marginal utility of money, and that everyone is honest, one should obtain the same answer as by the previous method.

[6] In general,

$$TB_a = TD_{a\ 0} - TD_a$$

where a: per cent abatement $0 < a < 1$

    TB_a: total benefit from "a" per cent abatement

    $TD_{a\ 0}$: total damage with no abatement

    TD_a: total damage with "a" per cent abatement

[7] C. W. Griffin, Jr., "America's Airborne Garbage," *Saturday Review* (May 22, 1965), p. 34.

[8] In 1913, the Mellon Institute estimated the cost of smoke nuisance in Pittsburgh. The $11 billion a year estimate for the United States is a 1959 price and population extrapolation from the Pittsburgh data.

[9] Hammond, "Epidemological Evidence on the Effects of Air Pollution."

[10] *Ibid*, p. 8.

[11] *Ibid*, pp. 13–14. See also J. R. Goldsmith, "Epidemology of Bronchitis and Emphysema," *Medicina Thoracalis*. Vol. 22 (1965), pp. 1–23.

[12] Hammond, "Epidemological Evidence on the Effects of Air Pollution," p. 19.

[13] *Ibid*, p. 20.

[14] *Ibid*, p. 23.

[15] T. A. Glenn, Jr., "Regional Air Pollution Warning System," *Journal of the Air Pollution Control Association*, (January, 1966), pp. 22–24.

[16] *Ibid*, pp. 23–24.

[17] Lawrence E. Niemeyer, "Forecasting Air Pollution Potential," *Monthly Weather Review*, Vol. 88 (March, 1960), pp. 88–96.

[18] Marvin Miller and Lawrence E. Niemeyer, "Air Pollution Potential Forecasts—A Year's Experience." *Journal of the Air Pollution Control Association*, Vol. 13 (May, 1963), pp. 205–10.

[19] For example, see D. B. Turner, "A Diffusion Model for an Urban Area," *Journal of Applied Meteorology*, Vol. 3, No. 1 (February, 1964), pp. 83–91.

[20] Azriel Teller, *Air-Pollution Abatement: An Economic Study Into the Cost of Control*, unpublished Ph.D. Dissertation, Johns Hopkins University, 1967.

[21] *Freedom to Breathe*, Report of the Mayor's Task Force on the Air Pollution in the City of New York (June 20, 1966), p. 27.

5. The Los Angeles Experience

GEORGE H. HAGEVIK

With the industrial growth and population boom caused by World War II, Los Angeles also gained an air pollution problem. The 1,200 square mile Los Angeles Basin, a mosaic of relatively small municipalities bounded on two sides by mountains, suffers frequent temperature inversions, light winds, and a high ozone content in its atmosphere. During the summer and autumn months, a large high-pressure area stagnates over the Pacific Ocean off the coast of California, sending warm air into the Los Angeles Basin over the top of the ocean-cooled breezes that skim along the surface. The warm air acts as a lid, preventing any vertical movement of the cooler air, at the surface. It was thus found in the mid-1940's that air pollutants originating anywhere in the basin are carried upward by surface air currents to the base of the lid or inversion layer where they accumulate, building up a reservoir of materials that can produce photochemical smog when acted upon by sunlight. This layer rises and lowers in response to changing meteorological conditions.

The first "smog attack" occurred in September, 1943, and such attacks increased in number and intensity during the next few years.[1] It became readily apparent that this "smog," visible as a light grey murkiness, restricted visibility and caused irritation to the eye, nose, and throat. In response to the worsening problem, Los Angeles officials brought in air pollution experts from eastern cities who declared that the smog was caused primarily by sulfur dioxide with assistance from smoke and dust.[2]

Mounting public pressure for the control of air pollution in Los Angeles resulted in the 1947 passage of the California Air Pollution Control Act, which authorized the creation of the Los Angeles County

George H. Hagevik, *Decision-Making in Air Pollution Control*. New York: Frederick A. Praeger, Inc., Publishers, pp. 81–92, 114–124. Copyright 1970 by Frederick A. Praeger, Inc.

Air Pollution Control District (APCD).[3] The District, established by the end of 1947, is governed by the five Supervisors of Los Angeles County sitting as the Board of Air Pollution Control, with jurisdiction over 75 political units and a large area of unincorporated land. Before the act was passed, the strongest threat to its viability was the opposition of the petroleum industry to the permit system which would require any industry building a new plant or revising an older plant to secure a permit to make sure that such plans and specifications met standards set by the District. The County Commissioners, by bringing this opposition to the attention of Los Angeles newspapers and holding a meeting with the major oil companies, convinced the companies to withdraw their opposition.[4] Initial control efforts were carried out on a broad front, but first priority was given to attacking visible sources of pollution—smoke, dust, and fumes. Much initial effort was given to the control of refuse burning and major industrial polluters.

Early Control Efforts

An across-the-board control effort was directed at industrial dust and fumes from metallurgical plants, rock-crushing operations, asphalt and paving processes, the food, paint, fertilizer, and soap industries, the thousands of orchard heaters used to prevent frost damage, and diesel trucks and buses. By the fall of 1948, it was determined by using air samples that there was a fairly high sulfur dioxide content in the atmosphere; this led to initial efforts by the District to control such emissions.[5] In response to proposed regulations aimed at them, the major oil companies said that the proposed recommendations were "inequitable, too strict, and would result in unwarranted expense to the petroleum industry without sufficient proof that the removal of the sulfur would cure the overall smog problem." [6] Powerful support for the District's position developed among the public on this issue and the Los Angeles Times publicly supported the District. Thus, the first of a long series of efforts to control the oil industry began.

By 1949, grey iron foundaries were controlled. The District's hearing board, in response to claims of excessive control costs, calculated that grey iron costs would be increased less than two mills per pound of product and concluded that this would not be a factor in pricing Los Angeles foundaries out of their competitive market. Within a period of 36 months from the date of the ruling, 36 bag-houses and three electrostatic precipitators had been designed, constructed, and approved by the District.[7] By 1951, the last of the open-hearth steel furnaces in the Los Angeles Basin had installed control devices, and floating lids on oil storage tanks to reduce evaporation of hydrocarbons were universally required.

By the early 1950's, the use of the Ringelmann Chart as a technique for the measurement of smoke emissions had aided in the virtual elimination of the problem of black smoke and soot from the Los Angeles area.* After this removal, it became apparent that there was a serious problem associated with gasoline vapors in that eye irritation and crop damage are caused largely by the oxidation of these vapors to form photochemical smog. These vapors—or hydrocarbons as they are more accurately called—enter the atmosphere from many sources, such as auto exhausts and losses in the storage, refining, and handling of petroleum products. Thus, the 1954 program of the District called for a major reduction of the emission into the atmosphere of gasoline vapors from automobiles and the control of automobile exhausts. (Since this study deals with stationary sources of pollution, only passing attention is given to automobile air pollution emissions.)[8]

By 1954, six different control approaches had been used in the five preceding years in about 28,000 enforcement actions[9] (a program of zoning to put objectionable industries where they would do the least harm from an air pollution point of view was also given some emphasis). Criminal proceedings, written notices of violations, office hearings, civil injunction actions, Hearing Board actions, and the granting and denial of permits were used. Written notices and cease and desist orders were issued for every violation observed. In more than 90 per cent of the actions that went to the next step of office hearings, compliance was obtained with no further action. In the small minority of cases that went to court, the District chose criminal actions rather than civil actions because of the long time required to complete a civil case. The District's permit system, however, was deemed to be the agency's most effective weapon.[10]

The Incinerator Ban

At the outset of the air pollution control program in 1948, the burning of rubbish was an obvious source of air pollutants; it was estimated that more than 500 tons of air contaminants were released from these sources daily. The first targets for control were the burning refuse

---

* The Ringelmann chart provides a scale for comparing the darkness and opaqueness of visible smoke to absolute levels. Published by the U. S. Bureau of Mines, the chart is a series of different line density squares which can be compared to smoke coming from stacks. It was developed in Paris and brought to this country in 1897.

dumps. Fifty-five of these were closed by the District, in many cases over bitter opposition and only after court action.[11] From 1948 to 1949, civil action and injunction proceedings were instituted against municipal and private dumps. After 1949, more direct action was employed by taking criminal action against the owners of individual dumps. Following this, all other open fires were restricted. One Los Angeles phenomenon—the backyard incinerator—and its several thousand commercial and industrial counterparts—proved to be more difficult sources to control. Suggested control measures were met with strong protests from delegations of homeowners and domestic incinerator manufacturers, and it was only when the smog continued to get worse that a control measure was approved.

A number of meetings were held in the early 1950's under the direction of the County Board of Supervisors by the District and the air pollution control committee of the Los Angeles County Division of the League of California Cities in which an attempt was made to find a substitute for the 1.5 million back-yard incinerators.[12] The alternatives suggested were collection by the municipalities or county and (a) county incineration or (b) sanitary landfill. In 1953, the District requested the County Counsel for an opinion as to the legality of a regulation forbidding the disposal of refuse by burning, except in multiple-chamber incinerators, or in an incinerator used in conjunction with a dwelling with not more than four dwelling units. The County Counsel reported that such a prohibition would be legal providing it was reasonable from a practical or engineering point of view. As H. Kennedy notes, the opinion held that:

> Since the burning of rubbish does give off substantial smoke and fumes it would be within the jurisdiction of the Air Pollution Control Board to forbid such burning if it finds that the air in the District is so polluted as to cause discomfort or property damage at intervals to a substantial number of inhabitants and that the regulation will reduce the amount of air contamination in the District.[13]

Although the California Air Pollution Control Act provided that air pollutants could be eliminated irrespective of their source and it was clear that the Air Pollution Control District could restrict these sources of pollution under its police power by adopting a formal rule at a public hearing before the Board of Supervisors, the District was still hard put to justify its decisions due to incomplete knowledge and inadequate data. Many people thought that incinerators were an insignificant source of air pollution that should only be controlled after industrial emissions were regulated. On the other hand, the automobile industry was reluctant to reduce the hydrocarbon emissions from cars as long as pollution from incineration remained untouched. A variety of "experts" for and against an incinerator ban were quoted in the newspapers and appeared on television. As a result, county residents were sharply divided on the value of the ban.

Partially as a result of a study that showed that about half of the total charge burned in a single-chamber incinerator escaped into the air, the County Board of Supervisors passed the incinerator control measure on June 9, 1955.[14] The first deadline for ending incineration was October 1, 1955, but, as that date approached, it became obvious that no other adequate means of refuse disposal could be provided in such a brief period. To permit the county and communities within the county to make suitable arrangements, the deadline was extended to October 1, 1957. However, as the extension was allowed only as a leeway for the municipalities to arrange service for domestic users, an advance deadline of July 1, 1957, was established for stores, factories, and apartment houses.

The controls on refuse burning instituted by the District thus occurred in four distinct phases:

(1) Elimination of municipal and private open burning dumps, which was accomplished by enforcement action in 1950.
(2) Elimination of all other types of open fire burning related to industrial, commercial, or residential activities.
(3) Elimination of industrial, commercial, and multifamily waste disposal in single-chamber incinerators, accomplished by July 1, 1957.
(4) The ban on all other single-chamber incinerators, which became effective on October 1, 1957.

As a result of these control measures, uncontrolled refuse burning has been effectively prohibited in Los Angeles County since the end of 1957. Disposal of refuse by burning now is possible only in multiple-chamber incinerators, with county collection and sanitary landfill the major means of disposal. Many apartment houses and industries turned to multiple-chamber incinerators in which the gases and particulates ordinarily emitted from single-chamber incinerators are further heated and burned at temperatures ranging up to 2,000 degrees. In operation, they proved to emit only 10 per cent of the pollutants emitted by the ones they replaced.

One of the most significant benefits associated with these abatement policies was the cessation of community recriminations traditionally associated with the Los Angeles smog control effort. Until the adoption of the ban, it was popular in Los Angeles County to argue against specific proposed control measures on the grounds that refuse burning was an obvious source of uncontrolled air pollution, and that so long as refuse burning remained uncontrolled, there was no point to controlling other lesser sources. This view was particularly ascribed to representatives of the automobile industry, who often pointed out that auto exhausts probably were unimportant sources of air pollution compared with the pollution emissions from refuse burning.[15] The refuse burning ban ended the relevance of this argument.

Benefits more susceptible to empirical measurement included a marked decline in public complaints against specific incinerator operations. Prior to 1957, complaints against such operations led the list of complaints received by the District. These complaints decreased 54 per cent from 1957 to 1958. From 1955 through 1957, three indicators of air pollution—reduced visibility, plant damage, and eye irritation—showed a downward trend, and the number of days during which smog alerts were called decreased. The fire department also found that, due to the incinerator ban, the number of individual responses to alarms was reduced by some 50,000 to 60,000 a year. The cost of removing the refuse formerly burned has been estimated at about one dollar per household per month.[16]

The Conflict Over Rule 62

The mid-1950's was the turning point for the District. From 1954 through 1956, more than $8 million was spent for District operation and research; the Federal Government was spending only $8.6 million nationally. By 1957, smog had been reduced to the level where any significant further reduction would have to be accomplished by automobile exhaust controls. The most important stationary sources of air pollutants left in the basin were steam electric power generating plants whose burning of fuel oil to generate electricity yielded large amounts of sulfur oxides and smaller, but still significant, contributions of oxides of nitrogen and particulate matter.

When oil is being burned in such plants, conspicuous plumes are emitted from stacks and particles that fall in the vicinity often cause property damage. The solution recognized by the District at this time was the substitution of natural gas for fuel oil, which would eliminate sulfur oxides, particulates, plumes, and localized fallout and possibly reduce oxides of nitrogen by more than half. By late 1957, the political climate for controlling sulfur-bearing fuels was favorable because the District could point to the fact that the households in the Los Angeles Basin had recently absorbed the costs associated with the back-yard incinerator ban. The obvious question being asked was: "If households can absorb these costs, why can't industry?"

The District concluded that large sulfur dioxide concentrations in the atmosphere should be reduced because of a rising tide of scientific opinion concerning the health effects of sulfur dioxide. Although there was little basic research, what has been done suggested to the District staff that sulfur dioxide in the air was a causative factor in certain illnesses or at least a factor that aggravated certain illnesses.* The critical turning point for decision was the discovery that the sulfur dioxide readings in the Long Beach area were as high as any place in the country and the realization that much of the sulfur dioxide was being emitted by public utility power plants.

Because the District realized that the only clear alternative to burning sulfur-bearing fuel oil for electricity-generating purposes at that time was the substitution of natural gas for the fuel oil,** there was concern for the fact that it would not be legally possible to force public utilities to change fuels unless there was a guaranteed source of alternative fuel. Thus, the District staff as early as 1956 was appearing before the California Public Utilities Commission in support of requests for increasing the allocation of natural gas to Southern California. In mid-1957, the County Board of Supervisors urged the Federal Power Commission to approve the request of the El Paso Natural Gas Company to allow the company to construct and operate facilities that would enable El Paso to carry out exchange agreements for the delivery of natural gas to the Los Angeles Basin. Shortly afterward, the board approved a policy urging all electricity-generating agencies to take whatever action necessary to make additional quantities of natural gas available for the use as fuel in the generation of power. By the middle of August, 1957, the District initiated a program calling for the voluntary use of natural gas in steam electric generating plants and large industries during smog alerts.

By October, 1958, the District was holding hearings on a proposed rule to require steam power plants to burn natural gas between May 1 and October 30—the period of minimal demand for natural gas for space-heating purposes. Although the use of natural gas was not to be specifically required, the proposed rule stated that fuel oils containing more than one half of 1 per cent sulfur were to be prohibited, together

* Although it was subsequently shown that sulfur dioxide was a minor agent in the formation of photochemical smog, the primary thrust of later legislation was that sulfur dioxide and sulfates were dangerous to health in and of themselves.

** Meeting the required limit of anticipated regulations using fuel oil was not considered feasible since imported crude oil of low sulfur content would have to be used and such crude oil was under strict federal control.

with gaseous fuels containing more than 50 grains of sulfur per 100 cubic feet of gas. The only fuel available to meet this requirement was natural gas.

Although the principal impact would be on steam plants, an estimated 20,000 firms, including manufacturing companies, oil refineries, and ferrous and nonferrous metal smelting industries would also be affected. At this time, steam power plants were using 30,500 barrels of fuel oil a day, refineries 8,000 barrels, and all other industrial sources 16,000 barrels. Whereas the fuel oil used in the basin at this time had a sulfur content ranging upward from $1\frac{1}{2}$ per cent, the District estimated that the measure would eliminate 400 tons of air contaminants of which more than 272 tons were sulfur dioxide. This would result in an estimated 50 per cent reduction in sulfur dioxide levels in the air. During this period, "interruptible"* industrial users of natural gas were using 400 million cubic feet daily from May through September. Local gas companies stated they could supply an additional 275 million cubic feet a day, which would be the equivalent of 48,000 barrels of fuel oil.

When the hearings on the proposed requirement to burn natural gas were started, public interest was greater than at any time since the prolonged debate over the back-yard incinerator ban.[17] The District took the position that the proposed rule was needed to prevent a major health catastrophe and relied on noted consultants to point out *possible* developments, such as the lengthy concentrations of sulfur dioxide that had occurred over Donora, Pennsylvania, and London. The District's position was that there had been a 100 per cent increase in sulfur dioxide emissions during the last seven years and that this rise transformed the sulfur dioxide problem from mainly a public nuisance to a potential health hazard even though a clear cause-and-effect relationship between sulfur dioxide concentrations and illness or death could not be specified.

The District also argued that to control one source and not another would be to undermine the entire pollution control program and would raise serious doubts as to the equity of other control measures. Failure to pass the rule was further viewed as allowing industry to continue to violate the state health and safety code as well as the rules of the District. Support for the District's position came from the Los Angeles

---

* Also referred to as "dump" gas, interruptible users receive this gas at a reduced rate during periods when it is not in demand by prime users. Interruptible customers can have their supply cut off when prime customers need additional gas.

County Medical Association and a citizens group based in Pasadena.

Conflicting testimony came from the former director of the Air Pollution Control District, who said that the new rule would do nothing to reduce air pollution and that the amount of sulfur dioxide in the air was well below the "allowable" limits specified by the state Department of Health. Oil industry representatives agreed that the rule would cause "economic disaster" for the local industry in that $25 million would be lost to the community without the assured elimination of smog. Western Oil and Gas Association (WOGA) representatives led the attack on the District's medical report by quoting numerous medical and chemistry authorities who denied that sulfur compounds were proven health menaces. These spokesmen also argued that the establishment of a "one fuel" situation would be dangerous in that natural gas supplies could possibly fail. At the same time, WOGA widely circulated a letter that called for political action to be taken "directly and indirectly" to block passage of the rule.[18] This letter led the County Supervisors to charge that the oil industry was guilty of applying political pressure. The Los Angeles Chamber of Commerce, although not appearing in direct opposition to the ban, suggested that evidence be produced that "the penalties fit the crime" due to the economic impact of the rule on the oil industry. Small oil producers who were not members of WOGA also appeared to testify against the ban.

A postponement of 60 days on a Board of Supervisors vote on the rule was proposed by opponents of the rule so that the data submitted by the District could be checked by "neutral researchers," but the plea was denied by board action. The position paper submitted by the District in support of its proposals emphasized that witness after witness had held that air pollution is not only a nuisance but also a possible health hazard and that these factors cause economic problems whose solution through pollution control would counterbalance the economic costs to industry of the oil ban. Aside from the health issue, the District argued that the rule was justified even on the basis of the visible plumes that cause local nuisances and reduced visibility. When the rule came up for a vote before the board during the middle of November, 1958, Supervisor Warren Dorn told his fellow supervisors that if the rule was not adopted a delegation of District officials going to the 1958 Air Pollution Control Conference sponsored by the Public Health Service would be in a very poor position when they tried to put pressure on the auto industry for a speed-up on the development of exhaust control devices. Without the passage of the rule, it was argued, the auto makers would say that the fuel oil situation needed to be cleaned up first, just as they had previously referred to the back-yard incinerators as the source of the problem.[19]

On November 12, 1958, the Board of Supervisors unanimously passed what became known as Rule 62 and stated their policy to be "to try to stop air pollution wherever we find it, no matter where it comes from." [20] In response to the oil industry's specific contention that the regulation would cripple the local economy, the board left the door open for later amendments. The law was to go into effect May 1, 1959.

The Los Angeles Experience Reviewed

In its 20-year history, the Los Angeles Air Pollution Control District has gained a reputation for combining militance and political adroitness in a very successful air pollution control effort. Since its establishment, the District has adopted more than 100 rules and regulations governing the emissions of air contaminants from stationary sources. These rules and regulations govern smoke, nuisance, particulate matter, sulfur compounds, combustion contaminants, dust and fumes, open fires, incinerator burning, storage of petroleum products, oil effluent-water separators, gasoline loading, sulfur content of fuels, gasoline composition, solvents, and animal reduction processes. These rules have been rigidly enforced, with a 97 per cent conviction rate of the more than 35,000 violators taken to court.

This abatement effort has been concurrent with the major effort to control the emissions of automobiles. From 1940 to 1960, the number of cars in the Los Angeles Basin increased from one million to three million, a rate of increase expected to continue in the future. Although Los Angeles has been the acknowledged leader in initiating control measures on automobile emissions, such emissions now account for a large percentage of the air pollution in the Los Angeles Basin. Because of the ubiquitous nature of the automobile, state and federal legislation have superseded the District's early control efforts in the sense that emission control devices are now required by the state and Federal Government.[21] Thus, even though the automobile emissions characterize the Los Angeles type of smog, the real indicator of the success of the Los Angeles County Air Pollution Control District is the control of stationary sources of pollution.

The Control Agency's Approach to Abatement

Prior to 1940, as far as is known, air pollution levels in the atmosphere in the Los Angeles Basin had not passed the threshold at which they had become conspicuous. Therefore, the District has in the past looked upon the level of pollution in the atmosphere existing before that date as the goal of their control efforts. But because no measurements of air quality were being made in those days, the specification of this objective could only be estimated. Because of the perceived seriousness of the air pollution problem in the Los Angeles Basin, the Board of County Commissioners has continued to give the District over the years a mandate: Get rid of air pollution. Thus, the District has operationalized its stated goal in the form of a "first and foremost principle" that all industrial, domestic, and vehicular operations should be carried out with essentially no emissions to the atmosphere. (In response to a request for a characterization of the stringency of the District's standards insofar as industrial pollution is concerned, County Supervisor Warren Dorn replied, "We just don't allow it.")[22]

The District's position is that during the time that the District has operated, Los Angeles has continued to have a severe air pollution problem and that the public has very clearly expressed its will that air pollution be eliminated. The District sees its function as the completion of this task as rapidly as possible. Due to the perceived severity of the problem, the opinion is that only now is the District approaching a position where it can "afford the luxury" of discriminating between different kinds of pollutants. Due to insufficient information, decisions have necessarily been made on the basis of judgment rather than from a position of complete understanding. As public officials, members of the District take the position that it is not possible for them to wait ten years for a study that will specify an A–to–B relationship when it is suspected that existing levels of air pollution have harmful effects.

Thus, the District does not feel the need to specify an exact relationship between air pollution and health, arguing that if success is achieved in reducing smog, the health situation would without doubt be improved.* The District's unsuccessful attempt before the FPC to specify such a cause-and-effect relationship probably reinforced this view.** Thus, in the District's presentation before the Secretary of

---

* The District has found that an argument for air pollution control based on aesthetic considerations is not considered in litigation proceedings to be pertinent. Assistant Director Robert Barsky, however, believes that the police power is perfectly designed to protect aesthetics even though few cases have been decided on it.

** As noted earlier, the FPC's decision was probably not based as much on the health arguments as on the fact that they did not want to establish the precedent at that time of providing natural gas for boiler fuel exclusively.

Interior on low-sulfur oil imports, the argument was related to gross manifestations—the visible plume, the visible fallout, the visible damage to property, and the "common-sense" relationship between these factors and the interference with the enjoyment of life and the general implications for health.* This view has also resulted in the policy of attacking photochemical smog, nitrous oxides, and sulfur dioxide by using available technology to control the visible plume, dust, and fumes, after emphasizing the visible effects such as damage to property and the fact that these emissions add to over-all levels of emissions.

It appears that the agency has adopted the general position that, because the close relation between health and air pollution is difficult to prove, its rationale for control should be that a nuisance interferes with comfortable living as a basic right and that there is no basic right to use the air as a sewer. Thus, the very important permit system used by the District is based on the "reservoir concept," which requires that the applicant demonstrate that he will not impinge on the basic rights of others by polluting the air.

The Permit System

The District believes that the permit system has proved to be a very effective means of controlling air pollution. Underlying the use of this system in Los Angeles is the concept that no one has a right to pollute the air, but rather that society has a paramount right that the air remain clean. Thus, if an individual proposes to conduct activities likely to create air pollution, he must first obtain a permit which is granted only after it is established that required safeguards are present.

The effectiveness of the District's permit system rests on a two-step method of issuing permits. The first step requires the applicant to obtain an "authority to construct" before any equipment capable of emitting or controlling air contaminants is constructed, altered, or replaced. If the applicant's plans and specifications show that the equipment can operate within prescribed limits, an authority to construct is granted. If the equipment is deemed capable of emitting air contaminants that will create a public nuisance, or of violating any of the sections of the State Health and Safety Code or the District's rules

---

* Due in part to the executive order from the President, as noted earlier, the Secretary of the Interior was also more open to environmental quality considerations than he was earlier.

and regulations, then permission to construct, alter, or replace such equipment is denied. Granting an authority to construct, however, does not constitute a "permit to operate." The second step requires that the applicant actually operate the equipment within the prescribed limits in the presence of an air pollution engineer, with approval of such source tests based on equipment performance. Only then is a "permit to operate" granted. This permit remains in effect only as long as its conditions are observed. The District charges a fee for these permits. The concept underlying the fee charge is that those requiring special service from the District should pay the major share of the cost of providing it.

Weighing the Benefits and Costs

The District staff views itself as being composed of "highly qualified scientists and engineers," but staff members emphasize that they make no pretense at being economists. Although some balancing of benefits and costs is done by the staff, benefit-cost analysis is viewed as a gambit to avoid and delay.[23] As such, they think of it as a strategic tool used by polluters to advance their case against control. But within the agency, benefit-cost analysis has been used in very generalized fashion to allocate staff resources and to serve as a final check on whether proposed regulations are feasible. The comparison has been between monetary costs of control and the amount of pollution emissions prevented. For example, in the late 1950's the District contemplated reducing the permissible level of particulate emissions until it was discovered that it would cost $150 million to reduce daily emissions by only 13 tons. This reduction was not considered worth the costs.[24] Rule 62 and the incinerator ban also exemplify the fact that the District's rules and regulations consider the economic impact but that this is not their primary thrust. In most cases, it was decided that particular sources *ought* to be controlled because they were identified as being major contributors of pollution, and tentative rules were prepared to do this. Important considerations have been (1) lack of technology or (2) the lack of available alternatives. As a general rule, regulations have been made as strict as existing abatement techniques would allow. No rule proposed by the District has been turned down by the County Supervisors because it was considered too expensive to implement.

The same sort of comparison between monetary costs of control and amount of emissions reduced has also been used to evaluate agency performance. Thus, it is pointed out that the cost to control

5,180 tons of air pollutants per day from stationary sources has been at least three quarters of a billion dollars and that these figures might be only half of actual costs.*

A Position of Power

A very important aspect of the District's strategy has been to develop a "position of power" based on public support, technical knowledge of air pollution and devices and processes for reducing emissions, and a well-defined legal and administrative structure. An early admitted mistake of the District was a failure to acquaint the public with all of its activities.[25] Thus, since the early 1950's, the District has carried on extensive public information programs. Much emphasis has been given to publicly rebutting arguments raised against proposed regulations or the application of existing regulations. In essence, the strategy is to put polluters of the air on the defensive by marshaling public opinion against them. The District does not dissuade "outraged" citizens' groups from having protest meetings and voicing their protests to the company or industry in question. The press and other media are also not discouraged from publishing or disseminating programs that emphasize the role of industry and public utilities in air pollution.[26]

The District's research on control technology allows it to counter potential charges by polluters that proposed regulations are impossible

* Louis J. Fuller, "Air Pollution Control—A Billion Dollar Problem," APCD news release, April 17, 1969. Another 1,140 tons are controlled by the installation of crankcase and exhaust control devices on automobiles. Some of the monetary cost can be measured with exactness, while the remainder was estimated. For example, the permits issued for pollution control equipment installed in Los Angeles County contain a record of equipment cost. These show that industry has spent more than $135 million. This does not include the cost of maintaining or operating this equipment or the value of the land it occupies, nor does it take into account the cost of designing the building into other basic equipment or modifications necessary to meet District specifications without the use of separate equipment. Another recorded item is the amount paid for fees for these permits and the amounts paid as fines for convictions of violations of District rules. From 1948 to 1967, these totaled $2,875,000. Also known is the cost of operating the District for 18 years—$46,095,300, or about $2.6 million per year on the average. Of this total, $6 million was spent on basic research. Another item of expense is rubbish collection and disposal, which costs an estimated $55 million per year in Los Angeles County. Finally, there are the costs of the hearings before the FPC and the court suit challenging the District's constitutionality—more than $250,000.

to meet, and its basic research on the effects of air pollution has been a strong incentive for the Board of County Supervisors to pass control regulations even when these have been opposed by important segments of the business community in Los Angeles. A "climate to negotiate" has been created in which the polluter is aware of the high probability that he would lose a court fight and realizes that, even if he should win, he would receive a great deal of adverse publicity. Large industrial firms and public utilities are especially sensitive to such publicity.

One reason this strategy has been applied so successfully is the provision in the District's regulations that a variance cannot be granted where a showing has been made that a nuisance is present.* (For example, it was shown that the burning of high-sulfur oil constituted a nuisance in the immediate vicinity of power plants.) In a typical case, a polluter would be informed that in a presentation before the District's hearing board the District staff would present a nuisance argument and that, once the nuisance is presented, the hearing board would be precluded from granting a variance. The only recourse for the polluter would be to take the case to Superior Court and have the case tried before the whole community with the resulting publicity.[27]

The strategy has been effective to the extent that, since the passing of Rule 62 in the late 1950's, there has been no significant large-scale opposition. Since that time, the District and industry have not taken the overt position of being adversaries. The most significant example of this change is Rule 66, dealing with the emissions from solvents. Over a period of years, difficult technological problems were worked out cooperatively, and the adopted rule turned out to be more stringent than the original proposal of the District. Even though the solvent industry is spending a great deal of money on research in an attempt to prove the rule ineffective, this form of opposition can be contrasted with earlier opposition based on inadequate or nonexistent information.

The Sequential Approach to Problems

The District has approached the air pollution problem in Los Angeles in a sequential manner and has explicitly or implicitly recognized that all major decisions are interrelated. Early in the District's operation, it was believed that sulfur dioxide was the cause of much of the smog with help from the ubiquitous back-yard incinerator. Thus, early

---

* This has not always been true. Southern California Edison operated under a variance for a number of years.

major control efforts focused on sources of sulfur dioxide and these incinerators. The latter were given emphasis because of the pyschological impact of the obvious visible emissions and the presence of a viable solution at hand (refuse collection and sanitary landfill). The automobile industry also continually advanced the argument that the back-yard incinerators were the source of most of the pollution and not the automobile. As noted before, the removal of the incinerators negated this argument. At a later date, in arguing against the WOGA proposal to relate fuel oil burning to weather conditions, the District could state: "It would be a complete breach of faith to the people of Los Angeles County who were told that if they led the way by giving up their back-yard incinerators other sources of pollution would be eliminated." [28] It is probably difficult to overestimate the importance to the District of having been able to point to other large investments in control processes when proposing new regulations and enforcing existing ones. Remaining polluters cannot fail to see the crude equity that is involved.

The Role of Bargaining

Operating from their position of power, the District has always proposed to the Board of County Commissioners the strongest regulation —i.e., the most restrictive in light of available technology—it thought could be justified. To date, no proposed regulation has failed to be enacted by the Commissioners. Thus, formal bargaining in the adoption of regulations has not take place.* These rules have been applied both within the spirit and the letter of the law. This has been possible because the District has always had a large enforcement staff.

Within the bargaining framework outlined earlier, it seems that significant conflict resolution takes place within the context of the informal conferences the District employs extensively. At the District offices, views, positions, and information are exchanged with industry representatives. At this level, incrementalism, ritualization, continuing negotiation, and the determination of focal point solutions all play a part. This factor, not obvious in the chronological development of issues emphasized in the case study, cannot be given too much importance.

---

* Although formal bargaining is precluded by the agency's charter, one Los Angeles official candidly admitted that on occasion "deals" had been made with polluters, but they played a minor role in the overall pollution control program and, in any case, could not be revealed.

The Political and Institutional Framework

Both the issues of burning natural gas and low-sulfur oil, not to mention the federal jurisdiction over emission control devices, emphasize the fact that some significant decisions in air pollution control are beyond the control of the Los Angeles Air Pollution Control District. When higher levels of government have the responsibility, conflict between a state or federal functional agency's multiple objectives has in the past typically resulted in the downgrading of the relatively new objective of environmental quality. This has been particularly evident in the actions of the Federal Power Commission, which has been more concerned with pipeline management than air pollution control. The District's solution to this problem is Presidential leadership in changing administrative priorities.[29]

At the opposte end of the scale, industrial interests in Southern California have continually complained that they have been unable to obtain fair and impartial due process before the District's hearing board and the County Supervisors and that proceedings of the board have been conducted in an "atmosphere of hysteria." The California Manufacturers Association also has stated in the past that air pollution control in the Los Angeles Basin is based on politics rather than economics. Indeed, the Association has been criticized by Los Angeles newspaper columnists for fighting their battles on the wrong terms, for it continually asked a group of nonscientists—the Board of Supervisors—to rule on extremely technical arguments. There is some logic to the industry argument that the board was making political decisions rather than technical ones, particularly if one considers their interpretation of the public interest as an essentially political decision.

NOTES

[1] L. Herber, *Crisis in our Cities* (Englewood Cliffs, N. J.: Prentice-Hall, 1965), p. 50.

[2] *Ibid.*

[3] Air Pollution Control District Act, California Health and Safety Code, Sections 24198–24323 (West, 1967).

[4] H. Kennedy, "The History, Legal and Administrative Aspects of Air Pollution Control in the County of Los Angeles" (Report submitted to the Board of Supervisors of the County of Los Angeles, May 9, 1954), pp. 12–14.

[5] *Ibid.*

[6] *Ibid.*

[7] APCD news release, August 29, 1957.

[8] For a short history of air pollution from automobiles in Los Angeles, see Herber, *op. cit.*, pp. 48–55.

[9] Kennedy, *op. cit.*, p. 66.

[10] *Ibid.*

[11] Air Pollution Control District *Report*, October, 1957, p. 1.

[12] Kennedy, *op. cit.*

[13] *Ibid.*, 55.

[14] APCD *Report, op. cit.*

[15] Interview with Robert Barsky, APCD Deputy Air Pollution Control Officer, August, 1968.

[16] Interview with Arthur Atkisson, Institute of Urban Ecology, University of Southern California, August, 1967.

[17] The sources for the following sections include interviews with Robert Barsky, APCD Deputy Air Pollution Control Officer; and David Mix, Assistant County Counsel, County of Los Angeles; Los Angeles area newspapers; and unpublished information in the files of the Air Pollution Control District. Specific references are as noted below.

[18] *Los Angeles Herald*, October 10, 1958.

[19] *Los Angeles Examiner*, November 14, 1958.

[20] *Ibid.*

[21] The best history of this development is found in U. S. Senate, *Air Pollution—1967; Automobile Air Pollution*, Hearings before the Subcommittee on Air and Water Pollution of the Committee on Public Works, 90th Cong., 1st Sess., Part 1, February, 1967.

[22] *Ibid.*

[23] Interview with Robert Barsky.

[24] Interview with David Mix.

[25] Kennedy, *op. cit.*, p. 1.

[26] Interview with Robert Barsky.

[27] Interviews with Robert Barsky and David Mix.

[28] Unpublished testimony by Smith Griswold before the Board of County Commissioners.

[29] Interview with Robert Barsky.

III

WATER POLLUTION

The water pollution problem is serious in the extreme. It comes down to a matter of sheer survival. Lake Erie and many other water bodies are threatened or have already been "killed." And we face other dangers: the quality of the water we drink and the food we eat is in peril from pollution. The discharge of mercury and other heavy metals into our waters has created special hazards; already there are certain kinds of fish we can no longer eat, and there are lakes so laden with chemicals that it is dangerous simply to swim or wade in them—the skin flakes off when in contact with such water. And these are only indications of the perils yet to come unless effective corrective action is taken.

But the concern created by this problem can be offset by the knowledge that if the proper level of commitment can be made, methods presently available to deal with water pollution are fully capable of purifying the nation's water systems. In fact, officials can choose from three levels of treatment depending on the use to which the water will be put after purification, the nature and amount of the pollutants, and the funds available. Primary treatment, filtering water through screens and settling chambers, simply catches sticks, papers and dust. Secondary treatment, utilizing the trickling filter method, is a highly satisfactory approach for most pollutants—it can effectively remove 90 percent of degradable organic waste. Tertiary treatment, utilizing filtration and other mechanical and chemical processes, can remove almost all contaminants. Unfortunately, as the quality of the treatment increases so does the expense. It costs twice as much to build and three times as much to operate a tertiary sewage treatment plant as it does to run a secondary operation.

Due to the magnitude of the problem and the awesome expense of the remedies, responsibility for initiating abatement programs and enforcing standards as well as providing financial support has fallen on the federal and state governments. The federal government began to play a role in this area as early as 1899 with passage of a largely ignored Refuse Act which made it unlawful (without a permit from the U.S. Army Corps of Engineers) to dispose of refuse in navigable waters. Further action was not taken until 1948 with the first major Water Pollution Control Act which provided funding for sewage plant construction. Additional legislation in 1966 and 1970 raised the federal contribution for construction costs and dealt with the problems of oil spills and thermal pollution. The states, on the other hand, did not take any significant action until after 1965. In that year, the federal Water Quality Act required the states to establish and enforce water quality standards for all interstate waters within their boundaries and empowered the states to take legal action if these standards were violated. Since then the states have been increasingly active.

The end product of federal and state activity during the past two decades has been the expenditure of billions of dollars on water treatment facilities; nonetheless, in the United States today only 140 million of the country's more than 200 million persons are now served by any kind of treatment facility. "In the last 10 years, the quality of the nation's water has probably degenerated," noted David D. Dominick, Commissioner of the Federal Water Quality Administration.

One way of explaining this failure is simply to say that the level of commitment, high as it may seem, has not been sufficient to bring pollution under control. Two factors account, in part, for the difficulties facing those responsible for managing our water supply. In the first place, there is not enough water for present population needs; and in the second, every day more people demand more water. It is anticipated that 73.2 billion gallons per day will be required in the United States by 2020, over three times the 23.7 billion gallons required in 1969. The principal consumers—and water polluters— are specific types of industry: steel mills, petrochemicals, paper manufacturers and municipalities. Industrial wastes can be more harmful to the environment but are less costly to control; they can be treated at the source, and their content is usually limited to a few types of pollutants. Municipal wastes, on the other hand, most often be transported long distances to treatment facilities, and they contain waste of a greatly varied nature—sometimes domestic, sometimes commercial, and sometimes overflow from storms.

In the readings which follow, the authors deal with several examples of water pollution and water resources planning. In the first, "Approaches to Regional Water Quality Management," Allen V.

*Kneese examines the basis for approaching water quality manage-
ment from the regional, or river basin, viewpoint and reviews several
examples of this approach. Among these are the Ruhr Area in Germany, the English River Authorities, the French River Basin Agencies
and the Delaware River Basin. Analysis of these examples points up
several important criteria essential to water quality management
which Kneese discusses in his final section: (1) the ability to analyze
and implement a wide range of alternatives, (2) the ability to have
an appropriate influence on related land and water uses, (3) the
ability of the agency to articulate private and local government decisions in such a way as to achieve an efficient regional waste disposal
system incorporating what already exists with whatever it deems
necessary to add, and (4) the opportunity for affected parties to
influence decision-making.*

*Other examples of successful pollution control are available on a
smaller scale in San Diego, California, and Seattle, Washington, as
described by E. W. Kenworthy in the* New York Times. *Kenworthy
describes how in these two areas once heavily polluted water bodies
have been transformed within a few years into clear, attractive water
systems. These two cities have demonstrated that the combination
of aggressive and imaginative leadership and the willingness of the
electorate to pay for the bonds can have a significant effect on water
quality even of heavily polluted bodies of water. The total costs of
these undertakings amounted to $145 million in Seattle and $60
million in San Diego—the equivalent of $2 a month per household
in Seattle, $1.50 in San Diego.*

*The path to success was a rough one, as might have been expected.
Voters in San Diego initially refused to support proposed bond issues
to construct necessary treatment plants. By 1960—six years later—
the bay had become so polluted that swimming was prohibited and
residents were warned that contact with the water could be harmful;
the bond issue, nearly three times larger than originally proposed,
was overwhelmingly approved. In Seattle, similar problems were
encountered. The governmental jurisdictions affected by pollution
on Lake Washington were numerous but showed an unusual inclination to work together to deal with the pollution problem. Although
an initial attempt was defeated at the polls, a second try, with a somewhat modified proposal, was approved.*

In an excerpt from The Siberians, *Farley Mowat describes the
efforts to clean up Lake Baikal in south central Russia. Lake Baikal
is the world's largest inland lake and the producer of a tremendous
variety of foods—sturgeon being probably the most famous. Years*

*of harvesting these resources had nearly killed the lake and every-
thing in it. The final blow seemed to be a large chemical plant which
Moscow planners proposed to build on the south shores of Baikal.
This announcement caused a vast outburst of protest which resulted
in the closing down of the new plants until adequate treatment
facilities could be provided.*

*Another area of water management—protection of coastal wetland
areas—is discussed in the "Massachusetts Coastal Wetlands Protection Program." A number of states along our coasts can take little
pride in the destruction of their coastal wetlands. Connecticut has
lost nearly half its coastal wetlands in the past fifty years while
California has lost nearly 67 percent of its coastal wetlands. These
are only two examples of the rapid waste of limited natural resources.*

*Massachusetts was one of the few states to take steps to halt this
process. Although the Commonwealth had long been guilty of allowing its coastal wetlands to succumb to dredging and filling operations,
Massachusetts passed legislation in the mid 1960's which has effectively reversed this trend. The essay describes the importance of
wetlands, the background of the Massachusetts program and how
legislation was initiated and enacted. As a footnote to this program,
a letter is also included protesting possible restrictions on wetlands
development. The writer makes one particularly significant point:
The coastal wetlands program should be only one aspect of a total
land use policy that looks to the development of all our resources in
terms of their appropriate use. Protection of our dry lands, says the
author, is just as important as protection of our marshlands and one
resource should not be protected to the possible detriment of the other.*

6. Approachs to Regional Water Quality Management

ALLEN V. KNEESE

SECTION I—INTRODUCTION

General Background

Water quality has come to be recognized as a major problem for public policy in all the developed countries of the world. While concern with the quality of water courses is of venerable age, especially in those countries which early experienced the industrial revolution, attention to it has grown spectacularly in the post-War period.

Since the war a number of major industrial countries have enacted new water pollution control legislation—indeed some have passed several new laws. A common element in most of them is emphasis on the river basin as a region for administering water quality management programs. New laws in England and France are rooted in this approach. A new law in Germany refers to it and provides a certain amount of encouragement for regional undertakings. At the time of this writing, a law is pending in the United States which would substantially encourage such undertakings by providing federal government assistance to them.

Why has such a strong emphasis developed on regional approaches to the problem? There are many reasons and the prominence given specific ones will differ among concerned individuals and in different countries.

Allen V. Kneese, "Approaches to Regional Water Quality Management." Originally published as part of a four-volume post-conference publication, this paper was prepared for the National Conference on Pollution and our Environment, organized by the Canadian Council of Resource Ministers and held in Montreal, Quebec, from October 31 to November 4, 1966. Reprinted by permission of the Canadian Council of Resource Ministers.

Clearly, however, the idea of water quality management, as contrasted with conventional pollution control, has come to have a wide appeal and this, in turn, has contributed to a regional concept of the problem. I believe that the following concepts characterize the idea of water quality management.

1. *The concept of direct interdependence.* Damages associated with waste discharges largely fall upon subsequent users rather than upon the dischargers themselves, and normally voluntary purchase or sale of property rights cannot correct the situation. This is perhaps the most central reason for government efforts to control waste discharges. Water quality management must, however, go further and consider the fact that quality is affected by a host of influences. For example, releases from storage reservoirs during periods of low flow or the inter-basin diversion of water alters quality and therefore waste disposal-associated damages, often at remote locations downstream. Management requires that such effects be foreseen, evaluated, and incorporated into a systematic program of control. In water quality management interdependencies between water quality and water quantity must be recognized and brought systematically into decision-making.

2. *Wide range of alternatives.* Pollution control efforts are generally focused on treatment of waste at individual outfalls. However, water quality management conducted as a regional undertaking is not limited to this single and often economically inferior solution. It can involve numerous alternative measures. Some may consist of large-scale or special facilities which cannot be efficiently implemented at individual points of waste production. These include, but are not limited to, river flow regulation, direct treatment of streams—including direct oxygenation—collective facilities for treatment of wastes from diverse sources, sub-surface disposal and arrangements for transport and off-site disposal of wastes. Also, extremely important is the recovery of wastes and treatment attendant to reuse of water by industry. Regional quality management requires that the many possibilities be brought into some sort of optimal balance.

3. *Multi-purpose use.* Stream flow regulation for quality improvement may be achieved by large multipurpose impoundments which simultaneously yield recreation opportunities and perhaps other benefits. Ground water recharge practices may *simultaneously* accomplish quality improvement and utilize underground storage capacity. Numerous other instances of complementary effects could be cited. It should not be assumed, however, that multi-purpose uses are always preferable. Making provision for specialized use of impoundments,

streams, or reaches of a stream may, in certain circumstances, be the preferred way of utilizing the water resources. For example, a regional management agency might wish to preserve certain streams or reaches of streams for high quality recreation while others are used more heavily for waste disposal but still serve uses less sensitive to quality conditions than recreation.

4. *Comprehensive approach.* Comprehensiveness applies not only to geographical extent and multiple uses of water, but to the effects of the general development of land use. Clearly the proposed location of industries and recreation areas will influence the costs of water supply and waste disposal in the river-basin. These effects must, in some fashion, be evaluated and brought to bear on decisions of local, state and regional land-use planning agencies and upon the location decisions of industries. If stream specialization is used to provide high quality recreation opportunities, for example, it will be necessary to have some appropriate authority which can control land use and provide for equitable distribution of the costs and gains of such a policy.

Studies of Water Quality Management

By this time a considerable body of conceptual and empirical literature has arisen on the economic-engineering aspects of water quality management. On one conclusion there is universal agreement—major economies over the conventional pollution control approach often can be achieved by a regional water quality management system based on some or all of the concepts just noted. Clearly all the problems in engineering and economics are not solved. Still, this aspect of the necessary background for effective water quality management is rapidly outstripping the ability to devise legal and institutional arrangements which will permit effective but efficient and politically responsible implementation of water quality management programs. Compared to engineering and even economics, institutional studies of water quality management are in their infancy. No established pattern or criteria exist. This paper therefore sets forth on a relatively unmarked trail.

Objectives of This Study

The present study pursues modest, but I feel, significant aims. Its central objectives are:

(1) to present a certain amount of information concerning legal and institutional approaches to water quality managament in various parts of the world in a reasonably systematic way;

(2) to assess these regional programs in terms of a number of specific criteria.

The Instances to be Discussed

The instances chosen for discussion are ones that appear to be the most highly developed regional approaches. In some cases, they are little more than good intentions at this point, new laws having been passed which have not yet had an opportunity to produce results. In other instances, the background includes a long history of activity on a regional basis.

Obviously, these two situations have to be assessed somewhat differently. Many factors other than the "inherent merit" of legal and institutional arrangements will influence outcomes. Despite the limitations imposed by difficulty of making comparisons at this point in time, it is felt that the dscussion will be useful to North American readers. It is clear from legal developments and from professional lay debate that we are trying to find our way toward suitable institutions for dealing with the quality problem. In this regard, it is useful to review the experience of other areas which in some cases have long had to face problems of an intensity we are just beginning to meet.

The particular regional approaches to be discussed are (1) the Genossenschaften or river associations in the Ruhr area of Germany which have been in operation for various lengths of time up to sixty years, (2) the English River Authorities which were created by Parliament in 1963 to supersede the existing River Boards established in 1948, (3) the French River Authorities which were created by a law passed in 1965, and (4) the Delaware River Basin Commission which was established by an interstate federal compact in the United States in 1961 to supersede an earlier interstate commission. Other instances could be discussed; for example, regional authorities exist in Belgium and Holland, and there is currently underway a major research project which points toward a regional approach in Upper Silesia in Poland. A long standing and relatively successful effort in the United States is that on the Ohio River Valley Water Sanitation Commission. The instances selected do, however, appear to represent those efforts which are likely to be of the greatest significance in the coming years.

The Criteria

The proposed evaluation criteria rest in a broad sense on the concept of economic efficiency. That is, they are developed with a view to assessing the degree to which these programs can achieve the least-costly systems for obtaining these levels of water quality which tend to equate incremental returns associated with water quality improvement with the incremental costs of achieving improvement. No effort is made to be very precise about the nature of these criteria or the conceptual or computational problems of optimization. This objective has been pursued elsewhere.[1] Rather, emphasis is placed on the extent to which laws and institutions tend to encourage consideration of economically relevant alternatives for improving water quality, the distance they go toward recognizing interdependencies between water quality and other aspects of water and land management, the degree to which relevant values associated with water quality improvement tend to be considered in the decision-making process, and the availability of management tools (such as performance standards and economic incentives) consistent with the objective of creating a regional system which will produce maximum net benefit. The criteria are restated and elaborated at the start of Section III.

SECTION II—THE CASES

The Ruhr Area Genossenschaften

1. *Situation and Accomplishments.* The "Ruhr Area" actually spans several watersheds, aggregating about 4,500 square miles. It contains some 10 million persons and one-half of Germany's industrial capacity. Eighty to ninety per cent of Germany heavy industry—coal, steel, heavy chemical—is found there. Clearly such a massive complex must exert a great water demand and produce an immense waste load. The streams in the area are, nevertheless, very small. Annually expected low flow of the main ones, the Ruhr, the Emscher, and the Lippe is only about 400 cubic feet per second. Still, the Ruhr River is kept suitable for a variety of uses including the production of drinking water, recreation and other less quality demanding uses. Furthermore, the drinking water in the area receives no unusual treatment and indeed is among the least costly in any German urban area.

These results were obtained by eight Genossenschaften or river basin associations which are a form of compulsory cooperative. They came into being at various times since the formation of the Emschergenossenschaft in 1904. Several of these organizations now work together to produce integrated regional systems for water quality management. They have implemented a wide array of measures including waste treatment in large collective plants, waste treatment at individual municipal and industrial outfalls, methods for treatment of the entire river such as mechanical reaeration, retention ponds and

The seven river basins of the Ruhr district.

diversions of the stream through a treatment plant, low flow regulation by releases from upland reservoirs and specialized use of certain streams or stretches of streams. The cost of these facilities attributable to water quality management has largely been met from effluent charges levied upon all waste disposers in the region whether they discharge directly into the Genossenschaft plants or to the river.

2. *Historical background.* The Emschergenossenschaft is the prototype upon which the other organizations were modeled. Many important changes in policy in the natural resources field have come about as the result of crisis situations and the Emschergenossenschaft is an excellent example.

The valley of the Emscher is quite flat and has naturally poor drainage. After 1860, coal mining moved northward into the Emscher region from the Ruhr area where it had started because the seams were shallowest there. As a result conditions in the Emscher became steadily worse. Steel, steel finishing and chemical industries came in the wake of this northward movement into the Emscher. Subsidence became a particularly severe problem as the low areas filled with the wastes of industries and municipalities. The region began to experience epidemics. Individual mining enterprises and small associations of mines attempted to improve drainage conditions, but to little overall effect.

A rather well worked out plan for a regional drainage effort proposed in 1883 failed because of inability to agree on how interested parties should be represented.

Meanwhile, industrial development of the Emscher area accelerated quickly. From 1870 to 1900, population rose from 350,000 to over 1,250,000. Also, by this time individual communities and industrial enterprises had begun to pump water from the Ruhr watershed for use in the Emscher area. Court cases involving claims of damages resulting from pollution became frequent. Mines and steel mills were often forbidden to discharge their waste waters—an obviously futile ruling. Also, the communities faced difficult if not impossible situations. There were a few treatment plants, but hygienic circumstances became rapidly worse.

In 1901, during a typhoid epidemic, the number of ill in the Emscher area was three times as great as on the average in Prussia. Gradually, the concept that it would be necessary to have a unified regulation of the Emscher from its headwaters to its mouth, if the situation was to be substantially improved, became widely accepted. However, a severe problem was that the Emscher area fell into over two hundred separate political jurisdictions.

In 1899 various industrial and municipal officials met in Bochum to appoint a commission to devise a technical plan for the area. The commission was made up of representatives of municipalities, industries and members of the scientific and technical community. Besides the task of preparing a plan, the commission was also confronted with the question of how an organization could be formed politically and administratively so that it could successfully carry through the needed works. There was no organization that could be taken as a model. The commission was convinced that the plan could succeed only if a feeling of community were established among the involved groups. This, in their view, required an organization with self-government and with a carefully structured political representation. It was clear that some higher unit of government would have to assume some responsibility but it was also deemed important that that authority be limited to oversight. It was argued that a continuing self-governing management agency would be the best means for economical operation including an elastic adaptation to the dynamic industrial area and a close association with the technical and economic resources of the region. At this early stage, the need for technical competence and research work was stressed.

A question of great importance was who the members of the association should be. It was decided that the membership should consist of all dischargers of waste water and those benefiting from the regulation of the stream. Not surprisingly, the matter of distribution of costs was prominently discussed by the commission and the principle was generated that costs should be distributed on the basis of the benefits received from the operation of the organization and the costs made necessary by the activities of the membership. In the Emscher, the most important of these were subsidence associated with coal mining and costs imposed by the discharge of waste waters.

In 1903 and 1904 the proposed law passed the Rhennish and Westphalian Landtags and was approved by the King of Prussia.

The members of the Genossenschaft fell into three groups, mines, industrial and business establishments, railroads and other productive facilities and communities. The law creating the Genossenschaft sets out its duties in general terms as the regulation of the stream and treatment of waste waters in the area. The statute indicates that this is to be done in accordance with a general plan, but it also provides scope for adaptation to changing circumstances in the course of time.

All the Genossenschaften created in later years have followed the general Emschergenossenschaft pattern. In none of the other cases was there so critical a situation to deal with as had existed in the Emscher. Rather the formation of these Genossenschaften reflected the bringing to bear of what had proven to be an effective instrument on additional difficult problems.

For example, in order to control pollution of the Ruhr and to support the water supply functions of the already existing Ruhrtalsperrenverein (Ruhr reservoir association), the Ruhrverband was formed in 1913. It general assignment was to provide, and to maintain and operate, those facilities that are necessary in order to control the pollution in the Ruhr and its tributaries that would otherwise occur through individual waste discharge activities of the Genossen.

3. *The Administrative and Organizational Arrangements.* The basic political power in the Ruhrverband as in the other Genossenschaften lies with the members of the governing board. These consist of (1) the owners of business and industrial establishments and other facilities that lie in the Ruhrverband area and that contribute to water quality deterioration in the Ruhr or its tributaries. Also, those are included who benefit from the activities of the Ruhrverband to the extent that they make a specified minimum financial contribution to its activities, (2) those communities that lie within the Ruhrverband area and (3) the Ruhrtalsperrenverein (combined under a single direc-

tor with the Ruhrverband in 1938) as a representative of the water-works and other water withdrawal facilities.

The political organs of both organizations, as of the other Genossenschaften, are the assembly (Genossenschaftsversammlung) and the board of directors (Vorstand). The assembly members execute the most basic functions, they elect the board of directors, approve or disapprove the plan for water quality management, approve or disapprove the assessment of charges, and decide upon the basic method for calculating the level of charges on specific Genossen. The assembly reaches its conclusions on the basis of absolute majority with the number of votes cast by each Genossen being dependent upon the amount of his financial contribution.

As the major organ of the Genossenschaft, the board of directors is elected by the assembly from among its membership. The board consists of a chairman, his deputy, and seven additional members. As previously mentioned, since 1938 the chairman of the Ruhrverband has served simultaneously as the chairman of the Ruhrtalsperren-verein.

It is required by the law creating the Ruhrverband that all Genossen groups, that is, the business establishments, the communities and the Ruhrtalsperrenverein have to be represented on the Board of Directors.

Since the directors are part-time and not necessarily skilled in technical water resource matters, it is, of course, not possible for them to undertake continuous and detailed management of the Genossenschaft. Accordingly, the board selects a director under whose leadership there now are around 450 professionals and 400 other workers active on the staff of the Ruhrverband-Ruhrtalsperrenverein.

In the course of its roughly fifty-year history, the Ruhrverband has built over 100 treatment plants on the Ruhr and its tributaries. The Ruhrtalsperrenverein has built and/or manages six large upland reservoirs with an additional one now under construction. When completed, this reservoir will be the largest of the group. The Ruhrverband also operates water power facilities and a series of shallow lakes in the Ruhr itself which provide retention and oxidation for the water source and are part of the regional treatment system. The costs of these activities have been considerable. Construction funds are obtained from the capital market while the expenses for interest, operation, maintenance and replacement are yearly obtained from the Genossen through a system of charges. The basic charge for the Ruhrverband quality management activities is contingent on the amount and quality of the effluent discharged by the industries and municipalities in the region. Based on waste discharge information, lists of charges are prepared by the staff indicating the name of the member and an estimate of the charge he must pay. The member may appeal his charge to a commission established by the Ruhrverband or finally to the courts. The Minister of Food, Agriculture and Forests of North Rhine-Westphalia has general oversight powers in regard to the Genossenschaften and must approve the list, but his examination is limited to determining whether the listings follow the form prescribed in the laws cerating the Genossenschaft. The assessments on the individual members established through the indicated procedure are public obligations and can be enforced by law as taxes. However, because of particularly good relationships between the Genossenschaften and their members, it has been rare that use had to be made of this provision. This favorable experience plus the public character of the obligations, has given the Genossenschaften a very strong credit rating. There is an international market for their bonds.

The English River Authorities

1. *Situation and Accomplishments.* In Britain, regional approaches are in effect decentralization of uniform water policies laid down by central government. Accordingly, this section presents a more general picture of the situation and prospects than did the preceding one.

The British contributed heavily to the development of the basic biological sewage treatment processes and over the years constructed many plants. Indeed, most of the urban households are connected to some form of treatment plant. However, overloading and failure to deal effectively with industrial wastes in many instances have left the country with severe pollution problems.

In 1958, a survey of stream water quality was conducted with the following results:

Class I   Unpolluted or Recovering from Pollution
Per cent of total river mileage—73

Class II   Of Doubtful Quality and Needing Improvement
Per cent of total river mileage—15

Class III   Of Poor Quality and Requiring Improvement as a Matter of Urgency
Per cent of total river mileage—6

Class IV   Mostly Polluted
Per cent of total river mileage—6

At first sight, this survey looks quite encouraging. It indicates that only some 12 per cent of the length of all the rivers in England and Wales was suffering from gross or very gross pollution. However, it

AREAS OF RIVER AUTHORITIES

is the middle and the lower reaches of the rivers that would tend to fall in this category or into the 15 per cent of river mileage deemed of doubtful quality. These are the reaches which are close to urban areas. Also, the small proportion of river mileage includes some grossly polluted estuary areas.

The middle and lower stretches of the rivers are at the same time becoming increasingly important for water supply purposes, as ground water becomes depleted and upland reservoir sites become ever more distant from the urban areas.

The idea of entrusting the management of water resources to comprehensive authorities with jurisdiction over a whole river basin or group of basins is not new in Britain. It has been put forward from time to time over the years by Royal Commissions and government committees as well as professional groups. Experience in other countries including that in the Ruhr area of West Germany also received specific attention when new approaches were being considered.

Moreover, there had been certain moves toward river basin management in English water laws. Several river basins, notably including the Thames, have a long history of conservancy boards with certain powers in regard to navigation and pollution control. Catchment Boards in 1930 provided an organization for every drainage in England and Wales to carry out land drainage and flood control works and in a few cases river basin agencies existed with authority to enforce pollution control laws. But extremes of drought and flood plus mounting pollution problems in the post-war period emphasized the shortcomings of the limited approach to basin management embodied in these acts.

In broad outline, this is the background of the far-reaching legislation which passed in 1963 and created the River Authorities which began to function in 1965.

2. *Historical Background of the Present Situation.* England, like other European countries, has a long history of sanitation problems. In the Middle Ages, the streets of the unsewered cities of Europe were the receptacle for a variety of filth and excrement. Everything considered, this period must have been among the worst periods for urban life in the history of mankind.

On the other hand, the problem of river pollution was not severe. There are two main reasons for this. One is that the population was not large, and the other, the absence of water carriage sewer systems. Moreover, there were no large-scale industries producing liquid wastes. Stream degradation really began in England early in the 19th century. Industrialization itself produced massive amounts of wastes and in addition gave rise to an explosive increase in the size of the cities. At about the same time, the water carriage system of sewage disposal was introduced so that wastes no longer were disposed of in the streets but carried into the rivers. This combined with direct discharges to the rivers by industrial establishments meant that large amounts of untreated human and industrial waste began to find their way into the streams.

By the middle of the 19th century, pollution had become a very serious public health problem, particularly in such densely populated areas as Lancashire, Yorkshire, the Midlands and London. Epidemics, destruction of fish life, and grossly offensive esthetic conditions began to prevail to such an extent that two Royal Commissions on river pollution were appointed to study and report on the problem in 1865 and in 1868. The result of the work was the Public Health Act of 1875. In the following year, the Rivers Pollution Prevention Act of 1876 which applied not only to England and Wales but also to Scotland and Ireland was passed. This Act formed, until 1951, the basis for all legal actions, except for rare cases under the common law doctrine of riparian rights, connected with pollution of rivers.

The Act had rather strong provisions forbidding solid and liquid waste discharges but was largely nullified by a provision which required that no action could be taken unless the local government board was satisfied that "no material injury will be inflicted by such proceedings on the interests of such industry . . ." and other provisions which hindered its enforcement.

In the course of time, it became clear that the Act was not being successfully implemented and river authorities were set up in some of the most heavily developed watersheds to administer the 1876 Act. Between 1891 and 1932, the Mersey and Irwell Joint Commission (in the Midlands), the Ribble Joint Committee, the West Riding of Yorkshire Rivers Board and the River Dee Joint Committee were established. Two other boards, the Thames Conservancy Board formed in 1857 and the Lee Conservancy Board of 1868, were originally intended to control navigation but were given anti-pollution powers which in many respects were wider than those offered by the 1876 Act. These authorities became the only means of enforcing the law until comparatively recent times and especially the Thames Board which had rather broader powers than the others, seems to have conducted its pollution control activities rather successfully.

After World War II a feeling emerged that previous legislation had been a failure and a change in attitudes seems to have occurred which has been described by Craine as follows: "The administration of regulatory law prior to the end of the Second World War tended to favor established uses giving dominance to the doctrine of protecting individual rights unless the exercise of such rights implied a flagrant violation of the public interest. With the war and throughout the immediate postwar period, a rapid shift in public attitude gave greater weight to the collective interest in the quality of the natural waters of the nation." [2] In 1948, Parliament passed the River Boards Act which established river boards in each basin in England and Wales, a total of 34, and conferred on the boards or transferred to them functions relating to land drainage, fisheries and river pollution, and recognized them as local authorities so they could prosecute under the 1876 Act. In 1951, the Rivers (Prevention of Pollution) Act was passed and the River Boards were given the authority to enforce it.

This act (replacing the earlier statute of 1876) basically repeated the 1876 Act's general prohibition against pollution. The act also made it an offense for any person to make a new or altered outlet for the discharge of industrial or municipal effluent to a stream or to begin to make any new discharge of industrial or municipal effluent without the consent of the river authority. It further provided that such consent was not to be unreasonably withheld. This licensing authority was the primary new feature of the act. The act also permitted the River Boards to enact by-laws which could restrict existing discharges. None of the boards ever successfully used this authority.

The legislation (1948 River Boards Act, 1951 Prevention of Pollution Act) proved comparatively unsatisfactory and not much progress was made toward effective management of water quality in England. A major weakness was that the discharge license powers exercised by river authorities over industrial effluents basically applied only to new outlets or significant alterations in existing discharges, since no standards for existing effluents had been specified in the legislation. While the River Boards could, under the act, have passed by-laws establishing effluent standards, none of them did so. By-laws were proposed by some of the River Boards—the Mersey Board for example —but agreement on them was not reached with the Ministry of Housing and Local Government. Secondly, despite the existence of the River Boards, there still was not a central regional body charged with the general duty of providing for the development and efficient use of water resources generally.

3. *Present Organizational Arrangements*

POLLUTION CONTROL. In 1961, a new act supplementing the 1951 Act was passed. This is the Rivers (Prevention of Pollution) Act of 1961. Both acts are still in effect. The 1961 Act extended the idea of discharge licenses to all discharges by requiring the consent of the River Board to be obtained for the continuance of all pre-1951 discharges (i.e., those initially made before the passing of the 1951 Act).

Another new law, the Water Resources Act of 1963 (which creates the River Authorities) endeavors to deal with the whole problem of water conservation in a comprehensive manner. It has very little additional to say about pollution regulation. It is expected, however, that the existing regulatory powers of the Prevention of Pollution Acts of 1951 and 1961 will be more vigorously exercised as a result of being administratively associated in the River Authorities with broader responsibilities for the conservation of water. The new act creates river authorities which are to have jurisdiction over areas created by amalgamating the 32 River Boards into 27 River Authorities.

MULTI-PURPOSE FUNCTIONS. The 1963 Act for the first time gave River Authorities rather broad multi-purpose powers of water regulation and development. A bit of historical background will be useful in understanding these provisions. The Water Act of 1945 had provided for some integration of water "undertakers" (public and private enterprises distributing wholesale water). The number of undertakers was greatly reduced and thus certain scale economies were achieved. Still the act was very limited in its scope.

Perhaps most important for the contemporary situation was the creation of the Central Advisory Water Committee by the Act. This Committee went deeply into the matter of water supply and demand in England and made studies which became the basis for the enactment of the Water Resources Act of 1963.

The new Water Resources Act of 1963 had its immediate origins in a series of three reports issued by a subcommittee of the Central Advisory Water Committee. The first report was a general assessment of the situation. The second concerned irrigation and followed a severe drought during the 1959 crop season. It found potential irrigation demand sufficient to establish a need to control withdrawals from surface waters. The third and final report of the subcommittee, the so-called Proudman Committee Report, set forth in some detail proposals for comprehensive water policy and unified administration of water use and development activities in river basin areas. The government's "White Paper" followed quickly and the ground was laid for drafting and passage of the Water Resources Act of 1963. This took place with a minimum of controversy. The issues which emerged seemed to be largely concerned with financing and organization. The general objective of the act was to establish a comprehensive legislative basis for integrated water management.

Under the 1963 Act, the River Authorities possess extensive powers relating to regulation of water use. The following are particularly significant:

a. The River Authorities are authorized to operate a comprehensive system for licensing water withdrawals from surface and ground water sources.

b. The River Authorities are authorized to introduce "charging schemes" under which water withdrawers will be charged on the basis of the quantity they have been authorized to abstract. The law authorizes differential rates based upon different relevant circumstances such as characteristics of source of supply, season of the year, uses to which water will be put and the way water is disposed of after use.

c. As already mentioned, the River Authorities are given the powers originally assigned to the River Boards by the Rivers Prevention of Pollution Acts of 1951 and 1961, including responsibility to license all discharges of waste water to streams. The 1963 Act extends this authority to discharges to underground strata as well.

These regulatory provisions in the Water Resources Act are associated with extensive multi-purpose development powers which now reside in the River Authorities. These multi-purpose development functions may generally be described as follows:

a. The functions and power transferred from the River Boards to carry out development works relating to land drainage, flood control and fisheries.

b. Important new development powers given to the River Authorities by the Act which permits them to construct, operate and finance multi-purpose facilities, including conservation storage for municipal, industrial, and agricultural uses. This broad authorization is not explicit in the Act, but it is made possible by an aggregate of specific authorities.

The 1963 Act further strengthens River Authorities by giving them a key role in the collection and analysis of basic data and information and in the formulation of specific development proposals.

Of particular interest for our purposes is the provision that each River Authority is required to determine a minimum acceptable flow at each of designated and agreed upon control points. "In determining the flow to be specified . . . the River Authority shall have regard to the character of the inland water and its surroundings (and, in particular, any natural beauty which the inland water and its surroundings may possess) and the flow so specified shall not be less than the minimum which in the opinion of the River Authority is needed for safeguarding the public health and for meeting (in respect both of quantity and quality) the requirements of existing lawful uses . . . whether for agriculture, industry, water supply and other purposes, and the requirements of land drainage, navigation and fisheries . . ." Sec. 19 (5)

At the national level, the Ministry of Housing and Local Government and the Ministry of Agriculture have long been the dominant cabinet agencies concerned with water. Under the new law, they continue to play a major role in their respective areas of concern. In addition, a new Ministry of Land and Natural Resources has been created to give supervision to data collection, surveys and research related to water resources. A fourth agency of major significance is a newly established Water Resources Board, located administratively under the Minister of Land and Natural Resources, but with wide ranging water policy, planning and advisory authority, particularly with regard to inter-basin transfer of water. The Board also has specific approval and directive authority over river authorities in performing their function regarding hydrometric schemes, minimum acceptable flows, pollution control and proposals for action.

Craine has commented as follows about the overall situation:

> River authorities, however, are central to the new British scheme. The law provides that their managing boards will be composed of representatives of local governments and of the central government in such proportions as to always assure local governments a bare majority and no more. It is in these 27 semi-independent authorities that the grass-roots issues of water management are faced.[3]

The French Basin Agencies

1. *General Background.* In France, as in Britain, regional water management agencies are creatures of national law. Prior to the Act of 1964, which while not repealing existing laws fundamentally changes policy, French laws for pollution control were very piecemeal and complex. Many agencies at the central and local government levels were responsible for formulating standards for pollution control and supervising their application.

The central authority for industrial pollution control appears, however, to have come from the "Dangerous Objectionable and Unhealthy Establishments Act" of December 1917, and its various implementing decrees. The 1917 Act placed under the authority of the Prefect (Chief Administrator of a department) all industrial and commercial establishments endangering the safety, health or amenities of the community.

All these establishments are inspected by civil servants known as

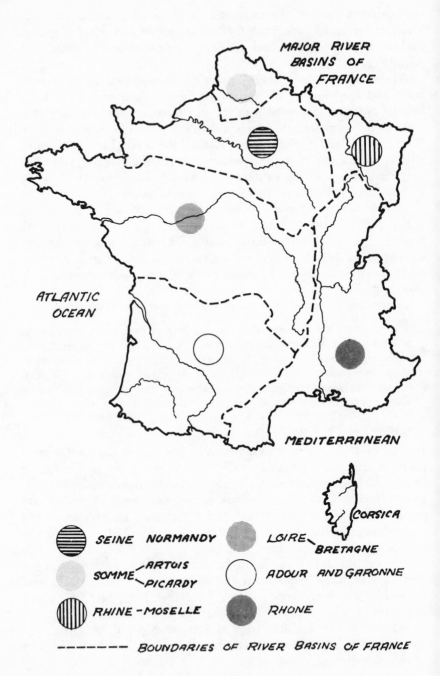

MAJOR RIVER
BASINS OF
FRANCE

ATLANTIC
OCEAN

MEDITERRANEAN

CORSICA

SEINE NORMANDY

SOMME ‒ ARTOIS ‒ PICARDY

RHINE - MOSELLE

LOIRE ‒ BRETAGNE

ADOUR AND GARONNE

RHONE

------- BOUNDARIES OF RIVER BASINS OF FRANCE

Inspectors of Classified Establishments. They operate under the instructions of the Prefect and their consultation usually weighs heavily in the laying of restrictions on industrial establishments. It appears that unofficial procedures and efforts to persuade have played a large role in these proceedings. Considerable emphasis seems to have been put upon negotiations and advice to the industries on a case-by-case basis. Should negotiations fail, there are legal arrangements to compel compliance. This approach has not prevented the development of a severe industrial pollution problem.

Other pollution control laws relate to fish life, protection of drinking water, protection of public and private water courses.

Under the Rural Code, any discharge harmful to fish life, reproduction and nutritive value is punishable by a fine of 50,000–500,000 francs and/or imprisonment for 10 days to one year. Water and forestry officials are responsible for enforcement, and since the penalties are heavy, they have tended to compromise with the offenders.

The Public Health Code, in addition to some more specific provisions, provides penalties for any person who has allowed substances which might be injurious to health to enter the public drinking water supply.

The highway engineers (Navigation Service) enforce the pollution control regulation concerning public (navigable) water courses. Authorization must be obtained for any discharges into these water courses. Infractions are under the jurisdiction of the administrative courts.

On so-called private (non-navigable) water courses, the Civil Code stipulates that a riparian owner has the right to use the water flowing along or through his property, but he must return it when it leaves his land to its initial condition. As in other countries having riparian law, this provision has been honored mostly in the breach. Additional provisions of the Rural Code entrust the Rural Engineering Service with pollution control functions on the "private" water courses.

Gentot explains that while this superabundance of rules and regulations concerning water pollution leaves the impression of confusion, a certain unity occurs because of the central role of the Prefect.

> But the fact remains that if any contentious matters that may arise are set aside, the concurrent laws that apply in this field all leave the Prefect as the representative of the central authority in his department the most important powers.[4]

Evaluations of the effectiveness of pollution control in France vary. Still, the preponderance of evidence seems to be that it has been rather ineffective. For example, the following statistics give for each watershed the approximate total number of industrial concerns which the French Government indicated in 1961 were discharging harmful effluents. The Seine, 1,000; Loire, 600; Garonne, 300; Rhone, 750; Rhine-Moselle, 500; Adour, 75; northern rivers, 350. Water courses flowing to the Brittany and Normandy coasts, 400; Atlantic coast water courses, 100; Mediterranean water courses, 150. As of 1965, as regards towns and cities whose population is above 2,000, only 3 million people out of 25 million were provided with any treatment facilities. This is a smaller proportion than in any of the other countries in this paper.

Discontent with the previous record of pollution control and the great diversity of responsibility for taking pollution control measures played a large role in the creation in 1959 of a Commission on Water, attached to the Commissariat Général du Plan. As the result of the work of this Commission, a comprehensive new law was passed by Parliament in December 1964.

2. *Present Organization Arrangements.* The law of 1964 might be described quite simply as revolutionary. While there is less experience in France with regional approaches to water quality management than in any of the other countries considered in this study, the new law foresees going further in some respects than has been done anywhere else in the world. This is particularly true in the area of using economic incentives for pollution control purposes.

Three features of the law are of particular importance: (1) it establishes regional agencies in each of the river basins of France—these are really regionalized agencies of the national government; (2) it gives these agencies far-reaching power to implement regional programs of water pollution control, and (3) it places primary emphasis on charges, particularly effluent charges, to finance the program and to coordinate private and local government waste discharge decisions with the objectives of the regional agency. In other words, it views charges levied on effluents as the primary means for controlling waste discharges. The act does not repeal previous pollution legislation, but it foresees that much of it will be displaced as the provisions of the new law become effective.

The act is extremely general. Indeed it is what the French term a "skeleton enactment." This means that Parliament has defined broad principles leaving the administration to state the provisions of the act in forms of rules (decrees in the Council of State) within a certain time. As of the present writing, very few such decrees have been published and consequently much of what the law intends must be

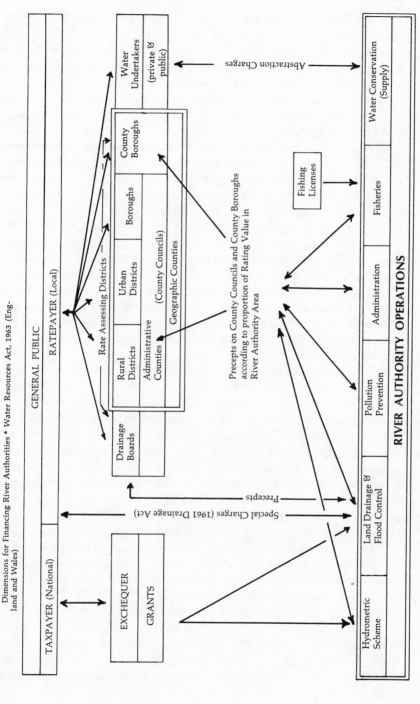

Dimensions for Financing River Authorities * Water Resources Act, 1963 (England and Wales)

RIVER AUTHORITY OPERATIONS

* This chart was prepared by Lyle Craine, School of Conservation, University of Michigan.

inferred from the statements of those who helped frame it.[5] The Act takes a very broad view of the quality problem as involving "any occurrence liable to cause or increase the pollution of water by altering the physical, chemical, biological, and bacteriological problems of surface water, ground water or sea water within territorial limits." It also sees the water quality problem within the context of overall management and the basin agencies are given general water resources management powers.

The generalities of the act have given rise to some disagreements over its proper interpretation. At first, some well-informed commentators (Levy-Lambert, for example) thought that it permitted the agencies to engage in direct investment in, and operation of, facilities. However, it is now agreed that it does not allow the basin agencies to act directly except for research and studies. Therefore, under the present law they must act primarily through grants, loans and contracts with private and public bodies. It is foreseen that these will be used in such a way as to achieve scale economies and lead toward an economically efficient solution. A new law will be needed to enable the basin agencies to build and operate control measures. Since it is now widely agreed that the new basin agencies should have this power, no difficulty is foreseen in getting such a law enacted by Parliament.

As shown by the accompanying diagram, the activities of the river basin authorities (Public Administrative Establishments) will be supervised by the central government which will also act in the capacity of coordinator between them. Each management area will be mapped out by the standing interministerial committee on development planning problems, and a national water committee under the direct authority of the Prime Minister will advise on all water resource development and distribution projects of major importance or common to several areas. In each area, a River Basin Committee will be set up (or, where appropriate, for a group of basins). The water users (including waste dischargers), local communities and the administration will be equally represented on it. They are to advise upon the desirability of any works or alterations contemplated in the area for the common benefit. Programs for water management (pollution control, for instance) must be discussed within the Basin Committee and approved by the central government before they are executed.

The basin agencies will be allowed to levy charges on corporations and individuals "taking into account the extent to which they have made the provision of facilities useful or necessary or will benefit therefrom." While the Act sees this is a way of financing large scale facilities—reservoirs, treatment facilities, measures to improve stream capacity, etc.—it also makes clear that the charges are not to be considered solely as a financing measure. The charges are viewed as a means to compel the waste dischargers to compensate for the "spill-over" costs they cause to the general economy. Thus, while the charges will promote the carrying out of works in the general interest, they are meant to provide an incentive for the waste dischargers to take all external costs into account when making decisions about the discharge of effluents.

The French organizations will cover the entire territory of France. Initially, the plan had been to set up executive organizations only in exceptional cases. The Parliamentary proceedings revealed a preference for the creation of organizations which could operate at the scale of the large basins. The reason is the recognized interdependence between water users and management facilities within the whole hydrological area. Although it was felt that interdependence between the users of the basin from the source to the mouth could no longer be neglected, it was also recognized that interdependence between distant points in the larger basins could be less strong than in smaller basins or sub-basins. It was therefore foreseen that some geographical decentralization of the agencies might be desirable. Thus the possibility of creating specialized authorities in particular sub-basins is left open. Such authorities would have rather large autonomy, but would remain under the general authority of the agency in charge of the whole basin.

Emphasis on the regional approach to water quality management in France appears to have had several origins. The first was on a conceptual plane, involving reasoning about hydrologic interdependency external costs, etc.

Clearly, however, another factor was the very close attention paid in France to regional undertakings in other countries. There are many references to the work of the River Boards in England in the French literature of the early 60's. Even more striking is the attention given to the developments in the Ruhr area.

While the basin associations of France appear to a considerable degree to have been modeled after the German Genossenschaften, they also diverge from that pattern in highly significant respects. This is primarily in the matter of their actual governmental structure and in the role they assign effluent charges in the management system.[6] These matters will be discussed further in the final section.

The Delaware River Basin

1. *Situation and Accomplishments.* By American standards the Dela-

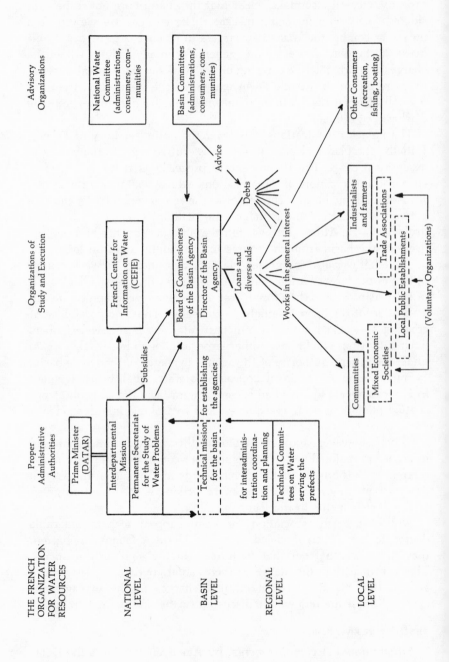

THE FRENCH ORGANIZATION FOR WATER RESOURCES

Proper Administrative Authorities

Organizations of Study and Execution

Advisory Organizations

NATIONAL LEVEL

BASIN LEVEL

REGIONAL LEVEL

LOCAL LEVEL

National Water Committee (administrations, consumers, communities)

Basin Committees (administrations, consumers, communities)

French Center for Information on Water (CEFIE)

Prime Minister (DATAR)

Interdepartmental Mission

Permanent Secretariat for the Study of Water Problems

Board of Commissioners of the Basin Agency

Director of the Basin Agency

Technical mission for the basin

for interadministration coordination and planning

Technical Committees on Water serving the prefects

for establishing the agencies

Subsidies

Advice

Debts

Loans and diverse aids

Works in the general interest

Other Consumers (recreation, fishing, boating)

Industrialists and farmers

Trade Associations

Local Public Establishments

(Voluntary Organizations)

Communities

Mixed Economic Societies

ware River Basin is rather small. Its drainage area (12,765 square miles) is less than $\frac{1}{40}$ the size of that of the Missouri. At that, it is about three times as large as the entire area administered by the Ruhr Region Genossenschaften. Its population however is somewhat less than that of the Ruhr Region amounting to somewhat over 6 million persons. Portions of it, however, especially the Lehigh sub-basin and the shores of the Delaware Estuary (a 43-mile reach of the Delaware River from Bristol to Marcus Hook, Pennsylvania), are among the most highly industrialized and heavily populated regions in the United States and indeed in the world.

Some of the problems associated with the use of the water resource of the basin result from the great variability in flow of the river. For example, on August 19, 1955, which was the date of the valley's worst flood disaster, the discharge from the river was 329,000 cubic feet per second. The early and middle 60's have seen a persistent drought in the basin with flows falling well under 1,500 cubic feet per second every summer and fall, even though reservoir releases were made for flow augmentation purposes.

The main water quality problems are in the Lehigh Valley and along the Delaware Estuary. Of these the Delaware Estuary is by far more important in terms both of the quantity of water affected and the number of people impacted. Much of the succeeding discussion will apply particularly to the Delaware Estuary.

2. *Historical Perspective.* By the late 17th century, water power was being developed at falls along the tributaries of the Delaware and by the time of the American Revolution, water-powered mills had made the Brandywine watershed a center for the production of flour, gunpowder, textiles, and paper. A combination of natural resources, including plentiful water, navigation opportunities and advanced cultural and political development caused the Delaware area, especially the estuary and the watershed of the Lehigh, to grow rapidly and hold its position as the center of American manufacturing for many years. Even today the estuary area is among the most intensely developed industrial complexes in the United States. It is a center for the manufacture of innumerable goods, prominent among which are chemicals, steel, and petroleum refining.

Despite the mass of industrial and municipal development, very little was done to deal with water quality problems until the last few decades. In 1940 little treatment of any kind was given to waste waters in the region.

During the decade of the 20's, the basin states were much occupied with proposals by New York to withdraw 600 million gallons a day

DELAWARE WATER BASIN AND SERVICE AREA

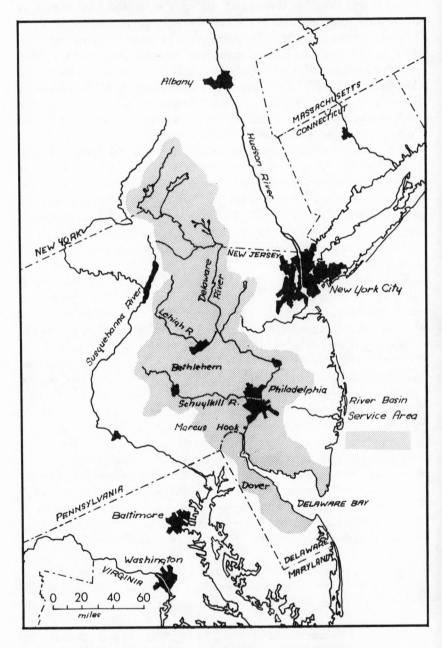

Source: Water Research Foundation for the Delaware River Basin.

of water from the upper Delaware for water supply purposes. A Supreme Court case evolved out of this proposal and the Court set a limit of 440 million gallons a day for the diversion.

Several proposed interstate compacts had been stimulated by New York's proposal in the 1920's and these had spoken in terms of a comprehensive development of the water resources of the Delaware. But the Court decision simply authorized a development of the upper Delaware designed primarily for New York water supply with incidental low flow augmentation to reduce claimed downstream damages.

In 1936, an agency called The Interstate Commission on the Delaware River Basin (or INCODEL) was formed. It was not in the form contemplated in the draft compacts for the 1920's, i.e., an interstate agency, but was created by parallel legislation among the states and operated from the beginning on the principle of voluntary interstate cooperation. The formation of this commission was partly the result of federal initiative, particularly that of the National Resources Committee, and was also encouraged by the Council of State Governments.

INCODEL had two main committees—a Committee on Water Quantity and a Committee on Water Quality. The latter had a membership from the departments of health in the four states. Its initiative and recommendations came to dominate the activities of INCODEL. The orientation was not toward comprehensive planning of the water resources of the basin but toward an effort to deal with certain immediate water quality problems. For this purpose, the committee prepared a reciprocal agreement on pollution control. The agreement classified the waters of the river and its tributaries into four categories or zones based on use and prescribed standards of treatment for each. The agreement was promptly adopted by the department of health in each of the four states. The committee also drafted a uniform pollution control law which was passed in all states other than Pennsylvania by 1941. There was strong opposition in the Pennsylvania legislature, stemming from industry and reflecting the fact that the City of Philadelphia had relatively little treatment for its sewage and accounted for a substantial portion of the untreated sewage discharged into the Delaware. Thus the plan failed to pass in Pennsylvania.

In 1945, INCODEL offered its plan again and with the assistance of a governor devoted to water quality improvement the measure passed unanimously through both Houses. Construction of treatment plants by municipalities along the estuary commenced immediately after the war. This was counted as a major victory by INCODEL and a period of what appears to have been "sitting on laurels" occurred. The importance of the treatment plant construction is by no means to be minimized, especially in terms of the removal of certain obvious and offensive pollutants from the water. Nevertheless, the standards of treatment achieved were not particularly high (on the average not much more than primary treatment) and the residual waste together with industrial discharges continued to place very heavy oxygen demands on the stream.

In regard to the broader possibilities of multi-purpose planning, INCODEL for a number of years did comparatively little. It displayed a preference for parallel state legislation against the preparation of a comprehensive plan for the river. In the late forties and early fifties, INCODEL did attempt an initiative toward broader planning in the basin. Several engineering firms were engaged and they presented a plan for the states to join in a compact for the construction of a number of reservoirs.

The plan, however, raised many controversial issues. Pennsylvania once more proved to be the critical state. Upon the negative recommendation of a special study committee, the proposal did not pass the Pennsylvania legislature. While the Pennsylvania study was going on, New York filed a petition with the Supreme Court in 1951 for modification of the 1931 decree to permit diversion of 800 million gallons per day.

The Supreme Court once more appointed a special master to conduct hearings among the litigants and to make recommendations to the Court. Agreement was finally reached on a plan which would permit New York to divert 800 million gallons per day with additional compensating releases and provide for additional diversions outside the basin by New Jersey without compensating releases.

In 1954, the Supreme Court without opinion adopted a decree as agreed upon among the party states and recommended by the master. By this time, the INCODEL compact proposal was virtually dead.

In 1955, severe hurricanes struck the Delaware Basin causing floods which took about 100 lives and did on the order of $125 million of damage. This set in motion a new study of the basin by the U.S. Corps of Engineers. Despite many discouraging setbacks, interest in interstate cooperation reaching beyond the limited role played by INCODEL continued in the basin as the Corps of Engineers prepared its study. Even before the flood and the initiation of the Corps of Engineers planning study, the governors of the four valley states and the mayors of New York City and Philadelphia organized the Delaware River Basin Advisory Committee. The committee working with leading citizens sponsored a study of interstate cooperation at Syracuse University. This study which helped to provide an intellectual and factual underpinning for further developments was completed in late 1959. Contrary to all expectations, the Advisory Committee completed a compact draft, agreed to among the states and federal agencies and ready for presentation to the federal Congress in one year's time. It took exactly two years from the completion of the Syracuse study to the final enactment of the Federal-Interstate compact.

In 1959, the Water Resources Association of the Delaware River Basin, another non-profit corporation, was founded. It is the representative of many citizens' organizations concerned with water problems. Via its publication, the "Delaware Basin Bulletin," it has acted as a friendly "watchdog" over the Delaware River Basin Commission.

The Corps of Engineers' Delaware River Basin Survey Report was completed in 1961 and approved by the states and federal agencies in 1962. This report formed the basis for the first comprehensive plan for the Delaware Basin adopted by the New Delaware River Basin Commission.

The launching of the Commission boded well for its future success, if the results of votes in the various legislative bodies can be taken as an indication. The vote was almost unanimously favorable in each instance.

Certainly the long history of efforts to achieve cooperation and the gradual building of conceptual and empirical foundations are related to this result as are the catastrophic floods of 1955. But another factor which, while difficult to document, is rated as important by those who observed the sequence of events is that the compact had an articulate, respected, and highly effective advocate in Walter M. Phillips. Mr. Phillips was Executive Secretary of the Delaware River Basin Advisory Committee from its formation in 1956. He and a few other leaders in the basin must be credited with a considerable role in achieving the compact.

Before turning to an actual description of the compact and its provisions, it should be noted that while water quality was mentioned in all discussions of the problems of the basin, it did not loom as the largest of them to the Advisory Committee or even to the Corps of Engineers during the preparation of its plan for the basin. Municipal and industrial water supply, navigation, and hydroelectric power were the central foci although the matter of the salinity of the estuary commanded some attention. It has now begun to appear to the staff of the commission and to the Water Resources Association that the quality problem is the most serious one they face.

3. *Present Organizational Arrangements.* The Delaware River Basin compact is a unique political instrument in the United States in that

it includes the federal government as a co-equal partner with the States. Moreover, it assigns more comprehensive powers to a regional agency than has been done previously in this country. The central objective of the compact is to create a river basin commission which will devise and administer a comprehensive multi-purpose water resources plan which ". . . will bring the greatest benefits and produce the most efficient service in the public welfare."

The document states that the United States "consents to, and joins . . ." an intergovernmental compact creating the Delaware River Commission which is to be "an agency, an instrumentality of the governments of the . . . parties." The commission consists of five members representing the four member states and the federal government. The commissioners are the governors of the four basin states and the Secretary of the Interior represents the President of the United States. Each commissioner may specify a voting alternate. In each case, these have been men with certain expertise in the field of water management.

The commission is charged with the duty of developing a "comprehensive plan . . . for the immediate and long-range development and uses of water resources of the basin" and to develop a shorter-range "water resources program" based on the comprehensive plan. The commission is granted the power to plan and execute the development of water resources by acquiring or building and operating and maintaining dams, reservoirs, and similar facilities to control and develop the water supply; regulate the flows so as to control water quality and pollution, to control and abate existing pollution, to provide for flood protection, and to institute sound practices of watershed management including the prevention of soil erosion, promotion of land reclamation and sound forestry practices, fishing and wildlife conservation measures; promote recreational uses of the river; develop and operate facilities for the generation and transmission (but not for direct consumer distribution) of hydroelectric power and to set rates and charges for such power and regulate and control withdrawals and diversions from the waters of the basin.

The commission also has a wide variety of powers for implementing the plan including the authority to delegate certain of its powers to instrumentalities of signatory governments, to establish cost-sharing standards and formulas for the apportionment of cost among the different purposes included in multi-purpose programs, for the sharing of financial responsibility with the signatory parties, public bodies, groups, and private enterprise. The compact authorizes broad borrowing powers and the power to issue bonds. It pledges the full faith and credit of the commission. The parties agree to provide capital funds for the projects of the commission in accordance with the cost-sharing provisions to be established by it. The compact provides for the apportionment of the annual expense budget among the signatories with all of them undertaking to include their portion in their respective budgets "subject to such review and approval as may be required by the respective budgetary processes." The commission has the power of eminent domain and the state signatories agree not to undertake any development projects in relation to the Delaware River unless the project is approved by the commission and is in accordance with the comprehensive program. The federal government agrees to substantially the same terms.

The compact gives the commission extremely broad power for the direct implementation of various measures affecting quantity or quality of water in the basin. It is intended that the commission shall exercise such powers only if another federal or state agency cannot or does not provide the same functions efficiently in accordance with the comprehensive plan.

Specifically with regard to pollution control, the commission is given the powers to undertake investigations and surveys and acquire, construct, operate, and maintain projects and facilities to control potential pollution and abate or dilute existing pollution of the water resources of the basin. It may invoke, as complainant, the power and jurisdiction of water pollution abatement agencies of the signatory parties. The commission may assume jurisdiction to control future pollution whenever it determines after investigation and public hearings that the comprehensive plan requires it. The commission, after public hearing, may also classify the waters of the basin and establish standards for treatment of sewage, industrial, or other waste according to such classes. It also has the power, after hearings, to amend and repeal rules, regulations and standards. The signatory parties also pledge themselves to pass whatever legislation may be necessary to control pollution in accordance with the comprehensive plan. The commission also has direct enforcement powers and may, after investigation and hearing, issue orders to any persons or person or public or private corporation to cease any discharge which it determines to be in violation of rules and regulations that have been adopted. The orders are subject to appeal in any court of competent jurisdiction.

To summarize, the commission has far-reaching powers to plan, design, construct, operate, and finance facilities for the abatement of pollution if it can demonstrate that these are effective and efficient means for achieving the objective and could not be so efficiently achieved by other units of government. It also appears to have considerable scope under federal law to proceed in the matter of standard-setting and control of discharges as it deems best.

SECTION III—COMPARISONS ON THE BASIS OF CRITERIA

The discussion of Section II has revealed marked similarities and contrasts in approaches to regional water quality management. The objective of the present section is to make these similarities and differences more explicit and to elaborate on them in the framework of certain specified criteria. The term criteria is used in a very loose sense since the experience with regional approaches is in some cases so limited that efforts at greater rigor would be misplaced. Still, if the matter is considered from the economic efficiency point of view (and the objective of economic efficiency is discernible in each of the regional cases), it seems that regional organizations must have certain capabilities.

First, technologic and economic study has indicated that efficient solutions cannot be achieved if the agency is constrained to focus on a narrow range of alternatives. Accordingly, the ability to analyze and implement a wide range of alternatives is one of the criteria.

Second, clearly there are often direct interdependencies between water management for supply and for quality improvement and between water quality and the pattern of land uses in the area. Therefore, the ability to have an appropriate influence on related land and water uses is another criterion.

Third, even an agency exercising far-reaching direct action in terms of investment in, and operation of, facilities, as do the Genossenschaften, must leave certain decisions bearing on the amount of waste discharge in the hands of industry and local government. For example, it is doubtful whether any regional quality management agency could or should directly dictate the design of industrial processes. Still, research on industrial water utilization has shown beyond doubt that design of industrial production processes is often the least costly way of reducing waste discharges. This means that the regional agency must have some way of properly influencing the design and operation of processes of a multitude of "independent operators." Similarly, local governments may be left to treat the waste from their areas themselves. In this instance, the regional agency must have tools of management, such as direct regulation or charging authority (such as the authority to levy effluent charges), if waste discharges are to be reduced to an appropriate level. Accordingly, the ability of the agency to articulate private and local government decisions in such a way as to achieve an efficient regional waste disposal system incorporating whatever works it provides directly is another criterion.

Finally, the parties who obtain the benefits and incur the costs of the management program should have an opportunity to influence the decisionmaking of the regional agency. This appears to be necessary from the point of view of efficiency for two reasons: (1) there are limits on the agency's ability to identify benefits and costs and evaluate them. Therefore, if representatives of the affected parties are brought together in the management board of a regional agency, their interactions in board decisions will tend to represent the confrontation and resolution of benefits and costs in terms of some judgment of marginal utility as collectively determined by the board members. (2) The regional agency is more likely to have a supporting constituency which will provide the necessary political support to allow it to implement an efficient system if the affected parties feel that they are represented where the real power resides. Therefore, the final criterion is the opportunity for affected parties to influence decision-making.

It is necessary to point out, however, that unless the larger framework of costs and rewards is so structured as not to make economically inefficient facilities financially attractive, the representation of interested parties may lead away from rather than toward an efficient solution. For example, of the costs of certain facilities are borne locally while others are subsidized by a larger unit of government, local interests may well unite to obtain the advantage of the income redistribution in their direction which is inherent in the latter, even if it is the less efficient alternative.

Again, the reader must be reminded that these criteria are meant simply to provide a framework for discussion and that it is unfortunately too early for a formal and rigorous assessment of the various cases.

1. *Ability to evaluate and implement a wide range of alternatives.* The results of engineering economic research clearly show that certain large scale regional measures for improving water quality can often improve the efficiency of a quality management system. These techniques include streamflow regulation, mechanical reaeration of streams, direct treatment of streams via oxidation lakes and other means, collection and treatment of municipal and industrial waste in central plants serving entire regions, piping of waste away from

critical reaches of stream, and others. Measures of this type will probably be most beneficial in highly developed basins, but should be examined in others as well. In general, the regional approaches discussed in this paper are cognizant of such opportunities and the laws governing them make provision for their implementation. The only exception is Britain where the law establishing the River Authorities, documents leading up to it and discussions following it, all suggest that the river authorities are not expected to undertake activities of this kind.

The Genossenschaften are, of course, in a different category from the other cases. Not only was the idea of an integrated river basin-wide system from the beginning a guiding conception for them but they have had a number of decades to implement such a system. The range of alternatives evaluated and implemented is wide. In fact, the works which have been instituted span virtually the entire range of possibilities which have been found feasible in at least isolated instances elsewhere across the world. Nevertheless, there are two factors in the operation of the Genossenschaften which may militate against the actual identification and implementation of an optimum system. One is that there still seems to be an excessive separation of water quality and water quantity considerations. This point is explained further below. The second is that, despite the sophistication of their operations in many other respects, they have used little or no formal systems analysis. While this may seem strange in view of the broad scope and responsibilities of the organizations and the fairly obvious utility which this mode of analysis would seem to have, not only for the design but for the operation of water quality management systems, it reflects a more general lag in the application of systems methods to water resource engineering and economics in Europe. To what degree such techniques as computer simulation and more sophisticated analysis of hydrology might improve the system must remain an open question. Limited information from U.S. research and practice suggest that these are important design and operation tools.

British practice historically has not been characterized by systematic implementation of regional scale quality management measures. Indeed, virtually complete reliance has been placed upon treatment at individual points of waste outfall. The only effort in the direction of achieving scale economies in waste disposal was embodied in the 1937 Drainage of Trade Premises Act. This authorizes the discharge of trade waste into public sewers with the approval of the local authority subject to such conditions as it might establish. Some small effort to integrate the sewer systems of local authorities was also embodied in the Rivers (Prevention of Pollution) Act of 1951. However, up to this time it cannot be said that there has been any systematic exploitation of the opportunities provided by collection and treatment of waste on a regional scale (with the exception of some efforts in this direction by the Thames Conservancy), not to mention the array of other possible measures which might be implemented on a river basin basis. The probable economy of broader regional scale measures has not gone unrecognized by certain water quality professionals, however. It is possible to find strong statement in the literature concerning economies to be achieved by these measures.

In view of the dense development of watersheds in England—especially in the industrial areas—and that a number of English experts have spoken out strongly on the matter, and perhaps especially in view of the fact that the Advisory Committee had visited and assessed the Ruhr area experience, it is strange indeed that the possibilities inherent in the central design and operation of regional scale measures for quality management received literally no discussion in the Final Report of the Sub-Committee on the Growing Demand for Water. This report was, as indicated, the basis for the river authorities' legislation. There is little or nothing in the law or the various available interpretations of it that could lead one to suppose that much emphasis will be placed on direct investment and operation of facilities for water quality improvement by any of the river authorities. This contrasts strikingly with the emphasis placed upon the river basin development and management approach to water supply and the strong role which the river authorities are assigned to it. The situation probably reflects a long history of pollution control based on efforts to impose restrictions on individual waste dischargers. This effort had produced several laws which had not yet been fully tested and which were not basically questioned during the studies and debate leading up to the river authorities' legislation.

Whereas there may be some ambiguity about the objectives of the other regional agencies discussed in this report, it seems clear both from the law and discussions of it that the objective of the French agencies is economic efficiency in the full sense of the term. It appears that they aim to establish a system wherein the incremental costs of further improvement of water quality balance the incremental benefits, and in which the full range of alternative ways of improving water quality is assessed and all measures brought into optimal balance. In pursuit of this objective, certain large-scale regional undertakings are envisaged, and an effluent charges scheme is contemplated as a means for making these collective measures financially possible.

While the current legislation does not appear to provide authority for direct investment in regional scale works, it does contemplate systems of grants and contracts aimed toward producing an economically optimal system. Moreover, there is now considerable sentiment to supplement the basic law by giving the basin agencies the authority to build and operate control measures. To what extent these objectives will actually be achieved in practice cannot now be foreseen.

It is clear from the Delaware Basin compact that the commission has authority to plan, construct, operate, and finance measures for water quality improvement. The compact also specifies, however, that the commission is to do this only if it can do so more efficiently than other agencies. The commission seems particularly well-suited to undertake measures of the kind we have been concerned with in the previous several pages. It appears also that such measures are potentially of great importance in the Delaware Estuary area and perhaps elsewhere in the basin.

The commission staff has been quite small and its capability for planning, economic evaluation, and program development very limited. While realizing the aspirations of the compact will necessarily involve expanding staff capability by a large multiple, it is true that over the years since the compact commission came into operation extensive and unusually high quality work on system planning has been done by other agencies. These include the Federal Water Pollution Control Administration, Harvard University, and the University of Pennsylvania among others. The Federal Water Pollution Control Administration study went far in identifying and evaluating alternatives both in terms of combinations of measures available to improve water quality in the estuary and in regard to objectives to be met. Without going into the details of the matter, it can be said that the Federal Water Pollution Control Administration study identified certain large-scale regional measures including mechanical reaeration of the estuary and piping of industrial waste waters out of the estuary which could greatly reduce the overall cost of a water quality management program. Further opportunities for realizing regional scale economies remain to be explored. Already, there appears to be justification for direct action in regard to the construction and operation of works on the part of the commission if it is to achieve the most efficient system for dealing with the water quality problems in the estuary. Moreover, in the matter of the systems analysis tools available to it, the commission is far ahead of any comparable regional agency in the United States or abroad. A board of consultants has strongly urged the commission to use these tools and to proceed to implement a program of regional measures. There is every evidence that the federal authorities would be pleased to see the commission taking a strong hand in implmenting the program which seems to grow out of the analytical efforts.

Whether the commission will actually implement such a program is an open question at the moment. The force of engineering economic analysis is in that direction, but skepticism about such an approach is evident in the basin. Industries continue to be doubtful, seeing it as a potential threat to their freedom of action and opening the door to inquiries about matters which have hitherto been considered confidential. The state agencies responsible for pollution control continue to be jealous of their prerogatives.

Finally, a point raised earlier should be re-emphasized. In every country with which we are here concerned subsidies from higher levels of government are provided for certain specific measures to control pollution (although this does not amount to much for the Ruhr area). In different places, these include subsidies to streamflow regulation, subsidies to municipal treatment plant construction, and subsidies to industrial waste control facilities. Such arrangements may cause an inefficient facility to become financially attractive even though it is not economically most efficient and therefore distort the planning and implementation of alternatives. This suggests that if a policy of subsidization is desired, regional agencies should have the option of taking a general subsidy for quality improvement based on the provision of a regional plan rather than having to obtain subsidies by implementing particular types of facilities.

2. *Ability to Appropriately Influence Related Land and Water Uses.* It has often been remarked that considerations for water quantity and water quality are basically inseparable. This is usually correct. Clearly streamflow regulation through reservoir storage while influencing the amount of water available for diversion, depletion, and in-stream uses at the same time affects the quality of water in the stream. Therefore, quality considerations should be taken into account in the design and operation of reservoirs. Furthermore, restrictions on water usage such as permits or charges for water supply withdrawal influence water quality. If an industrial enterprise is induced to recirculate its water, more than likely the waste load will be reduced through internal treatment or waste recovery processes. Moreover, the waste load left will be smaller in volume and therefore less costly to treat.

It is also clear that relationships between land-use patterns and water quality management may be significant. For example, establishment of a new industrial discharge immediately above a public water supply may impose a large enough burden to make it worthwhile for society to consider changing the pattern of development. Research has indicated that particular location patterns may greatly influence the costs associated with waste disposal along an estuary. Institutions for land and water management should be such that these interrelationships will be evaluated and properly taken into account.

In a broad way, interrelationships between water quantity and quality have been taken into account in each of the cases discussed by putting water quality and quantity under the authority of the same agency, although in France the primary reservoir construction and operation agency has been Electricité de France and it probably will continue to be.[7] Here, as in regard to other large-scale measures, the law foresees that releases would be arranged for with EDF for quality improvement on a reimbursable basis by the basin agencies and that they would participate in planning. It is conceivable that this kind of relationship between agencies could accomplish the indicated integration without having the authority of a single agency internalize all direct interdependencies.

Because of the wide scope of their water resources authority, the Genossenschaften are in a particularly good position to integrate all aspects of water management. Institutional development has, however, created a somewhat artificial distinction between water quality and "water supply" in the Ruhr which is still apparent. In view of the limited opportunities for flow regulation to improve water quality, however, it is doubtful whether this is very important. Through its charges for water withdrawal, the Ruhrverband has caused a far-reaching development of internal water recirculation systems in industry. This is recognized as desirable, not only from the point of view of water supply conservation, but because it reflects itself in lesser volumes of waste water and accordingly in the possibility for less costly treatment of residuals.

Closer coordination with land-use development and land management generally is considered one of the major future tasks of the Ruhrverband by its director. A certain amount of coordination is nevertheless already achieved by the working together of staff from the Genossenschaft with the Siedlungsverband (the organization charged with general land-use planning in the industrial region of Northrhine-Westphalia). Thus the impacts upon water management are considered by the land-use planning authority in devising its overall plan for the region. This is the only case among those here considered where there is a reasonably comprehensive and systematic interrelationship of land use and water resources planning although such an interrelationship has been developed to some extent in England.

The English river authorities have at their disposal several potentially effective management controls. They have the authority to directly regulate the withdrawal of water from natural water courses, to regulate discharges of waste water, authority to charge for withdrawal of water, and the authority to construct and operate water management facilities with primary emphasis on reservoirs to store water and modify its natural flow characteristics. These tools permit the authorities to exercise control over waste discharge and water withdrawal and bring them into some sort of balance with river flows. While charging schemes are also possible, there seems to be a strong emphasis on direct control. On theoretical grounds which cannot be fully explored here, direct controls are often inferior to price-like devices in reaching for an economic optimum. Nevertheless, a number of critical interdependencies are clearly recognized and tools provided to influence them. There is also some recognition of the influence on land use and development upon the waste management problem. Most of the River Boards had arrangements with local planning authorities for all planning applications involving new discharges of trade or sewage effluents to be submitted to the board for review and advice before planning consent was given. The river authorities are expected to make similar arrangments. At a minimum this provides a certain protection against gross miscarriages.

In sum, while most of the critical interdependencies appear to have been recognized in providing management tools to the English river authorities, the heavy dependence on direct controls and failure to systematically integrate water and land planning must be counted as deficiencies.

In principle, the French law provides for a thoroughgoing management of water quality and water quantity. For example, the new law contemplates that charges will be levied upon water which is diverted and lost from the system, as well as upon effluent discharges. It is envisaged that two inter-connected but distinct fees will be paid by those who withdraw water and return waste to the system. It is also foreseen that the basin agencies will use grant making, contract and subsidy powers to bring all elements in the water system into optimal balance. If, as is expected, they are given the authority for direct investment, this power will be exercised in the same context. While these are only intentions at this point, it is fair to say that interdependencies between water quality and water quantity have been clearly and explicitly recognized.

On the matter of interrelationships between land use and water supply or waste disposal cost, the French law is largely silent. The same is true of various discussions of the law. Apparently this aspect of the management problem will not assume any major role in the activities of the establishments. The act does provide for the setting up of protective zones around sources of public water supply where the public health may be endangered. This power is extremely limited in scope, however, and does not represent any thoroughgoing recognition of interdependencies.

The Delaware River Compact provides the basin commission with a wide array of control measures and operating functions. The compact itself gives clear recognition to interdependencies between water quantity and quality. In principle, there is no reason why the agency's authority to set standards, levy charges on effluents and on water withdrawals, and engage in direct investment and operation facilities should not permit it to take optimal account of all interrelations between various water uses including waste disposal. For reasons already indicated, it is somewhat doubtful whether in practice this will actually be accomplished.

In regard to the matter of associated land use, there were suggestions prior to the framing of the compact that the basin commission should have open-ended authority and jurisdiction permitting non-water functions to be added later by the states. It was however decided not to propose this. The reasons appear to have been that the water agency was not necessarily an appropriate unit of government to exercise these functions and that, it was thought, to open the door to other government functions would bring forth complexities and political difficulties certain to bring defeat to the whole enterprise. As a result the compact is silent on the matter of relationships with land use. A study of the Delaware estuary made by the Federal Water Pollution Control Administration, however, suggests that important water quality costs and gains could be associated with particular patterns of land use which develop in the area. It is possible that the commission might have some influence on land-use patterns via its stream classification powers, but in general the issue has not been confronted. Since location decisions should not turn upon water quality considerations alone, it may be that no appropriate consideration of this variable can occur unless there is an adequate regional land-use planning authority in the basin. This does not now exist in the Delaware.

In summary, in each of the cases considered, interdependencies between water quantity and quality are explicitly recognized and tools are provided for managing these interrelationships. Particular types of tools used or contemplated vary with some agencies placing heavy emphasis on direct controls whereas others rely more heavily on indirect measures such as withdrawal or effluent charges. The only instance of reasonably systematic recognition of interrelationships between merging land-use patterns and water quality management problems is in the Ruhr. One may speculate that this is more a result of the existence of a strong regional land-use planning authority than of any particular initiative by the Genossenschaften.

3. *Ability to Articulate Private and Local Government Decisions so as to Achieve an Efficient System.* The extent to which coordinate action on a regional basis is achieved through direct design and operation of structural works by the regional authority will vary from case to case. In some instances, such as the operation of a reservoir or an in-stream treatment facility it may unquestionably be in the interest of efficiency for the regional agency to provide and operate a facility directly since there is no other agency that clearly has this responsibility or capacity. In the case of treatment plants at individual industry and municipal outfalls, the central authority may or may not find it in the interest of efficiency to operate them directly. In the Ruhr area, the Genossenschaften operate all conventional treatment plants. Municipalities and industries have the option to introduce their own treatment, but none have done so although industries frequently have incorporated internal waste recovery and pretreatment processes. It is one testimony to the efficiency of the Genossenschaften system that the members have chosen to pay the effluent charges rather than introduce their own treatment.

In few—if any—cases, could regional waste disposal considerations justify the direct design and operation of industrial processes by regional agency. Still, one point which engineering economic research has established beyond any possibility of dispute is the immensely important role which internal process design and internal waste recovery procedures can play in reducing industrial waste discharges. Thus even a regional agency which goes quite far in the design and operation of treatment facilities needs to devise some method of causing industrial waste disposers to take account of the cost they impose on waste treatment facilities or successive users when they design and operate their production processes. Where the regional agency does not construct and operate treatment plants, it must also use indirect means to induce optimal levels of treatment at municipal and industrial outfalls.

As already indicated, the Genossenschaften operate all conventional and some unconventional treatment devices. However, opportunities for industries to reduce their waste discharges are recognized by the Genossenschaften and industries encouraged in several ways to undertake these waste reducing activities. The effluent charge which varies with the quality and quantity of waste discharge either to the Genossenschaft facilities or directly to the streams is one incentive in this direction. Combined with technical and marketing assistance from the Genossenschaft it has had substantial influence on the reduction of industrial waste loads. The effluent charge cannot be said to be an economically ideal price[8] placed on the waste dischargers, but it does have considerable practical effect in articulating the decisions of industrial waste disposers with design and operation of the regional works provided directly by the Genossenschaften.

We have already seen that the English authorities are equipped with a wide array of water management tools. They are authorized by law passed in 1951 and 1961 to license all waste discharges in their areas. It is foreseen that these waste discharges will be treated on a case-by-case basis, but once the decision is reached control will be by means of the license specifying permitted waste discharge. Since there is little or no evidence that the English authorities will place much emphasis upon possibilities of exploiting economies of large scale within their region, it appears that these direct discharge controls will be the primary means for controlling water quality. In principle, it is possible to devise a system of such direct controls tailored to conditions as affected by individual outfalls which would correspond to a regional economic optimum (considerations of regional scale economies aside). In practice, this technique requires more information and is less flexible than the effluent charges device.[9] However, it may have certain advantages of greater administrative ease. It does not, of course, provide a source of revenue for financing the activities of the regional agency, including the exploitation of economies of large scale in water quality management.

The English law does permit the river authorities to devise and administer "charging schemes" under which "abstractors" will pay for water removed from surface or underground suppies. The law specifies four different relevant circumstances which may influence the level of charge. These are (1) characteristics of the source of supply, (2) season of the year it is withdrawn, (3) uses of the water taken, and (4) the way in which water is disposed of after use. In principle, therefore, there could be much flexibility in rate-setting and the charges might be used as a flexible tool of management. One could, for example, interpret the law to mean that the charge could be used

to create an economic incentive for waste reduction activity by municipalities and industries and thus serve as a suppliment to the administration of licenses for effluent discharges. At best, this would involve
some problems. For example, some industries withdraw from the
system of a water "undertaker" but discharge directly to a stream.
It must be said also that neither the law nor the associated literature
actually suggests that the use of charges as an incentive for waste
control would be desirable or for that matter even mentions it. Indeed,
the discussion is almost completely in terms of abstraction (withdrawal) charges as such.

It has already been explained that the French river basin agencies
are to take cognizance of the economies inherent in regional action.
Thus where economic analysis reveals their desirability, they might
induce combination of municipal and industrial waste into large treatment facilities, flow regulation of streams, and other regional scale
measures. Such measures would be supported through a program of
grants, loans, and contracts with public and private bodies. It is also
foreseen that the law will be changed to permit basin agencies to
engage in the direct construction and operation of facilities. Their
water quality operations are to be financed by effluent charges which
are recognized to be not merely a source of finance but a way of
inducing waste dischargers to take account of the costs they impose
on the general economy when they make their waste disposal decisions. The law specifies that the rates of charges to be levied have to
be approved by the relevant river basin committee where the local
public and private users of the water course (municipalities, industries,
recreational interests, etc.) have two-thirds of the seats while the
central government has one third. To what extent the political forces
in the committee will be conducive to the establishment of levels of
charges, which actually reflect the external costs imposed on the general economy, is perhaps somewhat questionable. Nevertheless, it is
intended that the effluent charges become the basic device for achieving control of effluents, particularly from industry. Moreover, the
law specifies that all those affecting quality by their actions are subject
to charges. Thus any action which reduces the waste assimilative
capacity of the river—such as a deep impoundment might do, for
example—is subject to charge under the legislation.

At this point, it is unclear how the Delaware Commission will
proceed on these matters. It has an array of management tools at its
disposal which include both direct controls and pricing and changing
schemes. A Federal Water Pollution Control Administration study in
the estuary found that a system of control which minimizes the cost

of treatment on a regional basis (even neglecting the possibility of large-scale measures) is much less costly than one which adheres to the usual administrative procedure of requiring an equal percentage of removal of waste by all sources to meet a stipulated goal. In other words, given the water quality goal in the estuary, it is much less costly to remove waste to a high degree at certain outfalls and to a lesser extent at others. This results from a combination of factors including scale economies in treatment methods and the dynamics of waste assimilation in the estuary. Savings in cost of 50 to 100 per cent are possible in the estuary area if a cost-minimizing procedure is adopted. A further study by the same agency found, as one would expect on theoretical grounds, that effluent charges can be used to induce a pattern of treatment about corresponding to the least costly treatment system.[10] They also found that major regional economic readjustments from a charge of the necessary level (8 to 10¢ per lb. of oxygen-demanding material) would not be anticipated to occur in the area and they were further of the opinion that an effluent charge system compared to conventional methods of improving water quality would not only obtain the same goal at lower costs but with a more equitable impact on the waste dischargers. The Panel of Consultants to the Delaware River Basin Commission (mentioned earlier) has recommended that this approach be thoroughly explored and both the Delaware River Commission and the Federal Water Pollution Control Administration are making intensive studies of it. On the other hand, there is considerable misunderstanding of the concept in the region as well as a good deal of opposition. Whether it will prove politically feasible to implement the technique is still an open question.

4. *Opportunity of Affected Parties to Influence Decision-Making.* It is clear that achieving a supporting constituency and making sure that all relevant values are reflected in the decision-making process requires means of communication with, and perhaps even direct political representation of, parties affected by the decisions. Knowledge of institutional design appears to be too limited to permit one to set down any sort of a well-defined criterion concerning appropriate means of communication and representation. The matter has nevertheless loomed large in the deliberations leading up to the regional approaches considered in this paper and in each case the laws establishing the regional agencies have been quite specific on the matter even though very general in other regards. The patterns which have emerged are, however, quite different in each of the cases considered.

In the earliest discussions of the type of institution which might be appropriate for dealing with the Emscher's problems much attention was accorded the matter of representation of interested parties. One early effort at organization had failed largely because of the feeling on the part of certain industrial interests that they were not adequately represented. The outgrowth of further deliberation was the creation of a political structure which is highly unconventional—at least as viewed from the perspective of the United States. Here, private interests as such tend not to be represented on public bodies unless these bodies are formed for very specific purposes.

In the case of the Genossenschaften, however, which have very broad management authority, industrial interests were given a defined place in the assembly and on the board of directors. While we are not privileged to know how these organizations would have fared in the absence of such representation, it is the judgment of the Directors of the Genossenschaften that the direct and clear representation of industry has been very important to their success. They feel that it has created a strong sense of participation on the part of industry which has reduced resistance to the provision of information and other cooperative services by industry. Communities which are also represented in the assembly and on the board as a matter of legal right are meant to speak for and promote activities in the broader public interest. The question may well occur whether the representation accorded industry would not militate against adequate representation of the value of esthetics and recreation in the activities of the Genossenschaften. This is a very complex question having to do with various cultural values and standards. But one thing is clear, visitors to the Ruhr are impressed by the attention which is given to esthetics and to provision of recreation opportunities.

In summary, while questions may well be raised about the particular distribution of political power in these organizations, managers of the agencies believe that careful attention to representation of affected parties has contributed to effective and efficient operation in the general interest of the area.

In Britain, the Sub-Committee on the Growing Demand for Water (the Proudman Committee) in its report on a study trip to Western Germany noted with interest the form of organization which had developed in the Ruhr area. Its recommendation concerning the composition of the new river authorities apparently reflected the influence of the Ruhr pattern. However, a minority report objected and favored continuation of the River Board pattern of representation of local governments based on their rating (taxing) power and of relevant ministries. The government's "White Paper" on the Proudman Committee set forth a compromise arrangement, which is essentially followed in the legislation except for details of procedure.

The Proudman Committee had recommended a "new type of authority," small and compact with membership ranging from 10 to 15 which might be elected by the interests concerned or appointed by the Ministers in consultation with those interests. The recommended organization resembles the Ruhr pattern of a board composed of representatives from the user groups.

The committee recognized that its recommendation departed from "a principle underlying the present constitution of River boards that representation is partly related to the provision of finance." In the River Board operation, the source of finance had consisted almost exclusively of precepts (taxes) on the local authorities. It was anticipated that this would remain a major source of revenue under the river authoriies, although the charging schemes are a new element in the picture. The committee attached "less importance to representation as such than to the efficient and expeditious discharge of the wide range of functions involved." The minority report, however, held that "to give these sweeping financial powers to a small non-representative body such as our colleagues recommend is without precedent. The precept made by River Board on a local authority is mandatory without any right of appeal. Thus, the authorities called upon to pay have no control—over the amount demanded and no voice as to how the money is spent.

The cry of no taxation without representation (perhaps two centuries late) won the day. Apparently the lessons of the Boston Tea Party were well learned in Whitehall. The compromise which emerged specifies that the river authorities should range in size from 21 to 31 members, part of whom would be appointed by local authorities and part by Ministers "because of their knowledge of particular aspects of the river authorities' work or interests affected by it." The local authority representation is to be selected by having regard to taxpayers in the area of each constituent local authority in numbers as is sufficient to constitute a majority of the total membership of the river authority.

Thus, in contrast with the Genossenschaft assembly which emphasizes representatives of water user interests, and is a "purely representative body" the river authorities are at least in part an "expert body."

A particular departure worth noting from the political organization of the Genossenschaften is the absence of industry representation.

Central government appointments are expected to represent the expertise and local area representation to reflect the provision of finance via taxation. To the extent that revenues are to be obtained from user charges, the specific users are not represented in accordance with financial contribution. However, local authority representation is in part answerable to the same clientele, i.e., the water users and waste dischargers are more or less represented through the local political process. Still, the distribution of power will be quite different than if industry were represented in some proportion to its water utilization or role in the finance of the authorities.

The French public administrative establishments display still a third pattern. Half of the board of the regional agency consists of representatives of the central government. The other half is composed of representatives of the local public and private users—communities, industry, agriculture, fishing, boating, etc. It is intended that the activities of the regional agencies are to be governed to a far-reaching extent by their technical and economic studies. It is foreseen that intensive studies will be made to determine the benefits from water pollution control and the cost of optimal systems for achieving the various levels of quality. Since the functions of the establishments are of broad multi-purpose character, it is also foreseen that in devising their systems they will calculate and take into account the benefits and costs associated with other aspects of multi-purpose development and management. While there is a representation from the interests in the region, it is foreseen that decisions will turn more on technical calculation than is perhaps true in the case of the Genossenschaften or the river authorities. One has the impression of a more technical or "expert" orientation.

As previously indicated, a river basin committee will be created in each basin and made up of the users, local communities, and the administration, all equally represented. This will constitute an information and advisory body, but even more important, this body must approve the rates of charges to be levied. Since charges are the critical financing and control measures to be used by the basin agencies, one could argue that the basin committee which is two-thirds composed of private and local government interests will really have the central role in deciding how far-reaching water quality management will actually be. If this is true the actual distribution of political power may not be unlike that of the Genossenschaften even though the organizational pattern is, at least superficially, quite different.

Another quite different pattern emerges in regard to the Delaware River Basin Commission. The commission itself is composed of the state governors and alternates and the Secretary of the national Department of the Interior and his alternate. The governors, of course, are political representatives at a high level representing the interests of the entire state. The alternates, at least so far, tend to be persons with a claim to technical expertise in their respective fields. Thus, in the commission itself, there is no direct representative of the parties immediately affected by the activities of the commission. The commission is, however, empowered by the compact to appoint advisory committees. "The commission may constitute and empower advisory committees which may be comprised of representatives of the public and of federal, state, county, and municipal governments, water resource agencies, water using industries, water interest groups, labor, and agriculture." This is quite different from the French pattern in which advisory groups are also used, but in which the basin agencies are required by law to establish them and in which they have certain critical powers of approval. Of all the regional agencies considered in this report, the Delaware Commission has the least clear lines of communication and influence between itself and local governments and water user interests in the area. This may reflect the fact that the United States has three distinct levels of government and in each of the other cases there are two. While Germany is a federal republic, all the Genossenschaften are within a particular "land" or state.

The matter of an appropriate political structure for regional agencies is probably the least well understood aspect of regional water quality management or more broadly of water resources management in general. It appears that one of the most important issues is the degree to which representation should reflect financial contributions. This has been a consideration in defining the structure of each of the regional agencies. However, in no case, except the Ruhr area, is there a one-to-one relationship between financial contributions and political representation. Another but related issue is the matter of industry representation. In view of the importance of the industrial waste and water-use problem, and in view of the need for industry cooperation, one may wonder whether direct representation of industry does not ease the problems of implementing an effective pollution control program. The question is particularly significant in view of the long history of failures to control industrial pollution effectively in most of the developed countries. The Genossenschaft experience suggests that the possible desirability of direct industry representation cannot be lightly dismissed.

NOTES

I am deeply indebted to a number of persons for help in the preparation of this paper. Drs. H. W. Koenig and E. Knop, executive officers of the Ruhrverband-Ruhrtalsperrenverein and Emschergenossenschaft-Lippeverband respectively, have over the past several years been very helpful to me in understanding matters of Wasserwirtschaft in the Ruhr area. Professor Gordon Fair of Harvard has also contributed substantially to my knowledge of the activities of the Genossenchaften. I am especially indebted to Lyle Craine of the University of Michigan for help in preparing the section on the English River authorities. I have freely borrowed from the results of research he is conducting on these organizations. The French Basin agencies came to my attention through the work of Hubert Levy-Lambert, Centre Français d'Information de l'Eau, who prepared a French translation of my *Economics of Regional Water Quality Management* to which he appended a most illuminating chapter about these agencies. I have relied heavily on his interpretation of what is expected from them. Close communication over several years with the staff of the Delaware River Basin Commission, especially James Wright, Executive Director and Brinton Whitall, Secretary, has greatly aided my knowledge about this organization. Blair Bower of RFF read the section on the Delaware and provided useful criticisms. Last, but far from least, Edward Cleary, Executive Director of the Ohio River Valley Water Sanitation Commission, read the entire manuscript and made helpful comments. I know that none of those whose help I have acknowledge would agree with everything I have said. Some of them would perhaps dissent from quite a lot of it. Therefore, none of them should be held responsible for any errors of fact or interpretations which may be found in this manuscript.

[1] For a development of the coneptual background of this paper see my *Economics of Regional Water Quality Management*, The Johns Hopkins Press, 1964.

[2] Unpublished notes prepared by Lyle Craine, School of Natural Resources, University of Michigan.

[3] From "The River Authorities in England and Wales," an unpublished paper prepared by Lyle Craine for the American Society of Public Administration meetings in Washington, D. C., April 15, 1966.

[4] See Michel Gentot, "France" in Joseph Litwin (General Rapporteur), *Control of River Pollution by Industry, Cases in Comparative Public Administration*, International Association of Legal Science, International Institute of Administrative Science, Brussels, 1965.

[5] Largely Hubert Levy-Lambert who was rapporteur for the Commission and who commented extensively on the law in a chapter prepared for Allen V. Kneese, *Economie et Gestion de la Qualité des Eaux, Paris:* Dunod, 1955, translated and adapted for French readers by Hubert Levy-Lambert. The

projections concerning what will be done to implement the act presented in the following discussion are Levy-Lambert's.

[6] Also in that they do not have the authority to themselves construct and operate facilities. As previously explained, this is expected to change.

[7] It is worth noting that hydropower operations can have a particularly destructive effect on water quality especially if they are used for "peaking." In that case surges will alternate on a diurnal schedule with very low flows. This effect can be mitigated by regulating reservoirs.

[8] one which exactly reflects external or "spillover" costs.

[9] See the author's The Economics of Regional Water Quality Management.

[10] A document, "Report on the Effluent Charges Study," prepared by the Federal Water Pollution Control Administration is especially commended to readers interested in effluent charges.

7. A Study in Pollution Control:
How Seattle Cleaned Up Its Water

E. W. KENWORTHY

A few weeks ago, a Seattle newspaper carried a brief article under the headline: "Flow of Raw Sewage Into Elliott Bay Ends."

The gist of the item was that the last two sources of raw sewage on the bay, an arm of Puget Sound that forms much of downtown Seattle's waterfront, had been connected with a centralized metropolitan sewerage system.

The event, long anticipated here, attracted little attention among the nearly 400,000 users of the vast network of interceptor lines and treatment plants. But for people interested in pollution control, it was good news and it was important news.

For the forging of the last link in the sewerage system marks the culmination of a 10-year, $145-million program that is a case study in how a community willing to pay the price can clear up its water.

The ambitious program, carried out by an organization formally named the Municipality of Metropolitan Seattle but known locally as "Metro" for short, is regarded by environmentalists as exemplary in many ways.

Metro went to work long before saving the environment became a popular issue. It has succeeded in harnessing together the divergent interests and efforts of 18 separate metropolitan governmental units. And it has been paid for almost entirely by local bond issues.

The White House Council on Environmental Quality, in its first annual report, cited Seattle's Metro project as one of the two outstanding anti-pollution success stories in the nation. The other was the cleaning up of San Diego Bay.

Greater Seattle is 80 per cent surrounded by water, and its pollution problem was compounded by geography and political structure. On the west lies Puget Sound. To the east is the freshwater Lake Washington, 20 miles long and two to four miles wide, bordered by many incorporated towns. The outlet for Lake Washington is the Duwamish River, which empties into Elliott Bay.

This was the situation in 1958 when Metro was formed to deal with the sewage problem.

On the Seattle waterfront and the Duwamish, there were four primary treatment plans. (A primary plant settles out solids and removes about 35 per cent of the organic matter.) But there were also 46 "outfalls" dumping 70 million gallons of raw sewage a day into Puget Sound.

The deep sound, with its tidal flow, might have been able to handle

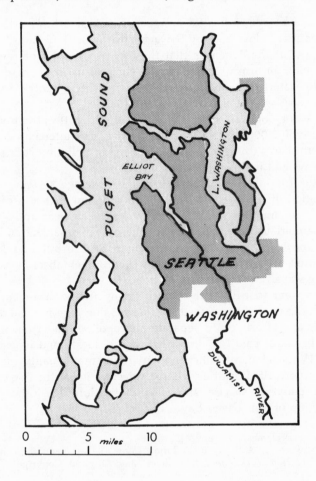

this if the outfalls had been located offshore in deep water with defuser attachments. But they were close to shore.

The result, according to Charles V. Gibbs, executive director of Metro, "was not only a terrible esthetic problem but a terrible bacteriological problem as well." The raw, stinking discharge floated around the docks and shoreline. Almost all beaches were closed as unsafe.

Around Lake Washington, where suburbia had proliferated since World War II, there were 10 secondary sewage plants discharging 20 million gallons of treated effluent into the lake each day from 23 cities and sewer districts. (A secondary plant removes 85 to 90 per cent of organic matter.)

The problem in Lake Washington was not bacteria; it was nutrients —phosphorus and nitrogen compounds in the effluent that stimulated the growth of algae.

When the algae died and decomposed, oxygen in the water was depleted. The result was a cloudy lake, foul-smelling and full of scum. The transparency of the lake—measured by the depth to which a white eight-inch disc is visible below the surface—decreased from 12 feet in 1950 to about two and one-half feet in 1958. Many of the beaches on the lake were closed. Salmon suffered as the dissolved oxygen became exhausted in the deep water.

Dr. W. T. Edmondson, a zoologist at the University of Washington who began to study the pollution of Lake Washington back in 1952, described the irony of the situation in the late 'fifties. Noting that 10 treatment plants had been constructed since 1941 to deal with the "intolerable" contamination from raw sewage, he wrote that "the situation had been changed from one in which the lake was contaminated with organic wastes to one in which it was being fertilized with inorganic 'plant food.'"

It was the studies of Dr. Edmondson and others by Dr. Robert O. Sylvester, a professor of civil engineering at the University of Washington, that provided the spur for the creation of Metro. The principal civic force involved was the Municipal League of Portland. And the principal leader was James R. Ellis, who in 1953 was 32 years old, just three years out of law school and deputy prosecuting attorney for King's County, which includes Seattle and its environs.

In 1953, at the urging of Mr. Ellis, the Municipal League set up a Metropolitan Problems Committee, which spent two years digging into the problem of sewage pollution.

It was obvious to the committee that the problem could be solved only if a system was developed to serve the entire drainage basin.

But such a system not only presented complicated design problems; it also raised jurisdictional problems on financing. Existing plants, some of them being financed by bond issues, would have to be abandoned. The suburban cities would have to be recompensed.

In 1956, the Municipal League recommended that the Mayor of Seattle appoint a citizens' committee to prepare a report and draft legislation to create a metropolitan authority to deal with areawide problems. The Mayor did so and named Mr. Ellis as chairman. The same year the state, county and city combined to hire Brown & Caldwell, a sanitary engineering firm, to prepare an area sewage plan.

The citizens' committee was ambitious. It wrote legislation permitting the formation of a "Metro" that would deal not only with sewage disposal but also with transportation and comprehensive land use planning.

The state legislature passed the bill in April, 1957. But the actual establishment of Metro required a majority vote in both Seattle and the county. In March, 1958 the voters of Seattle approved it, but it was defeated in the outlying county and thereby killed.

The citizens' committee thereupon redrafted the legislation to limit Metro's authority to sewage disposal, and city and county voters approved it in September, 1958.

Two Bond Issues Passed

As one of its first acts, the 21 members of Metro's decision-making body adopted the plan prepared by Brown & Caldwell. It provided for retention of one small existing primary treatment plant on Puget Sound, and the construction of four large new plants—three primary plants on the sound and one secondary plant on the Duwamish. A total of 110 miles of interceptor lines and 19 pumping plants would channel the sewage to the treatment plants. All 10 plants on Lake Washington would be abandoned, and no more effluent would go into the lake. All raw sewage discharges into the sound would be halted.

The original plan called for a bond issue of $125-million, but extension of the system to some suburbs not originally included has required a supplementary $20-million bond issue.

The bonds were to have been paid by additional sewer charges of $2.50 a month for each residential connection, with a proportionately higher charge for commercial and industrial connections. However, by careful planning, the residential fee was reduced to $2 a month before construction began in 1961 and has been kept at that figure.

Because it was begun long before passage of the Clean Waters Restoration Act of 1966, which provided Federal grants of up to

55 per cent of the cost of a sewage project, the Metro system has received less than 6 per cent of its financing from the Federal Government.

The system is now in full operation. The beaches on the sound and on Lake Washington are now open. In Lake Washington, phosphorus, which was 70 parts per billion in 1963, has fallen to 29 parts per billion, and summertime transparency has increased to nine feet. There has been a 90 per cent reduction in the oxygen demand of the effluent released into the Duwamish River, and salmon can now migrate to their spawning grounds.

"Without achieving a miracle or a utopia," Mr. Ellis said, "Metro has nevertheless brought its civic activists some satisfying rewards. It has demonstrated the great potential of local initiative in the Federal-state-local framework."

8. San Diego Cleans Up Once-Dirty Bay As Model for U.S.

E. W. KENWORTHY

In this sea-washed city where the sun shines an average of 353 days a year and the mean high temperature of the coldest and warmest months varies by only 14 degrees, autumn comes imperceptibly.

The warm waters of San Diego Bay are blue and sparkling and clear. They are also clean—with a purity well above the antipollution standards set by the State of California.

As recently as the summer of 1963, however, the bay was not blue. It had a brownish-reddish cast, imparted by the proliferation and death of phytoplankton, the salt-water equivalent of the algae that is causing the eutrophication of so many fresh-water lakes.

The transformation from the 1963 condition was cited last month by the President's Council on Environmental Quality as one of the two outstanding examples in the nation of water quality recovery by a municipality. The other example, cited in the council's first annual report, was Seattle's cleanup of Lake Washington.

These two cities have demonstrated that waters receiving sewage can be cleaned up by a combination of aggressive and imaginative leadership by a few citizens and a willingness by the electorate to pay off the bonds. In Seattle the charge is $2 a month per household; in San Diego it is $1.50.

Little Federal Help

Both cities undertook the job long before environmental decay became a national issue, and they finished it with almost no Federal subsidies. The Federal Government contributed about $8.5-million to Seattle's

E. W. Kenworthy, "San Diego Cleans Up Once-Dirty Bay as Model for U.S.," *The New York Times*, September 25, 1970, p. 28. Copyright © by The New York Times Company.

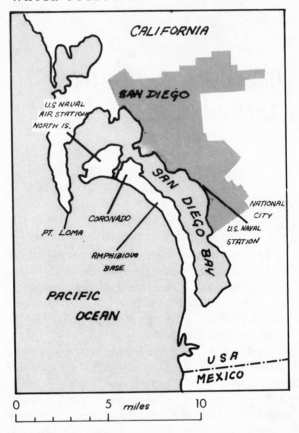

$145-million program and about $2.5-million to San Diego's $60-million program.

San Diego Bay is a crescent-shaped basin 15 miles long and one-quarter to $2\frac{1}{2}$ miles wide, with a single outlet to the Pacific at Point Loma. It is the home port for one-fourth of the Navy's active ships and 100 tuna fishing vessels and is a port of call for about 700 commercial ships a year.

On weekends the bay is dotted with white sails and churned by the wake of power boats. The bayside beaches opposite the United States Naval Station, where aircraft carriers, cruisers and destroyers are berthed, are crowded with swimmers and water skiers. The sea-walls of harbor and shelter islands are lined with fishermen.

Posh motels have recently been constructed on harbor and shelter islands.

In 1963, though, the plankton "bloomed" wildly as a result of the nutrients—phospates and nitrates—supplied by the sewage that was dumped into the bay from San Diego and its suburbs. The sewage discharge had risen from 37 million gallons a day in 1961 to over 60 million gallons a day. Most of the sewage received inadequate primary treatment (the settlement of solids) from a single, overloaded plant. The City of Coronado was dumping into the bay 2.5 million gallons of raw sewage a day, and the Naval Amphibious Base was dumping 200,000 gallons.

In addition, there were 3.7 million gallons a day of industrial discharges, mostly from tuna canneries and a kelp processing plant, plus an undetermined amount from naval and commercial ships.

Plankton Decomposition

The oxygen in the bay waters was consumed not only by these sewage and industrial wastes but also by the decomposition of plankton after death.

Water clarity—as measured by the distance from the surface that an eight-inch disc can be seen—was an average of six feet and was down to one foot in some areas.

Along one stretch of the waterfront in the central city, solids had formed a sludge mat on the bay floor 900 yards long, 200 yards wide and seven feet deep.

Most serious of all, from a public health viewpoint, was the density of coliform bacteria. In 1956, because of an alarming increase in the coliform density, San Diego, Coronado and the Naval Amphibious Base were ordered by the state's Regional Pollution Control Board at San Diego to chlorinate sewage discharges. While this emergency program reduced coliform intensity in some areas, it was not able to keep up with the city's increased discharge, and in some areas the count was 10 times the permissible level. Several beaches were quarantined.

The prelude to the San Diego success story was long, arduous and often disheartening. It began in 1949 when the State Legislature passed a water pollution control act, providing for nine regional pollution control boards to be appointed by the Governor.

The San Diego regional board was set up in 1950, and two men immediately stood out as leaders. They were Dr. J. B. Askew, the county health officer, who served for 19 years, 13 as chairman; and the late Harold E. Miller, a sanitary engineer who was the board's first executive officer and who later became executive officer of Seattle's metro sewerage system.

In 1952, the board employed the State Departments of Health and Fish and Game to make environmental studies of the bay. They revealed dangerous bacteriological concentrations, oxygen depletion and sludge deposits.

The same year a team of three engineers hired by San Diego County at the instigation of the regional board prepared a study of sewage disposal needs.

The engineers, Mr. Miller and the regional board all agreed that the problem could only be dealt with on an area basis; that interceptors should be built around the bay leading to a primary treatment plant on the ocean side of Point Loma, and that the treated effluent should be dumped far offshore in deep water through diffusers—openings in the pipe that would scatter the discharge.

In 1953 the city and county accepted the engineers' recommendations. The city decided that it should finance, construct, operate and own the core facility and negotiate contracts with surrounding incorporated suburbs and sanitary districts for tie-ins to the system.

New Sight is Sought

In 1954 the city went to the voters with a $16.5-million bond issue. There was no significant political or industrial opposition to the project because it was so grossly and dangerously polluted, that, as Dr. Askew said in a recent interview, the system either had to be enlarged or a whole new system had to be built.

Nevertheless the bond issue was defeated. Dr. Askew attributed this to three things—first, many people thought the planned plant on Point Loma was too close to a residential area; second, there was considerable opposition to the plan for paying off the bonds through an *ad valorem* property tax rather than by a standard monthly charge for each household, and finally, the inclusion on the ballot of a referendum on fluoridation of drinking water helped to defeat the sewerage bond issue.

As a result, the city spent $100,000 a year over the next five years for oceanographic and biological studies with the hope of finding an alternative site. Another engineering concern was engaged in 1958 to prepare a new plan.

By this time, the situation in the bay had become so bad that, despite emergency chlorination programs, the beaches had to be put under quarantine and the Navy issued warnings to all personnel about bodily contact with bay water.

The new engineering report moved the plant almost to the end of Point Loma. Where the old plan would have run the outfall only 7,500 feet into the ocean at a depth of 125 feet, the new plan called for discharge 11,450 feet—over two miles—from shore at a depth of 200 feet through two Y-shaped diffuser legs, each 1,368 feet long.

In 1960, the voters overwhelmingly approved a $42.5-million bond issue. Construction began in 1961 and the system began operating Aug. 15, 1965. The system now serves seven cities and six sanitary districts and all the naval shore installations.

The final cost of the core system was $51-million, and, with ancillary projects, the total cost was $60-million. The metro now serves a population of about one million; it is designed to serve 2.5 million.

The results of the project were prompt, according to Dennis A. O'Leary, executive officer of the San Diego Regional Water Quality Control Board.

From Brown to Blue

"Almost immediately," he said in a recent interview, "remarkable change occurred. We had expected slow improvement, but the bay quickly began to clear as if there had been a few, great tidal flushings. Where the bay had been brown and red, it became blue and sparkling."

The phytoplankton disappeared at the outset. As early as April, 1964—eight months after the system began operating—sculpin, sole, sand bass, steelhead trout, silver salmon, bonefish, black sea bass, barracuda, bonito, yellowtail, octopus, shark, seal and porpoise "were swarming back into the bay," according to a 1965 report by the United States Public Health Service.

Dissolved oxygen is now at safe levels, water clarity ranges from 10 to 30 feet and the sludge beds have been cut in half. Most important, coliform density has decreased so that the beaches are now safe for swimming, although it remains high near naval piers where ships continue to dump raw sewage.

The discharge of sewage, galley and laundry wastes from naval ships and of toxic industrial wastes from the North Island Naval Air Base is the biggest remaining problem in the cleanup of the bay.

The Navy in 1968 announced a five-year, $253-million plan to eliminate raw discharges from vessels. Congress, which must appropriate the funds, said in this year's Water Quality Improvement Act that all boats—naval, commercial and pleasure—must be fitted with waste disposal devices.

Outside the Navy, the most troublesome industrial wastes come from Helco, a kelp-processing plant, and from tuna-packing plants. But a tie-in with the metro system is expected to be completed within a year.

A year ago an official from the Federal Bureau of the Budget asked Dr. Askew, "What institutional mechanisms did you employ to get this cleanup of San Diego Bay?"

Dr. Askew smiled and said: "We said to the people of San Diego, 'you regard yourself as a high-quality community, then let's have a high-quality response to your problem.'"

9. The Siberians

FARLEY MOWAT

At least a million years ago one small group of mammals had given up the hard-won terrestrial way of life and returned to the salt seas from which all life originated. The sea was kind to these backsliders and they ultimately diversified into the many members of the seal family. Most of them chose to live in the open oceans where the greatest numbers of their kind still remain.

However, some hundreds of thousands of years ago, a few of the early seals entered the arctic estuary of one of the great Siberian rivers, the Yenisei, and worked their way south into the very heart of the Asian land mass to Baikal.

Here they found themselves in an inland sea where conditions were not so different from those in the greater sea—two thousand miles away to the north. The water was fresh instead of salt, but that was not material. Fish were abundant. Because of its great depth and the presence of convection currents of oceanic character, the ice formed late in the winter and there were always areas near the river mouths where it remained thin enough so that air-breathing mammals could keep holes open. In other areas of Baikal the mountain winds built up atop the ice heavy blankets of snow wherein the female seals could build snug caves in which to bear their pups.

When natural man arrived upon the scene he killed occasional seals, but his predations were so minor that they made no impression on a herd which, it is estimated, must have numbered several hundred thousand individuals.

When the European conquerors turned their attention away from

Farley Mowat, *The Siberians*. Boston: Little, Brown and Company, pp. 44–49. Copyright 1970 by Farley Mowat.

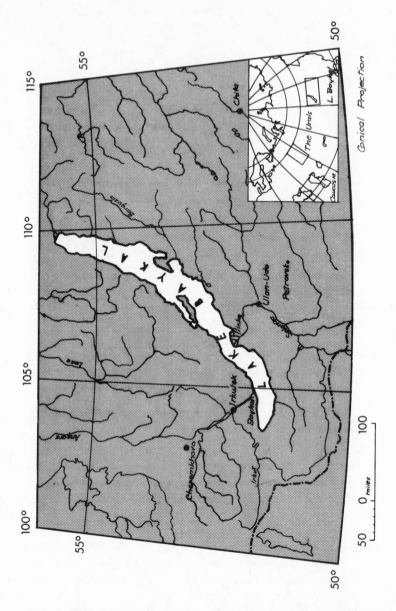

the forests where life was growing silent, and looked upon the sacred lake, they must have been incredulous at the amount of life it contained. Here was a killing ground worthy of their mettle. But that world of water was so vast (some sixteen thousand cubic *miles* of water) that the rape took some time to complete. By the early years of the twentieth century there had been solid victories. The giant Baikal sturgeon was virtually extinct. The apparently inexhaustible schools of fine-flavored whitefish called *omul* were fading fast. A number of other fishes were becoming scarce. And the seals were almost gone; no more than four or five thousand of them still survived.

The battle to destroy the living world of Baikal was being won. Fishermen and seal hunters were receiving indirect assistance in their work of destruction from landsmen. In the mountain valleys drained by Baikal's three hundred sixty inflowing streams and rivers, the forests where the sables were hardly more than a memory were themselves being razed. Siberian cedars, high-towering patriarchs, many of them more than a thousand years old, all but disappeared. Larch, and the lesser species, took their turn. The logs were floated down the once crystal rivers, gradually coating the stream beds with thick layers of bark until many of the lake fishes that used the rivers as nurseries could no longer find suitable spawning grounds. Tannic acid and other decomposition products from sunken logs and bark began contaminating the waters of the lake itself.

Then, in 1962, the economic planners in Moscow decided to build a gigantic cellulose and wood-chemical combine on the south shore of Lake Baikal. Even by Soviet standards the plans were grandiose. There were to be five plants with their associated towns in the combine. Secure in the conviction that the true good is to be found in more production, the planners turned their blueprints over to the builders, and in 1963 work on the first two plants began.

At this juncture something truly remarkable occurred. In the Soviet Union, that closed society where, so we are told, the voice of the individual is never heard, there arose a thunder of protests from individuals in every part of the land. The editors of the monolithic all-Union papers, *Pravda* and *Izvestia*, having proudly announced the birth of the gigantic new production complex at Baikal, found themselves inundated by letters of outrage. As the two plants neared completion the intensity of the storm strengthened.

An elderly, much respected Moscow writer described to me what followed:

"The word Baikal became a rallying cry even to people who knew very little about it except its name. They were acute enough to see that finally the high priests of progress-through-production had to be brought to their senses. The threat to Baikal made people understand that unless this was done the new world we were building would be no better than a ruined wasteland fit for machines, but not for human beings. Hundreds and thousands of professional writers, poets, artists and scientists took it on themselves to make Baikal the symbolic warning. They were joined by masses of workers and by revered members of the Academy of Science, and even by some State officials. Every magazine and newspaper heard the voice of what was a true mass movement of the people.

"For a while the authorities who had designed the cellulose combine tried to drown out the protests. There were long articles lashing out at reactionary sentimentalists who tried to stop the glorious march of our Revolution. There were some threats, and some of the more prominent of Baikal's defenders were told they would get into trouble if they did not keep quiet. They refused to be quiet. The fuss kept getting worse. The plants were completed and began operations. They began pouring their poisons into the sacred sea. Within three months there were reports of fish dying in Baikal and even of people getting sick from eating fish caught in the Angara. The fight of the people to save the lake became more furious and then, quite suddenly, the authorities gave in. The plants were closed."

I visited Baikal several times and on one occasion sat in a little café on the shore of the lake, watching its waters rage in the grip of a roaring October storm. Boris Arimov, an Irkutsk poet who spent seven years fighting for Baikal, sat with me and told me more of the story.

"When they closed the plants we suspected it was only for long enough to let things cool down. So, we did not let things cool down. We kept the fire going and gave it more fuel. Now we demanded that fishing be banned until the stocks returned to normal. No more slaughter of the seals, we said. We said that all lumbering must be stopped on the Baikal watersheds. We demanded that this treasure— one of the world's great treasures—be cleansed until it was again as beautiful as it had been before men began to desecrate it. All over the Soviet Union the friends of Baikal fought on.

"Some people thought we could not win. We knew we could. Things are not the same in our country as they were some years ago, and not the same as most foreigners seem to think. Lenin said the will of the people must be supreme . . . we *were* the people. In Moscow they listened, and at last they bowed to the people."

The battle to save Baikal brought, at its conclusion, one of the most significant human successes in recent times. It was a major victory of reason combined with deep instinctive feeling, over the senseless and suicidal passion of modern men to exploit the world around them into ultimate destruction.

To my Western mind the scope of the victory seemed staggering.

In 1967 the Presidium of the Supreme Soviet of the USSR voted to make the entire Baikal region—the lake and thousands of square miles of surrounding territory—into a national park. All fishing along the north half of the lake was prohibited for five years and along the south side for seven years. Sport fishing only will be permitted after that. Lumbering operations on all watersheds flowing into the lake have been halted for good. Extensive reclamation projects are under way to restore tributary streams and riverbeds to their pristine condition. A series of new fish hatcheries are being built. All forms of wildlife ranging from wolves to wild flowers are now under complete protection. By the end of 1969 the seal population had increased to forty-five thousand animals, and even the very rare Barguzin sable was staging a remarkable comeback. The sacred sea has again become a sacred sea in truth.

I asked Boris about the fate of the multimillion-ruble cellulose plants and their adjacent towns.

"It was unnecessary to abandon them entirely," he said, with the magnanimity of a successful warrior. "So we were content to have the two factories closed until a complete filtration system was built which guaranteed no effluent of any kind would ever enter Baikal. They will continue to work, but they will be fed with wood from other districts to the south of the park regions. They can now do no more harm. Of course, the plans for the three other plants were canceled."

One day I visited the Baikal Limnological Institute where more than a hundred scientists were doing research on the infinitely varied problems connected with preserving freshwater lakes. The men and women of the Institute were foremost in the fight to preserve Baikal, and their satisfaction in the victory knows no bounds.

"We have done more than save Baikal," a woman zoologist told me. "The fight woke up the whole of the Soviet Union to one of the grave dangers threatening mankind. We will not go to sleep again. Our leaders now understand how great the danger is and they are really listening hard to those who can tell them how to control and stop the damage done by a thoughtless modern industrial society. What happened here at Baikal will help set the pattern for the future development of our country."

10. Coastal Wetlands Protection Program in Massachusetts

CHARLES H. W. FOSTER et al.

I. BACKGROUND[1]

Massachusetts

Few reliable records are available as to the original extent of wetlands in Massachusetts. Miscellaneous Report No. 7 of the U.S. Department of Agriculture (1885) listed the amounts of salt and fresh marsh land upon the Atlantic Seaboard, and at that time the Commonwealth was credited with some 56,000 acres of coastal wetland.

In 1954, the national wetland inventory reported some 45,000 acres remaining on the Massachusetts coast, of which all but about 8,000 lay in the high or moderate value category.

It would appear that the state has already lost perhaps a full fourth of its most valuable coastal waterfowl habitat.

Looking more broadly at the state wetland situation, known agents, operating even now, are expected to reduce the total wetland acreage in Massachusetts *10 per cent* by 1960 and *66 per cent* in the foreseeable future!

From the brief review above, the wetland story appears sad indeed. The trend has been one of general indifference, unquestioned ignorance, and, in the final analysis, rather shaky resource economics. But this is, of course, pure hindsight.

In all fairness, even the most flagrant instances of abuse should be viewed within the context of their times.

Public Health

Of the two principal factors contributing to wetland destruction, the prevailing attitude towards public health would seem the most widespread and of the longest duration. It is still universally believed by the general public that marsh and swamp constitute hazards, if not actual menaces, to the public health.

For those of us who now live at the midpoint of the twentieth century, we can conveniently forget that malaria once affected many thousands of people annually in the nation. In fact, as late as 1951, nearly four thousand outbreaks of water-borne disease were reported in the United States.

The Commonwealth's encephalitis scare in 1956 did little to discourage the prevailing public point of view. At the close of an extensive chemical control program, which sprayed over 100,000 acres and some 700 miles of roadside in a single season, one prominent state official stressed the need for drainage of swamps and marshes as the only ultimate and permanent method of mosquito control in Massachusetts.

This attitude appears to have been shared liberally along the entire Atlantic Coast. From Maine to Virginia, a prime contributor to wetland destruction has been ditching for mosquito control purposes.

Agricultural Drainage

Agricultural drainage is, of course, the second major contributing factor responsible for wetland deterioration in the United States. There have, again, been historical reasons for this development.

In the years 1849, 1850, and 1860, Congress passed the Swamp Lands Act, which granted to some fifteen southern and western states all federal land within their borders made unfit for cultivation by its swamp or overflowed status. An important provision stated that "the proceeds of said lands . . . shall be applied, exclusively, and as far as necessary, to the purpose of reclaiming said lands by means of levees and drains aforesaid."

In this era it was prevailing public sentiment that wet areas were merely obstacles to land development—and should be treated in such fashion.

In a very real sense, the coastal and inland marshes of the United States have fallen victim to the same philosophy which so successfully opened the nation's frontiers to human occupancy.

Further incentives for reclamation were provided during the war years. Landowners were subsidized to convert seemingly unproductive wetlands to agricultural usage. Had it not been for a strong conservation ground swell in Congress within recent years, the practices instituted in 1944 would still be deemed applicable in this era of crop surpluses.

The points made above are designed neither to minimize nor condone the circumstances that have led the nation to its current wetland crisis. As the facts indicate, we have already reached the stage where clear-cut and decisive action is necessary in order to salvage a little of our once-rich wetland heritage.

And yet, before mounting his charger, the conservationist should properly define his objectives. He should recognize that disappearing wetland is merely a *symptom* of the disease, not the disease itself.

For what we are facing today is an appalling lack of knowledge about wetland—its values, uses, and reasons for remaining simply as marsh or swamp.

As technicians, we know little of the role played by wetland in the natural scheme of things. Nor do we have more than passing experience at managing a tract of marsh and swamp in order to maximize a given wetland value.

Proponents of wetland preservation can speak only in generalities or, unfortunately, in highly emotional terms.

Without a well-thought-out and well-substantiated case to lay before the public, the prospect of successful wetland preservation in future years appears dim indeed.

II. LEGISLATIVE HISTORY[2]

The pendulum of public opinion began to swing materially during the middle fifties, coincident with the publication of the wetland inventories. Scattered voices of protest were joined by many others; in Massachusetts one particular chorus of concern insured the preservation of the flood plain marshes of the Sudbury and Concord River valleys made famous by the journals of Thoreau.

In 1960 and 1961, a new voice began to be heard. A two year study of marine resources undertaken by the Commonwealth had revealed a surprising fact—that many of the most valuable commercial and recreational fisheries were dependent upon coastal marshes as sources of nutrients or as actual nursery grounds for young finfish and shellfish. The result was rapid legislative authorization for a careful study of coastal wetlands with an eye to their present and potential values and their eventual preservation.

In the interim, through local initiative, special legislation was secured, giving the Department of Natural Resources authority to modify any alteration project in the coastal area of the Commonwealth which might adversely affect the fisheries resource. By the stroke of a pen, therefore, the Department was given the authority to halt all construction activity in wetlands along the entire Massachusetts coast until the statutory requirements of hearings and evaluations had been completed.

Since the effective date of the act in May of 1963, more than 500 construction projects have been submitted for consideration—eloquent testimony to the explosive rate of activity now taking place along the Massachusetts coastline.

In the course of compliance with the act, it was inevitable that the conditions imposed on a particular marsh would be challenged in court. This proved the case at 78 acre Broad Marsh in Wareham, where a private corporation proposed to dredge a channel and boat basin, placing the material removed on the remaining marsh for subsequent real estate development. The condition imposed was a simple one: the dredging would be permitted but no fill could be placed on the adjoining marsh.

The owners commenced operations in violation of the condition imposed, and in the ensuing court proceedings posed four objections to the Commonwealth's actions: first, the condition was a prohibition rather than a condition of the work; second, the marsh was not necessary to protect the fisheries; third, the statute was unconstitutional; and fourth, the restriction was tantamount to an unlawful taking without compensation.

In an historic opinion, Judge Horace T. Cahill of Suffolk Superior Court upheld the Commonwealth on all four counts, granted a permanent injunction, and ordered the owners to remove the fill already placed on the marsh. Excerpts from this decision may be of interest.

For the first time to our knowledge, a court decision gave legal substance to the biologists' firm conviction that marshes are a vital part of the entire marine ecosystem.

"The Court finds the nutrients derived from Broad Marsh, and, in particular, the portion thereof intended to be filled by the respondent, play an important and integral part in sustaining the life of the shellfish and finfish in the areas adjacent thereto."

Note the particular weight given the nutrient contribution of the marsh as its prime biological significance.

The question of constitutionality was discussed as follows:

"Property is acquired by private citizens with the tacit understanding that it shall not be used to the detriment of the public—."

On the matter of compensation, the Court noted that when action is taken to regulate property in the general public interest, the owner is already compensated by receiving the benefit that accrues to the public as a whole!

Understandably unsatisfied with this decision, the owners petitioned for further review by the Massachusetts Supreme Judicial Court—this time on just two counts: the issues of total prohibition of usage and taking without just compensation.

Significantly, the Supreme Court made no final determinations, but ordered the case remanded to Superior Court for additional arguments. No actions have been taken to date by the owners to reopen the lower court proceedings. Although the permanent injunction and restoration ordered by Superior Court have been stayed, the temporary injunction remains in effect and Judge Cahill's findings still stand.

Earlier in 1965, at the request of the Department of Natural Resources, Governor Volpe included in his inaugural message a proposal for the permanent protection of some 45,000 acres of high value coastal wetland. The legislation differed materially from the existing statute under which alteration projects were regulated. It broadened possible intervention beyond merely marine fisheries to include public health, wildlife, or protection from floods or other natural disasters. Further, restrictions could be imposed before any alteration is proposed, rather than awaiting project initiation. Finally, the enabling of compensation would relieve both the owner and the administrative agency of uncertainty in the event that the restriction imposed was found to be excessive.

Thanks to unprecedented citizen interest, the measure received unanimous support at our legislative hearing and was reported without dissent by the Joint Committee on Natural Resources. It was passed by the House and subsequently by the Senate.

What conclusions can be drawn from the Massachusetts story? Here are some that come immediately to mind.

If you are starting from scratch in your own area, take heart from our experience within the Commonwealth. We have found our public to be extraordinarily responsive, and our legislative body willing to take even unprecedented steps forward when the facts are presented for their consideration.

Using the privilege of hindsight, I would begin first by building a strong team of public and private agencies to discuss just how your program should commence and who is best fitted for what job. The group should be broadly based, intensely practical, and representative of an impressive segment of your citizenry. Its first job should be to build public interest in wetland conservation—through speakers, conferences, special publications, and frequent use of news outlets, to name a few.

The next step is to gather facts about your particular wetland problem. Which marshes have the highest value and for what purpose

—where are they located and who owns them—how many acres are left and, of these, which are presently endangered?

If you can obtain legislative sanction for such a study, so much the better, because you will then have tangible evidence of official interest in your problem. The actual study should involve both public and private specialists to be sure that all facets of wetland usage are covered properly.

In our case, a high degree of public interest in wetlands permitted a system of interim controls even during this period of inventory. It is, of course, ideal to be able to hold the line on wetlands in general while particular areas are being defined.

Once the roster of high value marshlands is complete, the next and most difficult job is to devise a program for their protection. You may wish to take the route of outright acquisition, rather than the Massachusetts approach to zoning. Or local and private action may appear superior to efforts at some higher level of government.

The actual approach is immaterial, but it has been our experience that implementation by a number of entities, both private and public, provides both a broader base of support and a greater variety of tools for resolving individual marsh protection problems.

Borrow advice from other areas, but be sure to shape your program to fit your own particular circumstances! Be practical at all times— even to the extent of deliberately setting aside wetland areas which could be used to satisfy legitimate commercial or community needs.

Take steps to bury any past differences you may have had with bureaucrats like myself! Work *with* them despite their obvious failings—prodding, persuading, and actively assisting where red tape would provide interminable delays or public actions might raise the specter of official impropriety.

I cannot overstress the importance of good teamwork. Individual action does little more than satisfy the organization ego, whereas joint action, despite some small loss of identity, can move mountains.

A particular case in point is our own Massachusetts Audubon Society, whose officers and membership have never hesitated to respond when a conservation need has arisen. I am hopelessly prejudiced, of course, but honestly believe Massachusetts conservation programs are a shining example of what good teamwork can accomplish.

Lastly, don't be discouraged! In comparison with the glamorous era of Theodore Roosevelt and Gifford Pinchot, when million-acre national parks and forests were created overnight, our current problems might appear inconsequential.

But the twentieth century has raised frightening new areas of concern—resource shortages, for example, as fundamental as water and space—and unless I miss my guess, the biographers of the future will rate our wetland conservation struggles among the finest in history.[3]

III. MASSACHUSETTS COASTAL WETLANDS PROTECTION PROGRAM[4]

Objectives of Program

Protection of high value coastal wetland from alteration or destruction is the primary purpose of the program. It advocates a close partnership of private and public interests and specifically encourages protective action at the private and local levels. Outright acquisition of marsh areas is contemplated only where no suitable alternative exists, or where the use of the marsh for other purposes would justify its ownership in fee by the public.

Issuance of Restrictive Orders

Under the present legislation, the Department of Natural Resources is authorized to legally restrict the dredging or filling of coastal wetland for public health, safety, or conservation reasons by the issuance of a formal order filed with the local registry of deeds. Full notification is required to assessed owners on record and the order cannot be issued without a properly advertised public hearing. Once issued and filed, the order cannot be amended or repealed without the specific consent of the legislature, as is now the case with municipally-owned park land.

Rights of Owners

Once an order has been issued, the owner is faced with several possible courses of action. He may accept the order without seeking compensation, thereby retaining all rights to his marshland, including hunting, fishing, and assurance of personal privacy, except those of destruction or physical alteration.

If he should choose to claim loss of value as the result of the restriction, he may petition Superior Court and, upon proof of title and ownership, receive any award of damages the Court may determine equitable. Once damages have been awarded, however, title to the marsh would be vested in the Commonwealth and the issuance of the order would be considered the equivalent of an eminent domain taking.

Powers of Conservation Commissions[5]

A second section of the program empowers the board of selectmen in the case of a town, and the mayor and city council in the case of a city, once the necessary project approvals and funds had been voted by the community, to make land takings on behalf of a municipal conservation commission. This extends to conservation commissions the same privileges available to park commissions, town forest committees, and other local boards, and clarifies the authority of a town to exercise eminent domain for public conservation purposes. The poor condition of title to most salt marsh areas makes this extension of authority essential if coastal communities are to participate extensively in a protection program.

Financing a Protection Program

It is expected that the issuance of restrictive orders, and any compensation therefore, will be included as charges to the recreation bond issues authorized the Department of Natural Resources each year by legislative action. Principal and interest payments for these twenty-year bond issues are assessed annually on the cities and towns outside of the metropolitan parks district. A program of this sort would also be eligible for 30% financial assistance from the federal government through Title VII of the Housing Act of 1961.

It is suggested that outright acquisition of marsh lands of substantial size and value to wildlife be accomplished by the Division of Fisheries and Game through its proposed accelerated land acquisition program. It is expected that not less than 50% of these costs could be borne by federal funds under the Pittman-Robertson or Land and Water Conservation Fund programs.

Protection efforts by local conservation commissions are conducted through municipal appropriations. Conservation commissions, however, are eligible for state reimbursement under the Department's self-help conservation program up to 50% of the cost of a given project. The state's share of local acquisition or protection efforts would be financed through either the proposed Massachusetts Conservation Fund or allocations from the regular recreation bond issue.

Role of Private Organizations

It is also expected that many acres of marshland will be protected through private efforts. The Fund for the Preservation of Wildlife and Natural Areas, for example, has instituted a special program to assist private marshland owners in contemplated gifts of land or rights in land. Private conservation organizations such as the Massachusetts Audubon Society, Trustees of Reservations, and Nature Conservancy are also prepared to participate entirely in the overall protection effort.

MASSACHUSETTS GENERAL LAWS

Chapter 130 — Section 27A
(The "Jones Act")
An Act Relative to Removal, Filling and Dredging
of Areas Bordering on Coastal Waters

No person shall remove, fill or dredge any bank, flat, marsh, meadow or swamp bordering on coastal waters without written notice of his intention to so remove, fill or dredge to the Board of Selectmen in a town or to the appropriate Licensing Authority in a city, to the State Department of Public Works, and the Director of Marine Fisheries. Said notice shall be sent by registered mail at least thirty days prior to any such removing, filling or dredging. The Selectmen or in the case of a city, the Licensing Authority, shall hold a hearing on said proposal within twenty days of the receipt of said notice of which hearing shall be given by them by publication in a newspaper published in such town or city, then in a newspaper published within the county, and shall notify by mail the person intending to do such removing, filling or dredging, the Department of Public Works and the Director, of the time and place of said hearing. The cost of such publication of notice shall be borne by the person filing the notice of intention to so remove, fill or dredge. The Selectmen or Licensing Authority as the case may be, may recommend the installation of such bulkheads, barriers or other protective measures as may protect the public interest, and shall transmit forthwith to such person, the director and the department of public works a copy of any such recommendations. If the Department of Public Works finds that such proposed removing, filling or dredging would violate the provisions of sections thirty and thirty A of chapter ninety-one, it shall proceed to enforce the provisions of said sections. If the area on which the proposed work is to be done contains shellfish or is necessary to protect marine fisheries, the said Director may impose such conditions on said work as he may determine necessary to protect such shellfish or marine fisheries, and work shall be done subject thereto.

Whoever violates any provision of this section shall be punished by a fine of not more than one hundred dollars or by imprisonment for not more than six months or both, and the Superior Court shall have jurisdiction in equity to restrain a continuing violation of this section.

This section shall not affect or regulate the ordinary and usual work of any mosquito project operating under chapter two hundred and fifty-two, or under the provisions of a special act.

CITIZEN'S LETTER OF PROTEST

I was unable to attend the Marshfield [Mass.] public hearing that was held January 6th but I should like to comment upon your letter of December 14th.

Apparently, the Department of Natural Resources has already been convinced that the marshes and swamps of Marshfield should remain undisturbed, under the aegis of the State, in perpetuity.

Your bulletin advocates this action without acknowledging a possibility of error in the basic promises of those who sponsor the legislation, the probability of economic loss to wetland owners and the almost certain stultification of coastal marine economic development.

Personally, I should like to pass a bill designating the entire town of Marshfield as a Protected Area.

Unfortunately, as the population expands we must have space for additional homes, factories, roads, etc.

Once we accept this premise, which is irrefutable, then it becomes a simple matter of priorities—which is going to be destroyed next—the marsh-mudflat or the adjoining meadow or forest.

To sequester marshland is to accelerate the exploitation and development (destruction if you will) of adjacent upland.

I presume that your Department is concerned with the resources of the entire State. To save wetland is to consume dryland.

To make a few random comments on your letter in the order which various statements and/or conclusions appear:

1.—limit wetland uses to *protect public health*. These marshlands, or swamps as they are sometimes called, have been recognized as a *menace* to public health for generations.

Millions have been spent over the years to drain, dyke, fill or otherwise eliminate such areas as a breeding ground for malaria, fever, insects, rats and reptiles. Now we are asked to believe that swamps are solubrious! This concept is positively mind bending. Has anyone thought to inform the Dutch that they have been on the wrong track for centuries? The kids in Holland will be delighted, no more cold night watches with their fingers stuffed in some damn dyke

2.—to protect public *safety*. The marshes themselves are not safe, particularly for children. Three youngsters have been drowned in Marshfield in my lifetime by slipping off the banks of a marsh creek.

I presume that safety has been mentioned in connection with the theory that marshland provides a "barrier" to the sea in violent storms.

Rather the opposite is true, wetlands provide the sea with access to vast areas in the interior of the town with borders so extensive that it has been impractical from a financial standpoint, to construct adequate seawalls or dykes. Therefore every major storm floods roads and property.

3.—protect wildlife. There is no question but that the marsh and swamp areas are splendid havens for migratory fowl An excellent reason for preserving our wetlands, but is it more logical to provide a part-time home for vagabond ducks or a year-round home for our residents

Citizen's Letter of Protest, continued

lent birds, squirrels, rabbits, etc. on adjacent uplands? Again, a matter of priorities.

4.—protect marine fisheries. This ecological area is one in which the answers are not yet definitive as many candid marine biologists will admit. It is possible that marshlands contribute some ingredient essential to the propagation of fish but I have travelled extensively and my observations suggest otherwise.

Except for shellfish, and perhaps shrimp, there appears to be no correlation between marsh acreage and fish quantity.

For example, the Gulf of Mexico is bounded on three sides by millions of acres of marsh, swamp and tidal flat. It also has a very extensive continental shelf. If the marsh/nutrient/ = fish theory is valid the Gulf should be teeming with fish.

In actual fact, except for shrimpers, the area is barren or nearly so. Commercial fishing is almost nonexistent. A small fleet of Company "Pogy boats" keep a fish meal plant operating part-time and a scattering of decrepit "snapper schooners" handline for bottom fish on a seasonal basis.

By contrast, the Pacific coast of North America is mountainous and almost entirely devoid of so-called wetlands, yet, the contiguous sea supports a huge fishing fleet.

Again, Florida is nearly half fetid swamp and marshland but fishing is better off western Mexico where the littoral is arid desert.

5.—produce *nutrients*. Several dedicated government and private organizations are at work to REDUCE the nutrients that are pouring into our oceans and coastal areas. The last thing needed at this stage of population density is more nutrient in the waters of Massachusetts.

Above a certain level nutrients inhibit life cycles of fish and certainly impair human health and recreational activity.

Excess "nutrients" have poisoned our shellfish beds around Boston and in Narragansett Bay. Marshfield flats are borderline cases.

Also, these nutrients promote the growth of slime, algae, and bacteria far beyond the immediate area of the swamp or marsh where they originate.

6.—provide food. This concept is nebulous and comes under the nutrient = fish theory. Since the colonials found that it was no longer worthwhile to harvest salt hay, marshes have not provided food except that their effluence may improve shellfish yields.

7.—provide employment. No one of my acquaintances is or has been employed as a result of a marsh except in efforts to reclaim, drain or otherwise improve upon the marsh area.

8.—provide recreation. Hardly anyone except the most devoted of naturalists or intrepid of duck hunters willingly ventures across our marshlands.

Marshes are stinking sulphurous bogs. No amount of romantic rhetoric will dissipate the smells or sooth the savage breasts of the bugs that inhabit these wastelands.

9.—enhance the (scenic) value of

Citizen's Letter of Protest, continued

nearby areas. This is *the* cogent reason for leaving wetlands undisturbed. Only an insensitive boor would desecrate the lovely sweep of the North River for instance.

In general, there are several controversial problems that will arise if the wetlands are expropriated by the State.

First; much of this land is in private hands. Will the State reimburse the owners at fair market value for their land?

If not then will the town forgo taxes on the property while it is being held in trust for public benefit?

Provided neither of these situations obtain we shall have a group of citizens providing a public park, involuntarily, at their private expense. The land will become a classic White Elephant, perpetual expense with no escape, except to forfeit title to the town. No one will be fool enough to *buy* wetlands in the future.

It seems discriminatory at best to penalize these people who have committed no crime. Let's include farmers and woodlot owners in the Protective Area, it's their town too.

Second; how will the marine industry continue to expand? Is recreational boating to be arrested at its present stage of development? Will newcomers to the sport be price gouged by those fortunate enough to own a marina before this freeze on wetland development or will they be told that they can't have dock or mooring space, that they were born too late?

Conservationists cite with passion (and truth) that it took millions of years to create our marshlands which are de-

stroyed in a few days by dredge or dragline. However, is it any more noble or prudent to rip up sod and destroy topsoil, equally long in creation, for "development," for State roads or State buildings.

Surely it is neither economic nor desirable to dig out an upland field or wooded area for a marina or parking lot when a nearby mudflat is available for dredging or fill.

If you have borne with me this far expect that you have come to the conclusion that—A. I own marshland or wish to develop same, B. I have a boat and am overcharged for its mooring or C. I have no regard for the preservation of our environment.

Wrong on all counts; my vacation home has a view improved by another taxpayer's marsh. I have an interest in a marina which will prosper if competition is restricted and last, I am most concerned about our environment. Although I can afford to live anywhere in the world I would much prefer to keep Marshfield habitable.

Then what the hell am I doing carping about this wetlands bill which is supposed to preserve the environment?

Two reasons; first, as pointed out above, if we are going to preserve the Wetlands, let's preserve the Dryland too. The latter will ultimately prove more valuable.

Second; and far more important, I feel that you are directing your attention towards the effect rather than the cause of environmental breakdown.

The wetlands bill is an attempt t

Citizen's Letter of Protest, continued

lunt one tentacle of a cancer which is estroying the nation.

The cancer is overpopulation.

People have to live somewhere. The ■etlands bill is futile and irrelevant un-

less the population is checked. In a few years the marshes will be developed, exploited and destroyed. It's simply a matter of time and biology.

NOTES

[1] Charles H. W. Foster, "The Wetland Story," *Massachusetts Audubon*, pp. 3–5.

[2] Excerpts from remarks by Charles H. W. Foster before the National Audubon Society Convention, Boston, Massachusetts, 1965.

[3] By the end of the 1970 fiscal year a total of 11,250 acres of coastal wetlands had been restricted and restrictions for another 9,524 acres are on the way. Thus, to date, 46 percent of the top priority acreage (45,000 acres) have been preserved from development under this legislation. (Editor)

[4] Excerpts from literature prepared by the Department of Natural Resources.

[5] See Chapter 16 for information on the Conservation Commissions in Massachusetts.

IV

NOISE POLLUTION

One price of progress and technological achievement has been an increase in the level of noise in every aspect of the world around us. The natural sounds of wind, streams and birds have been almost drowned out by the machines of man. In the urban environments in which most Americans live, noise (i.e., unwanted sound) is both constant and enervating. Furthermore, the trend is in the wrong direction; the proliferation of technology has created new and louder sources of noise.

As we have become aware of the pollution that inundates us, we have begun to realize that we must re-think what we mean by progress. Once we thought that smoke billowing from smoke stacks was a sign of new income and new opportunities. Similarly, we have equated noise with growth and power, the noise of a motorcycle or a sports car as proof of its speed and its "manliness." Air hammer, jack hammer, pile driver, heavy machinery rolling down the highway have come to indicate that things were in a state of progress, proceeding at a "muscular" pace.

Urban dwellers are exposed to noises in every area of their lives; they are surrounded by noise not only at work, but at home and at play. All in all, the most severe problems of noise occur at work where everyone is exposed to excessive noise for long, unbroken periods of time. And in order to get to and from work, one must pass through another wall of sound; transportation noise—motor vehicles and rail systems—often reaches excessive levels due to the fact that, with only a few recent exceptions, they all were designed with little consideration to noise.

The dangers of exposure to intense noise are found not only in heavy industrial and aircraft operations but also in light industrial, commercial and business areas. Noise levels in dwellings, particularly the 60 to 90 decibels found in kitchen areas, are beginning to approach those in factories, where progressive deafness on the part of long term employees is a common ailment. There is no conclusive evidence that the moderate noise, normally encountered domestically or socially, produces any obviously identifiable physiological effects; however, it is true that noise does prevent sleep, produce stress, and interfere with concentration, communication and recreation.

Generally two approaches have been used in controlling noise. First, noise can be dampened at its source or its characteristics can be made less annoying. The second and most costly approach is to replace the source of noise with a quieter machine or with one that is not noisier but performs better, thus reducing the number of machines required to do the job. Another approach schedules maximum machine use at those times when the fewest people are nearby to be disturbed. And, of course, one can simply separate the source of noise from people: for example, place airports away from residential areas. Often, rather than approach the problem at the source of noise, it is more practical to attack the problem where the noise is heard: for example, install acoustic insulation in homes and offices near airports and highways; or use ear protectors, such as those worn by employees working near airplanes.

Up to now, efforts at the federal level to control noise pollution have concentrated primarily on noise in the occupational setting. In this area the greatest success to date has been recorded in industrial safety regulations.

Transportation noise has not been so successfully managed. There are no federal laws or regulations to control surface transportation noise. The Transportation Act of 1966, which created the Department of Transportation, also directed the Department to undertake noise research. One study is now underway, but any control that might be recommended must first be authorized by Congress, while the enforcement would be left up to local authorities. Aircraft, on the other hand, is subject to some noise control. In 1968, Congress directed the Federal Aviation Administration to set standards for the control of civilian aircraft noise and sonic booms. Regulations announced by the FAA in November, 1969, apply mostly to new aircraft with compliance dates set so far into the future that almost all the new jumbo 747s, for example, will have been built. The agency has not yet decided whether to require noise limiting devices on existing aircraft.

The two articles in this section discuss two different attacks on noise pollution: the first regulates sound commonly found in any urban setting; the second concentrates entirely on motor vehicle noise.

Claude A. Armour, former chief of the Memphis Fire and Police Departments and now Commissioner of Tennessee's Safety Department, in the "Nation's Quietest City," describes the Memphis noise control program, often cited as the outstanding example in the field. A close look at the city's noise control ordinance prompts the reader to question why this legislation should be so effective. Other cities and states have proposed similar regulations and found them unenforceable. Why then has Memphis been able to achieve quiet while other cities have not? Armour says that the methods used to establish the program in Memphis included not only the control ordinance, but also zoning regulations, enforcement procedures, education, public participation and many other factors. The most critical of these seems to have been education and public participation. For some reason, the idea caught hold; an attitude was formed among the citizens and a way of life was developed and has been maintained which places value on a quiet environment. Unfortunately, other cities have yet to develop this attitude.

California, on the other hand, has approached the problem of transportation noise with strong legislation which carefully defines standards and provides a strong stick for enforcement. Ross A. Little of the state's Highway Patrol, in "The Motor Vehicle Noise Problem and What is Being Done About it in California," describes how California faced the problem of controlling noise levels of vehicles operating on the state's highways. Working closely with motor vehicle manufacturers, the state has developed procedures for measuring noise levels. The overriding concern in the development of this legislation has been to design regulations which could be readily understood and enforced.

Noise, only recently recognized as a pollutant, may be easier to curb than air or water pollution. But government at all levels, except for recognizing it as a work hazard, has all but ignored the problem. To date, most legislation enacted at the state and local levels has been unenforceable because it fails to spell out enforcement techniques and maximum noise levels. And it becomes apparent, if we are to achieve better legislation and enforcement procedures, that we must know more about sound, especially how to measure it and what its effects upon human beings are. But the chances are that the world of the city dweller will continue to get noisier and noisier in the next few years.

11. Noise Abatement—Memphis Style

CLAUDE A. ARMOUR

Memphis is recognized as the nation's quietest city. Of this achievement every citizen is proud.

This title was not attained through any easy method but by sincere work and the full cooperation of the citizens of Memphis and its civic organizations, service clubs, newspapers, radio stations and television.

The rewards of this achievement are too numerous to mention, but the citizens of Memphis have realized what its means to their health and happiness and to the progress of their growing city.

It is gratifying to hear the expressions of tourists and visitors when passing through the City of Memphis, and also the many inquiries made by other cities and some foreign countries as to "How is it done?"

One of the major factors of the growth and progress of the City of Memphis has been the quietness which prevails.

In order to convey to you a complete picture of the noise abatement program in Memphis, I would like to summarize the history of noise abatement in our city.

In 1940 a noise abatement program was adopted and all efforts were made to accomplish the ideals set forth as a result of a good program. At this time Memphis had a population of 292,942 people and a vehicular registration of 70,588 vehicles. At the present time Memphis has a population of 432,250 people and a vehicular registration of 139,628 vehicles. This is approximately 70% increase in population since 1940 and around 100% increase in vehicular registration since 1940. Through this tremendous period of growth of population and vehicular registration, Memphis has maintained and expanded its noise abatement program.

From year to year the noise abatement program has been improved,

Claude A. Armour, "Noise Abatement—Memphis Style." *Proceedings of Fourth Annual Noise Abatement Symposium* (Chicago, Illinois, 1953), pp. 32–38.

more ordinances adopted, new fields have been explored in the reduction of noise. At the present time the entire citizenry of Memphis are proud of the achievements made during these years.

It was no easy task when noise abatement was first started in Memphis but the Honorable Joseph P. Boyle, then commissioner of fire and police, recognized the importance of noise abatement. He instituted a program; was often criticized and the most outstanding criticism was "we are required to have a horn but they won't let us blow it." A car must have a horn in order to pass the automobile testing station. Musical horns were being used, horns for door bells in the early hours of the morning, and many other unnecessary uses, too numerous to mention.

Commissioner Boyle did not become discouraged but insisted on noise abatement and all the fundamentals necessary to accomplish this worthy endeavor. It is needless to say what the results have been, as you gentlemen are well aware of noise abatement in Memphis through the years and up to the present time.

We have found in Memphis that noise has to be eliminated in all fields, such as, industrial noise, mufflers, horns, low flying aircraft and many other fields in which noises are made unnecessarily and should be eliminated. The methods used in Memphis to attack and suppress unnecessary noise have been through ordinances, zoning, enforcement, education, public participation and many other factors which I will discuss later.

One of the first steps to control noise is by enforcement of ordinances, such as the Anti-Noise Ordinance in the Memphis Municipal Code, Chapter 28, Paragraph 769, which covers noises generally.

The anti-noise ordinance follows:

Subject to the provisions of this section, the creating of any unreasonably loud, disturbing and unnecessary noise within the limits of the city is prohibited.

Noise of such character, intensity or duration as to be detrimental to the life or health of any individual, or in disturbance of the public peace and welfare is prohibited.

The following acts, among others, are declared to be loud, disturbing and unnecessary noises and noises in violation of this section, but this enumeration shall not be deemed to be exclusive; namely:

1. PROHIBITED NOISES ENUMERATED

(a) *Blowing horns*—The sounding of any horn or signal device on any automobile, motocycle, bus, or trackless trolley while not in motion, except as a danger signal if another vehicle is approaching apparently out of control, or if in motion only as a danger signal after or as brakes are being applied and deceleration of the vehicle is intended; the creation by means of any such signal device of any unreasonably loud or harsh sound; and the sounding of such device for an unnecessary and unreasonable period of time.

(b) *Radios, phonographs, etc.*—The playing of any radio, phonograph, or any musical instrument in such a manner or with such volume, particularly during the hours between 11 p.m. and 7 a.m. as to annoy or disturb the quiet, comfort or repose of persons in any office, hospital or in any dwelling, hotel or other type of residence, or of any persons in the vicinity.

(c) *Yelling, shouting, hooting, etc.*—Yelling, shouting, hooting, whistling or singing on the public streets, particularly between the hours of 11 p.m. and 7 a.m. or at any time or place so as to annoy or disturb the quiet or repose of any persons in any hospital, dwelling, hotel or any other type of residence or of any persons in the vicinity.

(d) *Pets*—The keeping of any animal, bird, or fowl, which by causing frequent or long continued noise shall disturb the comfort or repose of any person in the vicinity.

(e) *Use of vehicle*—The use of any automobile, motorcycle, or trackless trolley so out of repair, so loaded or in such manner as to cause loud and unnecessary grating, grinding, rattling or other noise.

(f) *Blowing whistles*—The blowing of any steam whistle attached to any stationary boiler except to give notice of the time to begin or stop work or as a warning of fire or danger, or upon request of proper city authorities.

(g) *Exhaust discharge*—To discharge into the open air the exhaust of any steam engine, stationary internal combustion engine, motor vehicle or motor boat engine, except through a muffler or other device which will effectively prevent loud or explosive noises therefrom.

(h) *Building operations*—The erection (including excavation), demolition, alteration or repair of any building in any residential district or section, other than between the hours of 7 a.m. and 6 p.m. on week days, except in case of urgent necessity in the interest of public health and safety, and then only with a permit from the chief building inspector, which permit may be granted for a period not to exceed thirty days while the emergency continues. If the chief building inspector should determine that the public health and safety will not be impaired by the erection, demolition, alteration or repair of any building or the excavation of streets and highways within the hours of 6 p.m. and 7 a.m. and if he shall further determine that loss or inconvenience would result to any party in interest, he may grant permission for such work to be done within the hours of 6 p.m. and 7 a.m. upon application being made at the time the permit for the work is awarded or during the progress of the work.

(i) *Noises near schools, hospitals, churches, etc.*—The creation of any excessive noise on any street adjacent to any school, or adjacent to any hospital, which unreasonably interferes with the working or sessions thereof.

(j) *Loading and unloading operations*—The creation of a loud and excessive noise in connection with loading or unloading any vehicle or the opening and destruction of bales, boxes, crates and containers.

(k) *Noises to attract attention*—The use of any drum, loud speaker or other instrument or device for the purpose of attracting attention by creation to any performance, show or sale or display of merchandise.

(l) *Loud speaker or amplifiers on vehicles*—The use of mechanical loud speakers or amplifiers on trucks or other moving or standing vehicles for advertising or other purposes.

2. EXCEPTIONS

None of the terms or prohibitions hereof shall apply to or be enforced against:

(a) *City vehicles*—Any vehicle of the city while engaged upon necessary public business.

(b) *Repair of bridges, streets, etc.*—Excavations or repairs of bridges, streets, or highways, by or on behalf of the city, Shelby County or the State of Tennessee, during the night season, when the public welfare and convenience renders it impossible to perform such work during the day.

(c) *Noncommercial use of loud speakers or amplifiers*—The reasonable use of amplifiers or loud speakers in the course of public addresses which are non-commercial in character.

AMENDMENT TO SECTION B

(b) *Radios, phonographs, etc.*—The playing of any radio, phonograph or any musical instrument or sound device, including but not limited to loud speakers or other devices for reproduction or amplification of sound, either independently or in connection with motion pictures, radio, or television, in such manner or with such volume, particularly during the hours between 11 p.m. and 7 a.m. as to annoy or disturb the quiet of persons in any office, hospital or in any dwelling, hotel or other type of residence or of any persons in the vicinity.

After the above ordinance it can be seen readily that this ordinance covers noises in general, but we have found that it takes other ordinances to support and make an effective enforcement program such as an ordinance known as:

HOSPITAL ZONE—Streets in the vicinity of hospitals are hereby designated as "hospital zones," and it is hereby made the duty of the chief of police to mark such zones by appropriate signs, and designate the boundaries of such zones. It shall be unlawful for the driver of any vehicle, except apparatus of the fire department, or for any person, to make or cause to be made any unnecessary noise or other disturbances within such "hospital zone," as designated by the chief of police.

Another supporting ordinance which we have found necessary is:

WHISTLE NOT TO BE BLOWN EXCEPT WHEN REQUIRED BY STATUTE—It shall be unlawful to sound or blow the whistle or other similar device of any engine operated on any railroad in the city within the city limits except when the same is sounded as required by the statute laws of the State of Tennessee.

Another supporting ordinance which is most important and the noise abatement program could not be successful without is:

HOURS OF OPERATION OPERATING IN NOISY MANNER— The owner or operator of a mechanical amusement device shall not permit the same to be operated between the hours of 12 p.m. and 8 a.m. It shall be unlawful for any person in charge of any mechanical amusement device playing or emitting music or sound to permit such device to be operated in such a manner that the sound created, emitted or transmitted by the mechanical amusement device shall be audible to persons on any public street or highway or upon any adjoining premises.

Several other supporting ordinances which are also necessary for a complete noise abatement program are as follows:

DISCHARGE OF FIREWORKS—It is prohibited for any person to use or discharge any fireworks within the limits of the city, except at such points as may be authorized by the mayor.

DISCHARGING FIREWORKS—It shall be a a misdemeanor to fire or discharge any cannon, or explode or set off any rocket, squib, torpedo, cracker, or any combustible fireworks of any description, in the streets or public grounds of the city; provided, that nothing herein contained shall be construed to extend to any military parade, exercise or review, or fireworks exhibited by order of the mayor, or to any exhibition authorized by a permit from the mayor to exhibit the same for public amusement, or to any officer of the city acting in obedience to law or ordinance.

DISORDERLY CONDUCT—Shouts or making a noise either outside or inside a building during the nighttime to the annoyance or disturbance of any considerable number of persons.

DISORDERLY HOUSES—KEEPING—It shall be unlawful for any person to keep a disorderly house, by making or causing to be made therein, loud or improper noises, or by collecting therein drunken, noisy and disorderly persons, to the annoyance of others and the disturbance of the neighborhood.

DISTURBING PUBLIC PEACE—It shall be unlawful for any person to use rude, boisterous, offensive, obscene or blasphemous language in any public place or to make, aid, countenance or assist in making any improper noise, disturbance, breach of the peace or diversion, or conduct one's self in a disorderly manner, in any other place, to the annoyance of others.

DISTURBING PUBLIC WORSHIP—It shall be unlawful for any person to disturb any congregation or assembly, met for religious or other lawful purpose, by making any noise, or by rude and indecent behavior, or by boisterous or profane discourse within or near such place.

HORNS AND OTHER DEVISES —

(a) Every motor vehicle when operated on a street shall be equipped with a horn in good working order and capable of emitting a sound audible under normal conditions from a distance of not less than two hundred feet, but no horn or other warning device shall emit an unreasonably loud or harsh sound or a whistle. Only such warning devices shall be permitted as may be approved by the commissioner of public safety, or by ordinance duly passed by the mayor and board of commissioners of the city.

(b) No vehicle shall be equipped with nor shall any person use upon a vehicle any siren, whistle or bell, except as otherwise permitted in this section. Any authorized emergency vehicle may be equipped with a siren, whistle or bell, capable of emitting a sound audible under normal conditions from a distance of not less than five hundred feet and of a type approved by the department but such siren shall not be used except when such vehicle is operated in response to an emergency call and then only when necessary to warn pedestrians and other drivers of the approach thereof.

(c) No bicycle shall be equipped with nor shall any person use upon a bicycle any siren or whistle.

One of the most annoying types of noises being experienced by all cities more than ever at the present time are mufflers.

While the ordinance requiring mufflers in the City of Memphis is a very good ordinance and is one of our supporting ordinances to our anti-noise ordinance, it is still a difficult job to control the loud noises made by large truck and other vehicles with mufflers as the excessive noise is still very aggravating.

It is being seriously considered by Memphis officials at the present time that more strenuous effort should be put forth in the curbing of this excessive noise which would not hinder the operation of a motor in its efficiency and performance but quiet its offensive roar.

There are arguments both ways with reference to mufflers that the more an engine is muffled the less efficiency is received from it. From our experience in Memphis it is believed that motors can be properly muffled to eliminate excessive noise and still operate efficiently and economically without undue wear and tear on a motor.

There are two ways in which to combat and abate the excessive noise of mufflers; one of these being by strict ordinance and enforcement of this ordinance and the other by routing trucks around the city, if possible, or by truck by-passes.

A major truck route plan is under way at the present time in the City of Memphis for a truck route system that, in the most part, will keep trucks on commercial and industrial streets and keep them away from residential areas and streets.

An ordinance is also being prepared to enforce this regulation.

Approximately 6% of all the cars inspected by the Memphis Inspection Bureau were turned down for defective mufflers in the year 1952. For eight months of the year 1953, approximately 1% of the cars inspected were turned down for defective and noisy mufflers. The City of Memphis will not accept any other muffler other than a standard approved muffler or equal for any vehicle regardless of make or type of vehicle. We feel that the standard approved muffler should be the only muffler accepted because it is engineered and manufactured for whatever vehicle regardless of make, model or type and will not hamper its efficiency.

We do not accept gutted mufflers and several other types of mufflers which have been manufactured recently that have been adopted as a fad and tend to increase the exhaust noise for the appeasement of some drivers' desires and also causes or incites speeding and recklessness.

MUFFLER REQUIRED—No person shall drive a motor vehicle on a street unless such motor vehicle is equipped with a muffler in good working order and in constant operation to prevent excessive gas, steam or oil. All exhaust pipes carrying exhaust gases from the motor shall be directed parallel with the ground or slightly upward.

MUFFLER CUT-OUT PROHIBITED—It shall be unlawful to use a muffler cut-out on any motor vehicle upon a street.

The noises made by street cars, overhead trolleys and any other type rail vehicle for public transportation in the cities have been eliminated in the City of Memphis entirely. Every public transportation vehicle in the City of Memphis at the present time is either electric trackless trolley, gasoline or diesel buses.

Another step that Memphis has taken toward the abatement of noise has been dealt with by the complete re-zoning of the city. Efforts have been made in our new zoning law to place commercial areas where they do not interfere with our residential areas. This has also been done when dealing with industrial areas by completely separating the industrial areas, as nearly as possible, from any residential areas.

Before any commercial or industrial establishment can start to build in the City of Memphis a hearing is required before the Planning Commission as to location, type of business, amount of traffic and what noises are made by whatever type of business is applying for permit to build.

In some cases some types of industry are not allowed to go into industrial zones due to the noise, dust and other obnoxious features. These places are usually put entirely off to themselves away from any other residential, commercial or industrial areas. Both the City and County Planning Commissions have worked with the officials concurrently in the proper locating of commercial and industrial businesses.

Another important factor in combatting excessive noise is done in Memphis by an ordinance known as the "Aircraft Over the City." This ordinance deals with low flying aircraft and is used in some instances towards the advertising use of low flying planes pulling banners, honking horns and other methods of attracting public attention to such advertising. I am sure it is conceded by everyone that a low flying aircraft is not only noisy but is very irritating and worrisome at times. This ordinance was written to deal with the type of noise and has been used successfully.

AIRCRAFT OVER THE CITY—It shall be unlawful for any person to operate an aircraft in and over the city at any height or speed, or in any manner which is unreasonable or improper under the circumstances, of the operation; or so as to endanger the property, life or limb of any person. Operation of any aircraft in violation of the air traffic rules of the Civil Aeronautics Board of the United States Department of Commerce shall be presumptive evidence of unreasonable and improper operation. In no event shall an aircraft be operated over the City of Memphis at an altitude less than one thousand feet above any obstruction and at a horizontal distance of less than two thousand feet, in any direction, from an obstruction; provided, however, that aircraft maneuvering for landing or take off are subject only to such rules and regulations as may apply thereto.

One of the most important features in any noise abatement program whether it be in Memphis or any other city is the selling of noise abatement to the public.

We might, for illustration purposes, use public officials as a big company and use noise abatement as a product; an unknown product which has to be advertised and sold to the public by pointing out its benefits and what it does for the health, happiness and progress of any community. When the citizens of our cities have been sold this worthwhile product, the job of selling noise abatement has been accomplished. No noise abatement program is successful unless the citizens have been sold and believe that it is worthwhile.

The problem of noise abatement can only be accomplished through public cooperation, advertising, education, ordinances, enforcement, and with full cooperation of public officials, planning commissions, service clubs, veteran oragnizations, civic clubs and all other groups who play a vital part in the rounding out of a complete noise abatement program.

It also takes the full cooperation of the press, radio and television which Memphis has had from the beginning of our noise abatement program.

The success of the Memphis noise abatement program through the years can be attributed to the full cooperation from the preceding.

This is the story of noise abatement—MEMPHIS STYLE.

12. The Motor Vehicle Noise Problem and What Is Being Done About It in California

ROSS A. LITTLE

The California Legislature became concerned in the early 1940's about truck and passenger car noise which resulted in the purchase of a sound level meter by the California Highway Patrol. Attempts to use the meter to support arrests for excessive noise were generally unsuccessful because no standards had yet been established.

Starting as early as 1959 the California Legislature, during each regular session, attempted to adopt maximum permissible noise limits for vehicles operating on California's highways. The 1967 session adopted two Vehicle Code Sections, 23130 and 27160, which finally achieved this goal by setting limits in decibels measured at 50 feet from the vehicle. The limits will be explained in detail later.

Many considered the limits too high so the 1969 Legislature attempted to lower them by 2 dB(A). The legislature was successful in lowering the limits in Section 27160 for new vehicles to become effective for vehicles manufactured after January 1, 1973. The proposed reduction of the limits in Section 23130 for vehicles operating on the highway was not totally accepted. The reductions adopted only applied to heavy trucks and to motorcycles. The limits were not lowered for passenger cars because data was not available to indicate the number and type of vehicles that would exceed the proposed limits.

The regulations required by the new sections were carefully prepared by members of the Engineering Section working with the vehicle manufacturers. We have continued to work with the manufacturers and also the SAE Acoustic Committee to attempt to improve the measuring procedures for new vehicles to more closely measure

Ross A. Little, "The Motor Vehicle Noise Problem and What is Being Done About it in California," presented at the 38th Convention of the Audio Engineering Society, May 4, 1970, Los Angeles, California.

maximum noise output. This cooperation has resulted in a better and more concise procedure for measuring truck noise which we plan to adopt into our regulations. We are also in the process of developing new test procedures for passenger cars and motorcycles which will more closely measure maximum noise.

Tests specified by the Departmental regulations to determine if new vehicles comply with Vehicle Code Section 27160 are performed by the Highway Patrol, Engineering Section, in Sacramento on a complaint basis. We have neither the time nor personnel to check all vehicles. Only those suspected to be loud and reported to us by our field personnel or citizens are actually tested. During 1969 the Engineering Section tested 96 vehicles which resulted in the recall of several models of vehicles for complete redesigning of the exhaust system.

Prior to the enactment of Section 27160, setting maximum permissible limits for new vehicles, it was common practice to manufacture heavy trucks with no or inadequate exhaust systems. These vehicles, as have shown up in our highway enforcement program, are naturally the noisiest vehicles on the highway.

The highway noise law, Vehicle Code Section 23130, is an operational law and relates to the driver's operating mode. The law is similar to the speed law which takes into account the fact that a vehicle is capable of driving at speeds greater than the posted speed limit.

This section states in part that no person shall operate a motor vehicle in such a manner as to exceed the noise limit for the category of vehicle based on a distance of 50 feet from the center of the lane of travel. The law also takes into account the fact that vehicle noise is somewhat dependent upon speed and that vehicles operating in the residential areas should be operating slower and in a quieter manner than when out on the open highway. Therefore, the law sets lower noise limits for areas where the speed limit is less than 35 mph and somewhat higher noise limits where the speed limit is more than 35 mph.

As you can see in Table 1, the limits established by the law are quite generous for the different vehicle classes and the speed zones. Also, a 2 dB(A) tolerance is applied to these limits, by regulation, to account for differences in measuring sites and differences between meters. We agree that the limits are high but we also believe that it is necessary to start someplace and begin gathering data to determine where to go.

Paraphrased Vehicle Code Sections

23130. (a) No person shall operate a motor vehicle at any time or under any condition in such a manner as to exceed the noise limit based on a distance of 50 feet from the center of the lane of travel.

Table I

	Speed Limit of 35 MPH or Less	Speed Limit of More Than 35 MPH
(1) Heavy trucks and large motorcycles:		
(A) Before January 1, 1973	88 dB(A)	90 dB(A)
(B) After January 1, 1973	86 dB(A)	90 dB(A)
(2) Any other motor vehicle	82 dB(A)	86 dB(A)

27160. (a) No person shall sell a new motor vehicle which produces a maximum noise exceeding the following noise limit:

Large motorcycles manufactured prior to 1970	92 dB(A)
Vehicles manufactured prior to 1972	
Large motorcycles	88 dB(A)
Heavy trucks	88 dB(A)
Other vehicles	86 dB(A)
Vehicles manufactured after 1972	
Large motorcycles	86 dB(A)
Heavy trucks	86 dB(A)
Other vehicles	84 dB(A)

To enforce the highway noise limits, the Department has purchased 6 sets of sound measuring equipment and trained 6 teams to measure vehicle noise in various locations throughout the state. During the first 10 months of operation 519,348 vehicles were measured with 2,387 violations. Of the vehicles in violation, 84% were heavy trucks, 14% were passenger vehicles, and 2% were motorcycles.

In order to determine the effect of the noise limits of Section 23130 on passenger vehicles, the Department undertook a special study to attempt to establish the average noise level for vehicles under 6,000 pounds GVW, the noise distribution from these vehicles, and if possible what was causing the noise. The survey was also made to determine if the limits of the Vehicle Code Section were adequate or should be lowered. The survey was started in September 1969 and ran through November 1969.

The data was gathered for the survey in two steps by members of the California Highway Patrol noise teams. Step one was intended to determine the source of noise from vehicles in violation. To accomplish this the noise enforcement teams were instructed to investigate every vehicle under 6,000 pounds GVW stopped for noise violations within a three-month period and determine if possible the cause of the noise.

During the three-month survey, the teams measured 54,576 vehicles under 6,000 pounds and stopped 105 for noise violations. Ninety of these vehicles were stopped for muffler violations of Vehicle Code Sections 27150 or 27151 because the mufflers were obviously modified or defective. Only 15 of the 105 vehicles were stopped for exceeding the noise limits of Vehicle Code Section 23130.

In other words, the remaining 90 vehicles were equipped with either modified or defective exhaust systems but did not exceed the noise limits. Also, of the 15 vehicles that did exceed the noise limits of Section 23130, 9 of them had modified exhaust systems including two vehicles with no mufflers, 5 had defective exhaust systems, and one had engine noise. Of the total 105 vehicles, 58% had defective systems, 40% had modified exhaust systems, and 2% had engine noise problems.

Step two was a noise distribution survey. To accomplish this two teams were instructed to measure and record the sound level of motorcycles, pickup trucks, and passenger vehicles for a period of 20 days each. Measurements were made on city streets with speed zones of 35 mph or less as well as in speed zones in excess of 35 mph.

During this time, the two teams were instructed to only measure vehicle noise and take no enforcement action. Readings were taken in 21 locations on city streets, 4 locations on country roads and wide high-speed city streets, and 10 locations on freeways. All readings were made in the regions of Los Angeles and Sacramento. Each of the vehicles measured was identified by type, make, year model, type of noise, noise level in dB(A), and lane in which vehicle was operating.

During the two 20-day distribution surveys, the two teams measured a total of 14,786 vehicles with only three vehicles exceeding the statutory noise limit plus 2 dB(A) tolerance.

Twenty-one locations were used in speed zones of 35 mph and less. A total of 9,395 vehicles under 6,000 pounds GVW, excluding motorcycles, were measured in these locations. The average noise level for these vehicles was 68 dB(A). Only one vhicle (a Porsche with a modified exhaust system) or 0.01% of the vehicles exceeded the statutory limit of 82 + 2 dB(A) (Figure 1).

When considering a level of 4 dB(A) below the present noise limits for comparison purposes, only six vehicles or 0.06% exceeded a level

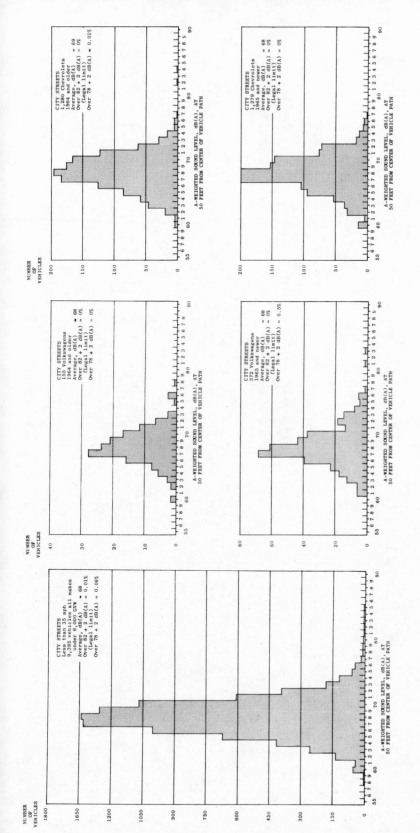

Figure 1

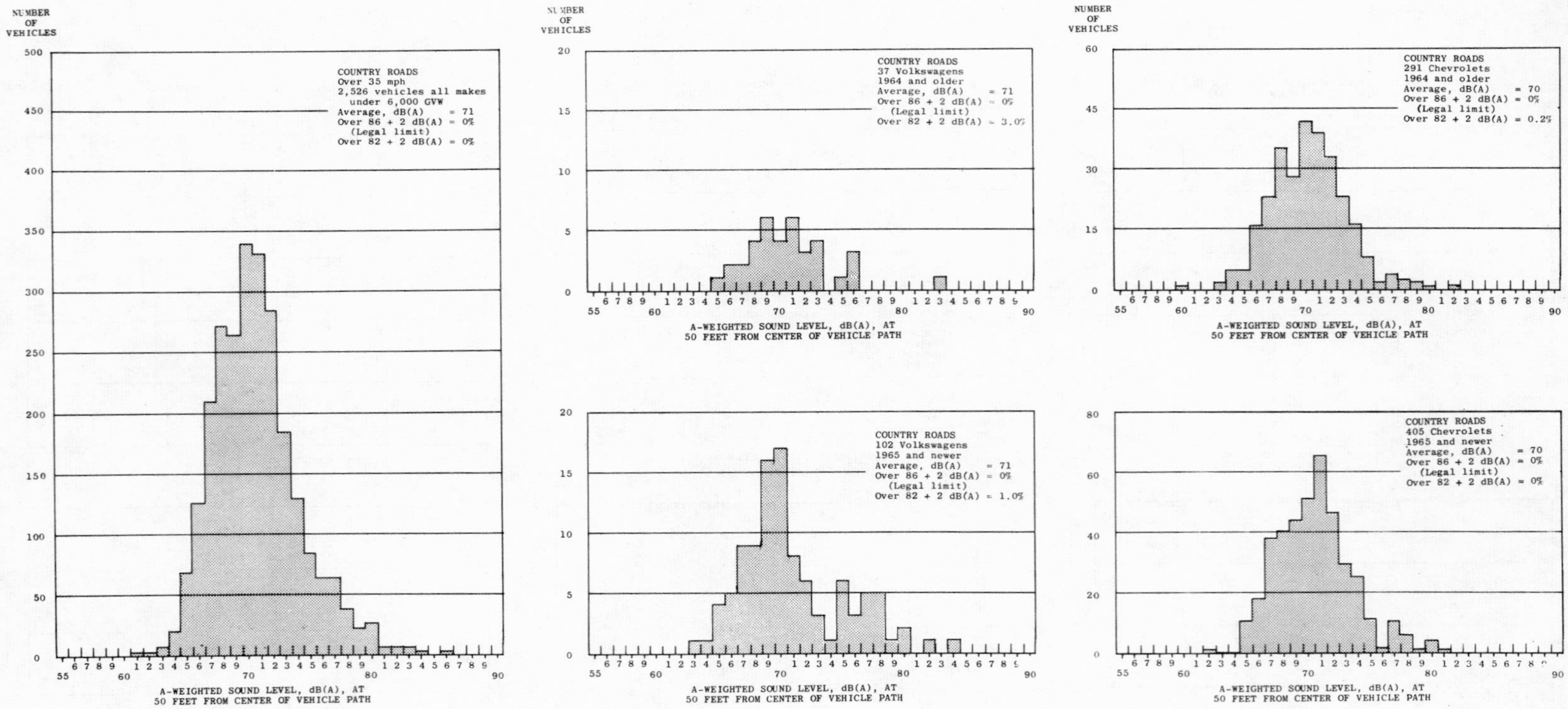
NUMBER OF VEHICLES
COUNTRY ROADS
Over 35 mph
2,526 vehicles all makes under 6,000 GVW
Average, dB(A) = 71
Over 86 + 2 dB(A) = 0%
(Legal limit)
Over 82 + 2 dB(A) = 0%
A-WEIGHTED SOUND LEVEL, dB(A), AT 50 FEET FROM CENTER OF VEHICLE PATH
COUNTRY ROADS
37 Volkswagens
1964 and older
Average, dB(A) = 71
Over 86 + 2 dB(A) = 0%
(Legal limit)
Over 82 + 2 dB(A) = 3.0%
COUNTRY ROADS
102 Volkswagens
1965 and newer
Average, dB(A) = 71
Over 86 + 2 dB(A) = 0%
(Legal limit)
Over 82 + 2 dB(A) = 1.0%
COUNTRY ROADS
291 Chevrolets
1964 and older
Average, dB(A) = 70
Over 86 + 2 dB(A) = 0%
(Legal limit)
Over 82 + 2 dB(A) = 0.2%
COUNTRY ROADS
405 Chevrolets
1965 and newer
Average, dB(A) = 70
Over 86 + 2 dB(A) = 0%
(Legal limit)
Over 82 + 2 dB(A) = 0%

Figure 2

of 78 + 2dB(A). Of these six vehicles, five had modified exhaust systems and one had a defective system.

We reviewed information on each vehicle and each year model measured, and have chosen to discuss the data for Chevrolets and Volkswagens as representative of all vehicles. The report submitted to the Legislature in March contained data on four makes of vehicles.

Chevrolets, both old and new, had an average of 68 dB(A) with a maximum of 84 dB(A) for the older vehicles and 77 dB(A) for the newer vehicles. Two of the older vehicles exceeded 78 + 2 dB(A) and both had modified exhaust systems.

Volkswagens in both categories had an average of 68 dB(A) with a maximum noise level of 78 dB(A) for the older vehicles and 83 dB(A) for the newer vehicles. Two vehicles exceeded 78 + 2 dB(A) and both had modified exhaust systems.

Four non-freeway locations were used in speed zones of 35 mph and more. A total of 2,426 vehicles under 6,000 pounds GVW, excluding motorcycles, were measured in these locations. The average noise level for these vehicles was 71 dB(A) with none of the vehicles exceeding the statutory limit of 86 + 2 dB(A). (Figure 2.) When considering for comparison purposes, a level which is 4 dB(A) below the present noise level, none of the vehicles exceeded a level of 82 + 2 dB(A).

Chevrolets, both old and new, had an average of 70 dB(A) with a maximum of 82 dB(A) for the older vehicles and 81 dB(A) for the newer vehicles.

Volkswagens, both old and new, had an average of 71 dB(A) with the maximum of 83 dB(A) for the older vehicles and 84 dB(A) for the newer vehicles. Both vehicles which made these values were equipped with modified exhaust systems.

Ten locations were used on freeways with speed zones of 35 mph or more. A total of 2,865 vehicles under 6,000 pounds GVW, excluding motorcycles, were measured on freeways during this period. The average noise level for these vehicles was 74 dB(A). Only one vehicle (with a modified exhaust system) or 0.03% of the vehicles exceeded the statutory limits of 86 + 2 dB(A) (Figure 3). Again for comparison purposes, only six vehicles or 0.02% exceeded a noise level of 82 + 2 dB(A) which is 4 dB(A) below the present limit. Of these six vehicles, one had a modified exhaust system, one had no muffler, and two were speeding. There were no comments relative to the other two vehicles.

Chevrolets, both old and new, had an average of 75 dB(A) with a

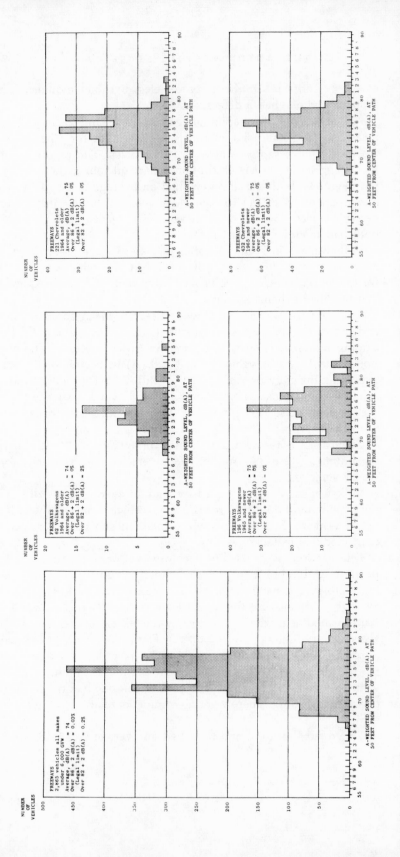

Figure 3

maximum of 83 dB(A) for the older vehicles and 82 dB(A) for the newer vehicles.

Volkswagens had an average of 74 dB(A) for vehicles manufactured prior to 1965 and an average of 75 dB(A) for vehicles manufactured after 1964 with a maximum of 85 dB(A) for the older vehicles and 83 dB(A) for the newer vehicles. The 85 dB(A) maximum was obtained from a vehicle which had no muffler.

In separating data from old and new vehicles it was found that there was no significant difference between makes or between the older and the newer year models of vehicles. However, the noise source survey showed that the biggest percentage of vehicles with modified exhaust systems were Volkswagens and Chevrolets. (Table 2.) Source of noise from vehicles in violation will bring it in.

Table II / Source of Noise from Vehicles in Violation

Vehicle Make	Number of Violations	Defective Exhaust	Modified Exhaust	Engine Noise	Exceeded 84 dB(A)
Chevrolet	30	19	10	1	4
Dodge	4	2	2	0	0
Ford	13	11	2	0	5
Volkswagen	26	8	18	0	0
Other	32	21	10	1	6
Total	105	61	42	2	15

It seems a common practice to make these vehicles more noisy with the misconception that noise is power, or at least this is the impression given by the operators. Noise has become synonymous with power, which may be true for some things but not for the motor vehicle.

Motorcycles (Figure 4) were also included in this study because they are passenger vehicles even though different noise limits apply to them. During the two 20-day noise distribution studies, only 127 motorcycles were measured. Because of the small sampling of vehicles the data was not broken down in the graphs to show city streets, country roads and freeways but was combined into one graph shown here. Only one of the motorcycles measured exceeded the noise limits specified for the speed zones in which it was operating. This vehicle was producing 91 dB(A) on a freeway where the legal limit is 90 dB(A). This point is not shown on the graph as it is beyond the limit of the graph.

Upon reviewing the data shown in Table 3, it can be seen that the

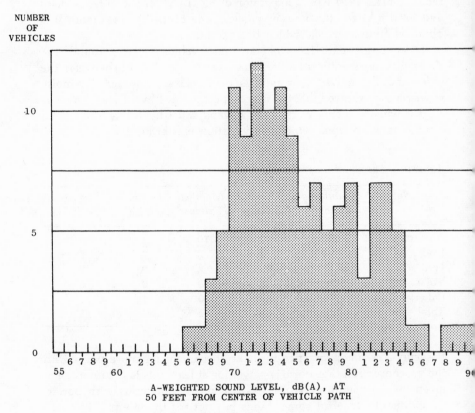

127 MOTORCYCLES
CITY STREETS, COUNTRY ROADS, FREEWAYS

Figure 4

noise limits for passenger vehicles, including motorcycles, could be reduced without causing any hardship to the public operating on California's highways. Most of the vehicles affected by the comparative reduction of 4 dB(A) discussed earlier were in violation of the older muffler laws because they have defective or modified exhaust systems. Proper maintenance of these vehicles would greatly reduce the noise problem.

There appears to be a lack of interest in enforcing against vehicles

Table III / Passenger Vehicles

The following chart shows the number and percentage of passenger vehicles that exceeded values from 2 dB(A) above the present limits to 10 dB(A) below the present limits:

db(A) Variation from Present Limit	SPEED ZONES					
	35 mph and under (9,296 vehicles)			Over 35 mph (5,391 Vehicles)		
	db(A)	No. of Veh. Over	% of Veh. Over	dB(A)	No. of Veh. Over	% of Veh. Over
+2	84	1	0.01	88	1	0.02
+1	83	2	0.02	87	1	0.02
0	82	3	0.03	86	2	0.04
−1	81	4	0.04	85	2	0.04
−4	78	10	0.1	82	25	0.5
−3	79	10	0.1	83	12	0.2
−4	78	10	0.1	82	25	0.0
−5	77	16	0.2	81	55	1.0
−6	76	26	0.3	80	88	1.6
−7	75	65	0.7	79	156	2.9
−8	74	119	1.3	78	250	4.6
−9	73	228	2.4	77	486	9.0
−10	72	304	3.3	76	751	14.0

Motorcycles

The following chart shows the number and percentage of motorcycles that exceeded the present limit and values to 10dB(A) below the present limit:

dB(A) Variation from Present Limit	SPEED ZONES					
	35 mph and under (38 vehicles)			Over 35 mph (82 vehicles)		
	db(A)	No. of Veh. Over	% of Veh. Over	dB(A)	No. of Veh. Over	% of Veh. Over
0	88	0	0	90	1	0.1
−1	87	0	0	89	1	0.1
−2	86	0	0	88	2	0.2
−3	85	0	0	87	3	0.4
−4	84	0	0	86	3	0.4
−5	83	1	0.3	85	4	0.5
−6	82	2	0.5	84	5	0.6
−7	81	3	0.8	83	9	1.0
−8	80	3	0.8	82	14	2.0
−9	79	3	0.8	81	19	2.0
−10	78	3	0.8	80	21	3.0

making excessive noise by the local municipalities because noise violations are not necessarily accident causing violations. The officers rightly spend a major portion of their time enforcing against operators committing unsafe acts which are accident contributory. Perhaps this situation will rapidly change with the emphasis now being given to environmental pollutions including noise.

There has been some concern by the public or representatives of the public that the noise limits for new vehicles are too close to the highway noise enforcement limits. Even though the values are somewhat the same, the limits themselves are actually considerably different because of the measuring and the testing technique. Testing for compliance of new vehicles for Section 27160 is done by the Highway Patrol, Engineering Section, in Sacramento. To determine if the vehicle complies with the limits established by this section, the Department conducts a rather severe full throttle acceleration test procedure which in most cases measures maximum noise output. In order for a citizen to make that much noise on the highway, he would likely be exceeding the speed limit or breaking other vehicle code sections for unsafe operation.

Passenger vehicles are not often driven on the highway under maximum acceleration and under full power. This is however, not altogether true with a commercial vehicle such as the heavy diesel truck. The normal mode of operation for this vehicle is to operate at full throttle in almost every gear. As you can see from the result of the highway enforcement, this vehicle is the major contributor to our highway noise problem. These vehicles can be quieted but it takes time. Several models of vehicles with two particular engines have caused the most problems, and it has been difficult to adequately silence them to compy with the law. The engine and muffler manufacturers have, however, completely redesigned their exhaust systems on these big engines to be quiet.

These big trucks have another problem in that the engine compartment is oftentimes exposed with little or no shrouding around it to shield and absorb the noise. We have been informed by some of the truck manufacturers that the cab configurations are being changed so that shrouding will come down over and around the engine and absorb some of the noise in acoustic material placed on the shroud. The 1969 model trucks which were sold and were not in compliance with the California Vehicle Code, are being recalled and refitted with the new designed exhaust systems to bring the vehicles into compliance.

Even though heavy trucks are the major contributor to highway noise and some models are difficult to silence, they can be effectively silenced. This is quite evident if you will take a picnic lunch and park where you can observe the flow of traffic. Many heavy trucks will glide by with not much more noise than the passenger car traffic. The noisy ones can be picked out without the use of a sound level meter. The limits of the law as amended by the 1969 Legislature for these heavy vehicles appear to be about as restrictive as it should be until the noisy ones are cleaned up.

Legislation has been introduced again this year to lower the noise limits for passenger vehicles, including motorcycles. Data has been submitted to support the authors of the bills.

The Department is continuing its enforcement by testing new vehicles and measuring vehicles on the highway and the program is due for expansion as money and men are made available.

In conclusion, I would like to emphasize that California has maximum permissible noise limits for vehicles and they are being enforced. There are still noisy vehicles on our streets and highways but the first step has been taken to eliminate them.

V

LAND USE

*Misuse of the land is one of the most serious and difficult challenges
to environmental quality; first, because mistreatment of the land is
apparently out of control and, second, because the process is virtually
irreversible. The United States has followed the frontier policy of
both the Old Testament and modern notions of "manifest destiny":
Man must conquer nature so that he can harness its limitless resources
for his own profit. Despite relatively recent efforts to alter an attitude
suitable for a small population expanding into a vast, almost unsettled
territory, land use is still not guided by any agreed upon standards
appropriate for a mature, urban society. Instead, we are faced with
a proliferation of overlapping government jurisdictions with their
competing responsibilities and programs, and we are confronted by
an odd mixture of private and public attitudes and biases. Generally
speaking distorted economic incentives have affected our land policy
beyond what we can afford to allow. This fact is accepted even among
conservatives wary of public intervention in behalf of the public interest. For example, President Nixon has proposed a National Land
Use Policy on the premise that: "Throughout the nation there is a
critical need for more effective land use planning, and for better controls over use of the land and the living systems that depend on it."* [1]*

*Part of the urgency underlying the calls for a national land use
policy is the tendency for most of the nation's population to crowd
into a tiny fraction of the nation's land resources. Although approximately three out of every four Americans now live in urban areas
(settlements of at least 2,500 population and metropolitan areas consisting of central cities and suburbs), these areas account for only
three percent of the land area of the United States. The most serious
land use problems, along with a desperate tangle of social and economic problems, are found in the decaying inner cities which house
the majority of the urban poor, many of them non-whites who ordinarily have little choice but to stay. Surrounding the inner city are
neighborhoods usually less old and less densely settled, populated by*

white working-class families. Beyond the city is suburbia. The "Suburbs" do not conform to a single stereotype; they are different kinds of communities that go by one title. Many are far from affluent but all share a common characteristic, i.e., they promise escape from many of the burdensome features of urban life while retaining some of the urban advantages; meanwhile, for the present, the schools are better, the crime rates lower, and there is more greenery and less litter.

In a democratic society, patterns of urbanization and economic growth are essentially the result of a multitude of decisions by individual citizens on where they want to live and work and by private groups and enterprises on which way they want to conduct their business. Municipalities have long exercised a significant role in allocating land uses through zoning, subdivision regulation and provision of vital services. But in most communities private enterprise called the tune leading to such well known abuses as "spot" zoning and other types of favoritism which weakened zoning regulations. The role of government in influencing land use decisions is gradually enlarging. But the limited, fragmented jurisdictions of municipalities and other agencies charged with land use responsibilities make effective planning for land use difficult if not impossible. Although a number of tools to control land use are at the disposal of public administrators at the local, regional and state levels, they are seldom brought to bear in a way that rationally shapes or directs development on a regional, state or national scale. The readings in this section include a variety of approaches at different government levels in the United States and in Europe to some specific problems of land use control.

In "London," Peter Hall records the experiences of London planners since the Second World War in devising a comprehensive plan with powers sufficiently strong to control the growth pattern of metropolitan London. The Green Belt Act provided the means to establish a zone of inviolate open countryside round the existing urban aggregation. The Town and Country Planning Act introduced a system of governmental machinery to control the use of every acre in Britain. For planning purposes, the Greater London Council, which was created in 1965, was made responsible for the 620 square miles which comprise most of the core of the London region. Thus, in this complex urban area, physical reality, statistical reality and administrative reality are all congruent.

A similar pattern is depicted in Shirely S. Passow's article, "Land Reserves and Teamwork in Planning Stockholm." Stockholm's development has been greatly affected by "an aggressive policy of acquir-

ing fringe area public lands and a well-coordinated political and governmental planning process." Passow speculates that many obstacles would have to be faced in trying to implement a similar policy in American cities; in particular, she cites the financial distress of most American cities, the large amounts of capital needed to be invested in land over long periods for future development, and, finally, the simple fact that most cities do not control the areas that surround them and affect them. Still, despite these manifold obstacles, she concludes that the task must be undertaken because the alternatives are so distressing. From the public viewpoint, advance land acquisition is the essential key to public implementation of planning.

Turning to the United States, Shelley M. Mark briefly recounts the background and distinctive features of Hawaii's Land Use Law. Produced in 1961 as the first and to date only statewide plan in the nation, Hawaii adopted state zoning for all public and private lands. It has also a statewide capital improvements program plus uniform statewide property assessment and tax collection. Mark concludes that Hawaii's experience with this ambitious legislation has not been smooth going. Yet, Hawaii's approach establishes a prototype for the reform of our nation's land use laws through a framework that provides a modicum of order while respecting the disorder, complexity, and spontaneity of man's aspirations.

An unusual approach to the preservation and control of our land resources was first established in Massachusetts in 1957 and has since spread to other states. The Conservation Commissions in Massachusetts are described by Andrew J. W. Scheffey. The commissions are made up of citizens who act as a conservation watchdog in the community, inventorying the municipalities' land and water resources and watching over the development or protection of these resources for the benefit of local residents. By mid-1971, 295 of Massachusetts' 351 cities and towns had created conservation commissions simply by adopting Chapter 40 of the state's General Laws. Scheffey describes the background of the commission movement and the experiences of several Massachusetts commissions.

While these examples illustrate some success in land use control, they fall short of leading the way to influencing land use on a larger scale. Standards and guidelines must be forthcoming from the federal government if uniform goals are to be established and the resources of the nation are to be developed for the public benefit.

[1] U.S., Council on Environmental Quality, The First Annual Report, (Washington, D.C.: Government Printing Office, 1970), p. xii.

13. London

PETER HALL

Even Londoners find it difficult enough to know what they mean by
London. Because there has hardly been a decade of recorded history
when London was not growing physically, it has never been easy to
determine with any finality where London ended and the rest of
Britain began. Paradoxically, in the mid-1960's it has become both
easier and more difficult than ever before. Easier, because since 1945
the outward growth of London has been limited by one of the most
powerful systems of land-use planning ever introduced in any country.
More difficult, because though the intention was to stop the growth
of London altogether, in fact the metropolis has gone on growing—
but in subtler and more complex forms than ever before.

By 1938, aided by the development of suburban electric railways
in the two decades since 1918, the suburbs of London had sprawled
out to a temporary limit roughly 12 to 15 miles from the centre.
In that year, the temporary limit became permanent: an Act of the
British Parliament, the Green Belt Act, created the means to fix a
girdle of permanent open countryside round the existing sprawl, thus
preventing further erosion of the countryside. And in 1947, when the
Town and Country Planning Act introduced at last a complex system
of local machinery to control the land use of every acre of Britain,
the preservation and even extension of the Metropolitan Green Belt
became a major policy objective. It happened that the built-up area
of 1938 coincided fairly neatly with a definition of London commonly
used for statistical purposes: Greater London, now known in British
official statistics as the *Greater London Conurbation*. It has an area

The London region. For local government, London means Greater London, an area roughly within 12–15 miles of the centre, which is similar to the 'conurbation' used for statistical purposes. Outside this is the Green Belt, and then the new towns created after 1945. The London region recognised for planning purposes stretches up to 40 miles from the centre; while some towns receiving London's overspill population are still farther out.

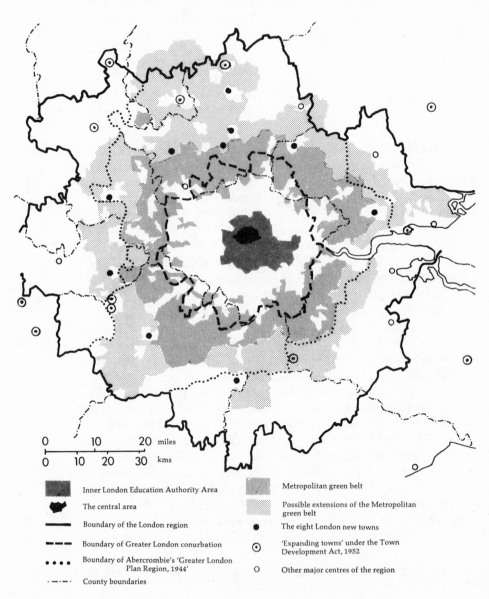

0	10	20 miles
0	10 20	30 kms

Inner London Education Authority Area

The central area

Boundary of the London region

Boundary of Greater London conurbation

Boundary of Abercrombie's 'Greater London Plan Region, 1944'

County boundaries

Metropolitan green belt

Possible extensions of the Metropolitan green belt

The eight London new towns

'Expanding towns' under the Town Development Act, 1952

Other major centres of the region

of 722 square miles, and at the 1961 Census it had a population of 8,182,550 which had been declining over the previous decade but which seemed to have reached stability by the early 1960s. And since 1 April 1965, following major reform of London's government, an area slightly smaller than this has become the territory of London's new administrative units: the Greater London Council, which administers the broader functions appropriate to the conurbation as a whole, and the thirty-two London boroughs which together with the ancient City of London administer the more local functions. The Greater London Council is responsible for an area of 620 square miles which in 1961 had a population of 7,990,161. So, from 1965, in London a situation obtains which is rare in any world city: physical reality, statistical reality and administrative reality are all approximately the same.

The difficulty is that there is another, deeper, sort of reality: the economic and social reality of people's jobs and homes, and the way they travel between them. Since 1945 London has continued to grow, and grow rapidly: but because the planners would not let it sprawl, because it has been hemmed in by the Green Belt, it has grown in new ways. In the zone beyond the original 5-mile-wide Green Belt, that is between 20 and 40 miles from central London, the existing towns have swelled; and new towns have grown out of villages, or on virgin fields, into major centres. Altogether, this "Outer Ring" added nearly one million to its population in the decade 1951–61, representing two-fifths of the net growth of the British population. Of course, not all these people look to the Greater London Conurbation for a living; but many—it is not quite certain yet how many—travel across the Green Belt into London's centre or its suburbs, each workday morning, to earn their daily bread. So, in an important sense, towns 20 to 30 miles out, like Guildford, Reading, Chelmsford and Maidstone have become parts of London too. Yet since 1945 they have grown in the way they always grew, not a part of a single sprawling urban mass, but as separate entities each with its own individuality: planning has seen to that.

In consequence a new sort of London is appearing in the 1950s and 1960s, a London so complex in form and function that it is difficult to describe or delimit it. The most useful working definition is the *London Planning Region* defined by the British Ministry of Housing and Local Government: it embraces an area of 4,412 square miles bounded by a roughly circular line with a radius 40 miles from Charing Cross and it contained a population of 12,465,941 at the 1961 Census. The International Urban Research definition gives a slightly smaller London, but it also makes London the biggest metropolitan area in Europe, and after New York—Northeastern New Jersey and Tokyo—Yokohama the world's third biggest in 1961. Its London Metropolitan Area, plus four small contiguous areas, contained 3,037 square miles and a Census population of 11,546,714 in 1961.

Greater London plus Outer Ring, therefore, equal London Region. These are the important definitions. But even within Greater London there are important social and economic distinctions between one ring and another. It is necessary to look now at the problems of the different parts of London in more detail: and the most logical place to start at is the centre.

Congestion at the Centre

Most of the least tractable of London's problems stem from the centre, even if they do not manifest themselves there. It is not merely a question of the increasing volumes of traffic on an inadequate street system, or of the increasing congestion of people in streets, cafés, restaurants, pubs; for the problem of the centre expresses itself also in the ever increasing crush on the suburban trains from Maidstone or Reading, the traffic congestion in the morning rush hours in Lewisham or Croydon or Leytonstone, and the problem of the isolated suburban wife in the "commuter country" of Camberley or Three Bridges or Chelmsford, outside the Greater London Conurbation and 30 miles or more from London.

As defined for the 1961 Census, London's "conurbation centre" is rather bigger than that of most other world cities. It covers just under 10½ square miles, mainly on the north bank of the Thames where it is bounded by the main terminal railway stations, but stretching about a mile south of the river as far as the traffic junction of the Elephant and Castle where government and other new office blocks began to go up in the early 1960s. With a resident population in 1961 of 270,395, the central core has a daily workforce whose precise size is unknown, but may have been about 1,400,000 in 1961, a little under one-quarter of total employment in the London Region. In the years 1951–61, the central employment total had increased by about 150,000, by far the greater part being office workers. And of the 1,400,000 workforce of 1961, probably just over half were office workers. These figures reflect the extraordinary office-building activity in central London in the 1950s. In 1939 there were 87 million square feet of office space in the central area. Bombing and displacement had reduced this to 77.5 million in 1948, and even in 1951 the total was only 80.5 million. Then additions to floorspace rose rapidly to a peak of 4.7 million square feet in 1957, subsequently falling back to 1.8 million in 1961. The net result was to increase total floorspace to 114.8 million square feet in 1962—an increase of over one-third in a decade. Because of increasing space standards in offices, employment did not rise proportionately, but only by some 25 per cent in the ten-year period.

These offices have powerfully changed the London skyline since 1950. The planners have eased the old rigid regulations which for centuries limited the height of London buildings, and the traditional landmarks of London are becoming lost among the new office towers. Yet London's skyscrapers represent only a physically different expression of a very old phenomenon. Office employment in Britain has been traditionally concentrated in London ever since the first offices were built by the government and the banks in the eighteenth century. But until the last decades of the nineteenth century, office employment was limited in scope. It was mainly restricted to the government offices of Westminster and the traditional commercial and financial functions of the City. Then, as the economy became more sophisticated, all sorts of new office functions multiplied: head offices of manufacturing organisations, concerned with sales; ancillary services like advertising, consultancy and operations research; non-profit organisations like trades unions, higher education research and professional organisations; journalism and broadcasting. The new functions colonised new areas; especially parts of the West End, which changed within a few decades from the home of the rich to office quarters, as deserted at night as the City. This was a change paralleled in other cities, for in the same decades offices took over from residences in the *Grands Boulevards* of Paris and in the Midtown district of New York.

The growth of offices has brought problems, of which the most obvious is traffic congestion. But here caution is necessary. Londoners are fond of saying that London's traffic is grinding to a halt: they have been saying it for at least a century, and probably since the Middle Ages. Though traffic volumes in central London have increased, according to police censuses, three to ten times between 1904 and 1962, the evidence is that improvements in traffic control, and in the speed and flexibility of vehicles, have just kept pace. No major street works were undertaken in central London between the creation of Kingsway in 1900 to 1910 and that of the Hyde Park Boulevard in 1962; but the capacity of the existing streets was expanded enormously by increasingly complex systems of traffic-light control, waiting restrictions, parking meters—which by 1965 extended almost right across the central area—and one-way street systems. Nor is it necessarily true that conditions for pedestrians or the ordinary worker and traveller have deteriorated. Few now remember the horrors of noise and smell which were the inevitable accompaniment of horse-drawn traffic on cobbles or wooden paving. Nevertheless, in 1963 an offi-cially-sponsored report appeared with the revolutionary suggestion that in terms of civilised urban life, to keep pace was not enough. *Traffic in Towns*, the report of a working party under Professor Colin Buchanan, was published by the Ministry of Transport with govern-ment blessing in autumn 1963. The report's central argument was that it was possible to define an environmental standard for any street or street network—a standard in terms of noise, fumes, danger and inconvenience—and that this standard would then automatically de-termine the amount of traffic which could be allowed to pass through the system. Once given the standard and the existing system, the amount of traffic could be increased only by comprehensive recon-struction, which might well be costly; but if the community were unwilling to pay for this, it could achieve the same standard of en-vironment with the existing system by restricting traffic flow. The primary objective of urban traffic planning, according to the Buchanan philosophy, is no longer to carry maximum traffic flows, but to main-tain environmental standards and adapt traffic flows to the amount of investment that is possible.

For central London, the implications of this approach are radical. Here, it is clear that congestion and regulations have long kept traffic flows well below potential maximum. The London Traffic Survey found that during the morning peak period (8 to 10 a.m.) in 1962, only 12.6 per cent of entrants into the central area from homes in the survey area were using private transport. And only 8.1 per cent (70,000) were car drivers. The majority of the vehicles on central London streets on working days are carrying people rather than goods; but they represent commercial traffic, which can be displaced only with difficulty. A case study by the Buchanan group in part of the West End showed that the present road system, even with the costly improvements shortly to be carried through, would not hold all the essential traffic expected by the year 2010. Some of this traffic might be diverted out of working hours, by insisting that commercial vehicles loaded and unloaded at night; but this might not offer very substantial relief. If this is the case then acceptance of the Buchanan principles will mean very costly reconstruction. An economist, Chris-topher Foster, has calculated the total costs of the more ambitious types of alternative reconstruction in the report at £6,500 million for inner London alone. This compares with the projected urban motor-

The South East Study: main proposals. The British government planners have based their proposals on a prospective population increase of 3.5 million, of which 2.4 million represents natural increase inside the metropolitan area of England. Their strategy is to divert as much as possible of this growth more than 50 miles from London, by the creation of big new 'counter-magnets,' including three new cities.

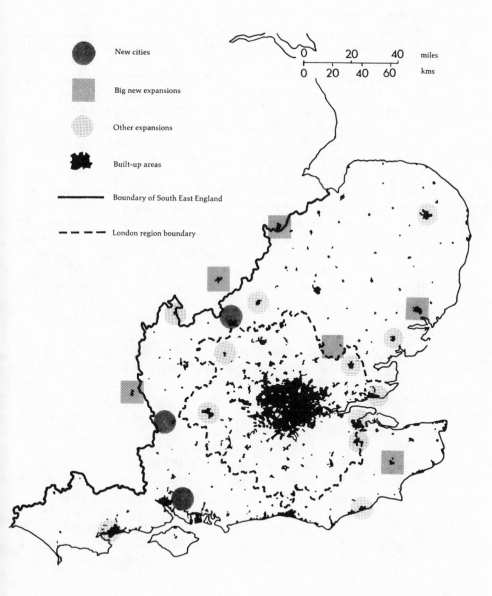

way network for inner London which is estimated to cost £450 million, and the current level of road expenditure in inner London which is only £100 million per decade.

The other critical effect of office growth is on the journey to work. Between 1951 and 1962, total arrivals in central London in the morning rush period (7 to 10 a.m.) rose by 157,000 to 1,238,000, and arrivals by British Railways trains alone into the central London termini increased by 97,000. Almost all of this latter increase represents long-distance commuting from beyond the Green Belt, that is from places more than 20 miles away. A reliable estimate was that the number of commuters to the centre from outside the conurbation, only 100,000 in 1951, had risen to about 200,000 by 1961. These long-distance commuters represent a new element in the social geography of London. Like their New York counterparts, they make relatively long journeys on express trains every morning, and then must transfer at the terminals to buses or tube trains which take them to their offices. Their journeys may take up to two hours each way and their fares are proportionately heavy. Already, their services are deteriorating because whole sectors of the outer suburban system have been overwhelmed by extra passengers and are working at beyond planned capacities. And fares are rising because of the increasingly uneconomic character of carrying heavy loads at peak hours. If money has to be found to provide extra capacity—which seems likely in the later 1960s—some or all of it will have to be collected from the commuters themselves; and the result will be increasingly expensive journeys for everyone.

East and West

Surrounding central London in a close-built, 5-mile-wide belt is the Inner Ring of the London Region. Together with the central area, it represents the physical growth of London before 1914, before electric railways allowed the suburbs to sprawl; and the two toegther are roughly coincident with an important administrative unit, the area of the Inner London Education Authority. The I.L.E.A. area of 117 square miles contained 3,200,484 people at the Census of 1961: 27,184 on average to the square mile, compared with only 8,235 to the square mile in the interwar suburbs just outside. But inner London is still built up to an extraordinarily low density by international urban standards. Its 27,184 to the square mile compares with 44,139 for Manhattan and Brooklyn (a bigger unit of 4,325,600 in inner New York) in 1960, or 73,152 in the *Ville de Paris* (population 2,970,091) in 1962. The difference stems from London's unique development since medieval times. As Steen Eiler Rasmussen points out in his book *London the Unique City*, London grew rapidly outside its medieval city walls, establishing a tradition of low-density suburbs for almost everyone, which has persisted ever since. London did not build apartment houses to accommodate its enormous nineteenth-century influx of population, as almost every other city of the world did; up to 1914 and in large areas up to the present day, the commercial core of London gives way immediately to separate houses with gardens, or at least small yards. Alike in the tiny, two-storey labourers' cottages of the East End, in the solid bourgeois houses occupied by city clerks and professional men in the streets and squares of Islington, and in the great stuccoed terraces of the rich in Kensington, this pattern persisted. It makes London, to this day, the airiest and least oppressive, and in summer the greenest, great city of the world.

Within Inner London, for centuries the classic distinction has been between east and west. In 1662 William Petty wrote that London was growing westwards to escape "the fumes, steams and stinks of the whole easterly pyle." The east, lying alongside the busy river port downstream from the city, was then already the home of London's poor, while the suburbs of the rich spread westwards and north-westwards from the court in Westminster. In the nineteenth century, the East End took in many of the poorest of the new arrivals in London, as an industrial revolution occurred in industries like clothing and furniture and as hundreds of thousands of Jewish immigrants fled here from persecutions and privations in eastern Europe between 1880 and 1910. In the late 1880s and early 1890s Charles Booth conducted the first large-scale modern social survey here: 12.45 per cent of East Enders were found to be "very poor," who "live in a state of chronic want," and another 22.79 per cent were "poor," "living under a struggle to obtain the necessaries of life and make both ends meet." In the years after Booth, conditions improved slowly. The population of the inner East End—the modern London borough of Tower Hamlets—fell from 597,000 in 1901 to 308,000 at the outbreak of the Second World War in 1939; then, evacuation and bomb destruction reduced the population still further to 231,000 in 1951. By 1961, the figure had fallen to 206,000—almost exactly one-third the level of sixty years earlier.

The bombing gave a unique chance for London to rebuild the East End; and London seized the chance. In the middle of the war, in 1943, appeared London's blueprint for reconstruction: the County of London Plan, prepared by the notable town planner Sir Patrick Abercrombie, in association with the planners of the old County of London which gave way to the Greater London Council in the reform of 1965. This Plan devoted much space to the problems of rebuilding bombed and blighted areas like the East End. Its analysis concluded that if the majority of East Enders were to be given housing suitable for family life, with houses and gardens on the traditional London pattern for the bigger families, then some people would have to move out of the area. Thus two important concepts were born, which have governed London planning ever since: the *net residential density* of 136 persons on each residential acre, which was to be applied to areas like the East End (and, in the event, to most of inner London), and the associated concept of *overspill* into new and expanded communities far from the congested redevelopment areas.

Working from this plan, even before the war ended, London took powers under a wartime act to combat "blitz and blight," to designate a huge area within the modern borough of Tower Hamlets as an area of comprehensive redevelopment, which meant that all reconstruction would be carried through according to a master plan prepared by the planning authority. By 1960 this area of nearly two square miles was still the biggest area of comprehensive development in Britain. The plan involved nothing less than the creation of a new town within the heavily built-up area of inner London, to hold close on 100,000 people —compared with over 100,000 in 1951 and over 200,000 in 1939. It is expected to be virtually finished by the late 1970s, and it has already been joined by two other schemes on the northern flank which will increase the total area under comprehensive reconstruction by nearly one-fifth as much again. The result on the ground, in the mid-1960s, is dramatic. Huge areas are in a state of travail. Bulldozers, cranes, steel frames and builders' fences dominate whole tracts of the East End. In other places are already finished neighbourhoods: here is a totally new world, dominated by the tall blocks of flats and by the lower terraces of three- and four-storey maisonettes, standing in spacious gardens and landscaped squares. Only a few yards away stand the reminders of the past: the long, squat rows of cottages inhabited by dock labourers or Jewish tailors. But they invariably already have the air of waiting for the demolition men.

The biggest comprehensive developments are concentrated east of the City: north of the river within the borough of Tower Hamlets, south of it in the Bermondsey area within the Borough of Southwark. These schemes were in large part conceived in the late wartime years of 1943 and 1944, to deal with the slum problems of the London of 1939. They are well on the way to completion; and, for the generation of planners of the 1960s, London's biggest housing problem lies in a different quarter. It is the west, home of London's rich; and paradoxically, the problem stems from that fact.

Though the landscape of inner London is almost everywhere still dominated by houses built for occupation by single families, these houses are very different in east and west. In the east, they are the small terraced cottages built in the 1840s and 1850s for the labourers who fled from the countryside into London's docks and industries; in Chelsea and Kensington and Paddington, they are the town houses of the rich and comfortable middle class of the mid-Victorian era, built on three or four floors above their basement kitchens. But progressively, as land values have risen, in inner London, after the First World War, and as the trek to more distant suburbs has taken place, the big houses of west London have been broken up into separate apartments or flats. Thus, in an area like North Kensington, middle-class houses have become working-class flats; they are occupied by people who drive buses or vans, or wait in restaurants and bars in central London and who have to live near their work. These people have been paying low rents for rather poorly equipped and poorly maintained property, and since rents were frozen as a result of two world wars, the maintenance has got worse and the property has deteriorated. In other areas, like Earls Court, houses have been fragmented into "bed-sitters" for students and secretaries without families, who can pay relatively high uncontrolled rents to be near their work in central London. As the growth of the central London economy has swollen the ranks of these people, so they have displaced others unless rent control provided a barrier. Now, as a result of partial decontrol of rents in 1957, many working-class families are finding themselves displaced. In some cases their homes pass to new immigrants, from the West Indies or other parts of the Commonwealth, who are willing to pay high rents because of colour discrimination elsewhere. Others pass, perhaps after a spell in the occupation of negro immigrants, to professional and executive workers who are willing to pay high prices to buy and re-convert them to one-family occupation. The process has made big profits for those who bought cheap and sold dear, and in summer 1963 evidence emerged that the West London property market had been unscrupulously exploited by speculators, who had used semi-criminal methods to eject statutory tenants and so free houses from rent control.

In 1963 the government appointed an official committee to investigate the problems of rented housing in London. But there is no simple answer to the problem of "multi-occupation" of former one-family houses in areas like west London. The local authorities have already been given considerable powers, under the Housing Acts of 1961 and 1963, to prevent mismanagement of rented housing. But a problem is bound to remain as long as population in London grows by natural increase and by rapid immigration; as long as coloured immigrants suffer prejudice and are so driven to offer high rents for cramped, insanitary accommodation; as long as London continues to attract disproportionate numbers of well-paid professional and executive workers who can afford high prices to buy houses near the centre. To build outwards is no necessary answer, for the pressure of people on space near the centre will remain; and no government could seriously contemplate the abandonment of the Green Belt policy. Yet to build higher and more densely in inner London is no necessary answer either: it will make at best a partial contribution because much of inner London does not need replacement; it will probably be more expensive, in real terms, than the present density standards for rebuilding; and as the housing authorities have stressed, it will almost certainly be less satisfactory for children. At bottom, the problem is not capable of solution; it may be relieved by giving people the maximum possible opportunity, incentive and help to move out of inner London, and even out of the crowded south east of England altogether.

The Interwar Suburbs

About five to seven miles from the centre of London, the outward-bound traveller passes, quite abruptly, from the more densely built inner ring to the suburbs built between 1918 and 1939. During the period 1921–39 the population of Greater London grew by about 1.2 million or 16.6 per cent; but the built-up area grew over three times. By 1939, the zone between about 5 and 12–15 miles from the centre was almost uniformly built up with housing at an average density of 12–14 to the acre. The new houses were not only more widely spaced than ever before; they were also built in much freer patterns, for it was everyone's ambition to own a house slightly different, in design or position, from his neighbour. The frequent corner shops of the old London were replaced by shopping parades, often built around the electric railway stations which took commuters into central London.

The interwar suburbs, in fact, were built on good communications— better than London had known before. Ironically, in the middle 1960s perhaps the chief problem they present is the problem of getting about. Between 1918 and 1939, the underground railways took their lines far into what was then open countryside, opening up the suburban ring to the commuter in areas like Hendon, Edgware, Wembley,

Harrow or Ruislip; south of the river, the Southern Railway electrified its suburban lines and built some new ones, with the same result. Underground or Southern suburban lines stretch, on average, some 15 miles from central London. They have frequent stops so that journeys—especially on the underground—are relatively slow. Because of considerable overloading on the inner stretches, again especially on the underground, they are also often rather uncomfortable. Those suburbanites who earn their living outside the centre—the majority, in most suburban areas—may travel by car, and many suburbanites travel exclusively by car in the evenings and at weekends; the London Traffic Survey shows that in most interwar suburbs at least 30 per cent, and in outer suburbs over 45 per cent of households owned cars in 1962. But here too, their journeys are far from smooth. The arterial roads which sweep through the suburbs are now thirty-five to forty years old, and are congealed with a volume of traffic for which they were never conceived. They are bad traffic carriers, with frequent sideroad access and frontage developments, including some major shopping centres. Already, in the middle 1960s, some are being relieved by new motorways (freeways), while others are being reconstructed as motorways. But it looks as if extensive improvements and new roads may be called for, on a much bigger scale, to deal with the traffic volumes expected in the 1970s.

Despite these disadvantages, it does not yet appear that the interwar developments are losing favour with commuters in competition with the newer suburbs farther from the centre, as may be happening in New York. Like the Bronx, many interwar suburbs of London are now experiencing slow population decline as their original inhabitants grow old and their children move away. The suburban zone as a whole has lost population since 1951. Many of the houses are already being bought by a second generation of occupants. These young people do not appear to find the houses of the suburbs obsolescent by the standards of the 1960s, possibly because fewer own cars than their New York counterparts, and even fewer own two cars. And to London suburbanites, the more distant suburbs appear less attractive because the Green Belt puts them so far away. So without any firm evidence, it would be wrong to suppose that the interwar suburbs will suffer rapid obsolescence. Pockets of older, smaller suburban housing, near to factory areas, may pass into the hands of coloured immigrants escaping from the overcrowded multi-occupied housing of the inner rings: a process observable in the immigration of Pakistani factory workers into Southall. But this will make relatively little impression on the suburbs as a whole. Overall, change is likely to be very gradual.

Green Belt and New Towns

London is the city of a thousand suburbs, but that perhaps is no longer the most remarkable fact about it. The unique thing is that the suburbs suddenly stop, to be replaced by open countryside. London's physical growth, some local rounding and infilling apart, has been stopped by the planners' edict at the point it happened to reach in the summer of 1939. The Green Belt has even grown. There is now the agreed Belt, about 5 miles wide, which still closely corresponds to the Belt shown in Abercrombie's Greater London Plan of 1944; around it there is a much wider penumbra, proposed by local authorities for inclusion in the Belt, but still to be approved by the central government.

In the period of rapid building in south east England since the mid-1950s, the Green Belt has been subject to intense commercial pressures; for the planner's decision to re-zone an area, from agriculture to housing, can put astronomical fortunes into private pockets. In the face of these pressures, successive governments have reiterated that the Belt is to be rigidly preserved. But in the government statement of February 1963, *London—Employment, Housing, Land*, and again in the *South East Study* of March 1964, the government admitted the principle that areas of doubtful agricultural or landscape value might be re-examined, to see if their inclusion in the Green Belt served any useful purpose. A frequently quoted example is the area of abandoned glasshouses in the horticultural district of the upper Lea Valley north east of London. The strong argument is that if land must be found for housing, it is preferable to take this sort of land than better land farther out.

This, though, is unlikely to make more than a marginal difference to the size and form of the Belt. The *South East Study* specifically rejects more radical solutions such as the replacement of the present belt by a series of green wedges running in less developed land between the main transport lines. Though this form is almost certainly preferable for a rapidly growing metropolis like London, the Study points out that London has been planned on the basis of a Green Belt for nearly twenty years and it is now almost impossible to change. But the Study does admit the force of the criticism that the function of the Belt needs re-thinking. The Scott Report on Rural Land Use in 1942, and the Abercrombie Greater London Plan of 1944, could not have anticipated the postwar explosion of population in Britain, and especially in the south east—or the threat of universal motorcar ownership by 1980. In wartime, and against the background of agricultural depression in the 1930s, it was natural that planners of 1942–4 should have been influenced by the need to preserve farming above all. But in the Britain of the 1960s, it is arguable that the needs of the city dweller should take first place, and his rights of access to the countryside should be greatly strengthened.

Strategically sited, at the outer edge of the original Abercrombie Green Belt or a few miles beyond, are the eight London New Towns, a complementary part of Abercrombie's grand strategy for London. Abercrombie proposed, and government and local planners accepted, that London should be developed at relatively low densities of population—136 to the residential acre over much of inner London, rising to 200 in a very small area at the centre but falling to 100 or less at the periphery of the Inner Ring. The inevitable consequence was a huge overspill population—1,033,000, in the calculation of the Greater London Plan—who must be re-housed elsewhere by public action, with perhaps another 250,000 moving privately of their own accord. A central feature of Abercrombie's plan was that these people should not be housed in outgrowths of the existing suburban sprawl; the Green Belt was to stop that. But as a complement to this restrictive policy, there was to be a positive programme of new, fully planned communities to receive the overspill beyond the Green Belt: the New Towns in the 20–35-mile ring, the expansions of existing small towns in the same ring and farther afield. Here people and jobs would move together, so that there would be no additional commuting problem.

The New Towns represent a uniquely English solution to a universal problem of metropolitan growth. They are communities of a finite size—generally 60,000 or less in the first conception, since increased to up to 100,000—built according to the English tradition at fairly low densities of fourteen to sixteen houses to the acre, with relatively few people housed in multi-storey blocks of flats. By the end of 1962 they had reached a combined population of 365,000, almost exactly two-thirds of the way to their final target population of 555,000. Because these targets allow for considerable natural growth after immigration ceases, there was room for only about 90,000 more Londoners in all the New Towns at that time. The Minister of Housing and Local Government was, however, asking two towns—Harlow in Essex and Stevenage in Hertfordshire—whether they could substantially increase their targets, from 80,000 each to 120–130,000 and 130–140,000 respectively; both Development Corporations later replied that this could be possible without detriment to the towns' structures, and the Minister has now formally proposed that the expansion of Stevenage take place.

The New Towns have on every criterion been a triumphant success.

They have proved phenomenally attractive magnets to industry, so that out-commuting has been kept to a minimum; their shopping centres, better adapted to the motor age than those of the older towns, have attracted shoppers from far afield; as examples of comprehensive and humanist planning they have attracted admiring visitors from all over the world. Yet curiously, their very success reflects a deeper failure of the Abercrombie policy. In his concept, they were instruments of a once-for-all planning operation—the removal of hundreds of thousands of Londoners from congested surroundings to new communities set among open countryside—within a London region which was no longer attracting jobs and people from outside. These postulates have not been fulfilled. Industry has grown rapidly in the New Towns partly as a reflection of the rapid growth in the south east as a whole; people, especially skilled workers, have come to the New Towns not only from London but from the rest of Britain; the rise in the birth rate is causing unexpected growth both in the New Towns and in London where it creates a new and a continuing overspill problem. Thus the problem of the growth of London, which the overspill policy was designed to solve once for all, has been exported to the New Towns and the ring of countryside within which they lie.

This belt—the Outer Ring of the London Region, between twenty and forty miles from Piccadilly Circus—has, however, witnessed even more radical and disquieting departures from the orderly planned development which Abercrombie foresaw. The ultimate effect of the Abercrombie Plan would have been to give this Ring a population of 4,224,000—1,166,000 above the level of 1938. Of this increase, all but about 250,000 would have been accommodated in fully planned communities. The postwar reality has been very different. By 1961, the New Towns programme was not nearly completed and the programme for planned town expansions—the other important instrument of Abercrombie policy for the Outer Ring—had hardly got under way at all. Yet the population had by then reached 4,284,000, or 60,000 above the "ultimate" Abercrombie level; and the increase of population in the decade 1951–61 had been 966,000, nearly 40 per cent of the net increase of the whole British population. The explanation lies of course in continued growth of population in the London region, both by natural increase and by migration, and in "spontaneous" migration into privately built houses, on a scale that Abercrombie never contemplated. Every one of the major towns in this ring—Reading, High Wycombe, Luton, Bishops Stortford, Chelmsford, the Medway towns, Maidstone, Guildford—has been ringed by a maze of new speculatively built estates in the 1950s. This is

London's new "commuter country," inhabited by people who make long journeys of thirty or forty miles to the London termini every morning. There is an important difference between these people and their New York counterparts. London's new commuters live in separate self-contained communities separated from each other by open land, because the Green Belt policy is being applied in practice around most of these towns. They also live at higher densities than the one-house one-acre American commuter, densities on average about the same as those in the interwar suburbs of London, but which the government planners are trying to raise still further in the future. London and New York commuters, however, suffer the same problems of the rising cost, discomfort and uncertain future of their commuter rail services; their children face the prospect that when their turn comes, the house they buy may be ten or twenty miles down the line.

So finally, this tour of the London region brings us round in full circle. The problem of the new commuter estates is also the problem of the centre. In London since 1945, the central set of problems has been the same as that of the decades before 1939: the continued growth of London, the dynamism of its economy, and in particular the attraction of the small area at the very centre for new jobs, especially the white-collar jobs which form an increasingly important part of the British economy.

People and Jobs in London: Past, Present and Future

The Abercrombie Plan of 1944 started from the simple and comfortable assumption that there would in future be no extra jobs and no extra people within the London Region. This belief, incredible in the 1960s, was not then entirely unreasonable. For one thing, the official forecast was that the population of Britain, 46.6 million in 1940, would be only 47.2 million by 1960; so plans could be made on the assumption of virtually no natural increase of population. (The actual 1961 population was 51.3 million.) For another thing, migration into London could also be discounted, because the Barlow Commission on the Distribution of the Industrial Population in 1940 had concluded that steps could, and should, be taken to control the establishment or extension of factory industry in the London area, thus stemming the inter-regional drift of population at source.

But after 1945 the planners were overtaken by two events. The population increased in every region because of a high (and, after 1955, a constantly increasing) birthrate. Between the 1951 and 1961 Censuses the population of the London Region rose by 801,000, but of this no less than 575,000 represented natural increase—the excess of births over deaths. In addition, the London Region continued to attract people from the rest of the country, to the extent of nearly a quarter of a million in the decade 1951–61. It was true that, as the Barlow Commission had recommended, an elaborate apparatus of control was established after 1945 to limit the growth of factory jobs in the London area. But this apparatus did not concern itself with shop and office jobs, which were the hard core of the London problem. Mr. A. G. Powell, a central government planning official, has estimated that, of the total increase of employment in the Greater London Conurbation in the 1950s, less than one-fifth was susceptible to the control mechanism for factory jobs set up after 1945. This was mainly because certain service jobs—retail trade, finance, and specialised professional and scientific services—were increasing rapidly in the national economy as a whole, but nowhere faster than in central London.

During the 1950s, though reliable figures do not exist, it is likely that total employment in the London Region increased by over 500,000 people—about one-third of the net national increase in Britain. Within the Region, the increases were distributed, very approximately, as in table 5.

Table I / London Region: employment growth 1951–61

Outer Ring	300,000
Suburban Ring	170,000
Inner Ring	—100,000
Central Area	150,000
London Region	520,000

Of the increases in the Outer and Suburban Rings, three-quarters were in factory industry and the other quarter mainly represented local service industries which are found anywhere, catering for the local population. Of the decline in the Inner Ring, perhaps half represented contraction in factory industry and another half a fall in service jobs, again mainly local in character. It is the growth in the Central Area that stands out as the real problem; almost all of it represents increases in office and retail jobs.

The continued strength of the London regional economy reflects structural trends in the British economy as a whole. Certain types of job—the services mentioned above, and manufacturing industries like electrical goods and vehicles—are increasing very rapidly. They have always been strongly concentrated in London and the South East, and it is very hard to break an established pattern of industrial location, because the existence of an industry in an area automatically tends to foster its further growth there. In addition, certain of these trades, especially the services, are extremely sensitive to the so-called "external economies" which stem from the close concentration of many firms in the same area. These economies tend to cause concentration of certain types of job not merely in the London Region, but in the very heart of central London.

For these reasons, it is not likely that the continued growth of jobs in the London Region will easily be stemmed. For the period 1961–81, the Technical Panel of the Standing Committee on London Regional Planning have estimated that the likely increases in employment, in very broad terms, may be as shown in table 6.

Table II / London Region: employment growth 1961–81

	1961–71 only	1961–81 total
Outer Ring	275,000	750,000
Suburban Ring	125,000	190,000
Inner Ring	25,000	40,000
Central Area	125,000	170,000
London Region	550,000	1,150,000

(Definitions here are slightly different from those given at the beginning of this chapter, but this does not significantly affect the overall picture.)

Of the total increase to 1981, about two-thirds—750,000—represents office employment, and virtually the whole of the increase in the Central Area, the Inner Ring and the Suburban Ring will be office jobs. Only in the Outer Ring will factory jobs make a substantial contribution—200,000 up to 1971 and in all 400,000 by 1981.

The big increases in the Outer Ring need not necessarily be regarded with alarm. They offer the hope that new jobs and new houses can be planned close together so as to minimise work journeys and traffic congestion. The increases in the Suburban Ring, and even more so those in the Central Area, are a different matter. For they must be seen against the prospect that the whole conurbation may suffer a decline in resident population, perhaps of 200,000, between 1961 and 1971. This may not happen because since 1958 the conurbation's population appears to have been roughly static. But if it did, the Standing Conference staff have calculated that commuting into central London from outside the conurbation—that is, from distances of over 15 miles—might rise by anything up to a theoretical maximum of 375,000 during the ten-year period up to 1971. British Railways reported in 1964 that by reworking their timetables and by spending about £100 million of investment money, they could cater for 450,000 extra commuters by 1981. With British Railways' working deficit running at £82 million in 1963, they are more than likely to pass the cost on to the commuters. And there remains the problem of distributing the commuters from the main-line terminals to the offices, which might involve heavy extra investment by London Transport.

The South East Study

The Ministry of Housing and Local Government's *South East Study*, published in March 1964, sets out a new strategy to deal with the problem of growth in the South East in general and in the London Region in particular. The existing growth trends are accepted as too powerful to stop; but they are to be modified by conscious planning, in two ways.

First, the total increase of population in the South East is to be kept below the level which would follow from mere projection of recent trends. The South East has attracted a higher relative rate of migration, from other parts of the country and from abroad, than other regions in the 1950s; if this differential is projected forward it gives a total of 1.4 million net immigration into the South East between 1961 and 1981. But the Study postulates that this can be cut to 1.1 million by energetic policies to secure economic growth in other regions of the country. This figure is then added to the natural increase of population within the South East—2.4 million in twenty years, which planning cannot be expected to prevent—to give a total projected population increase of 3.5 million within twenty years.

Secondly, within the South East, growth is to be diverted away from the London Region, and towards the fringe zone of South East England, between 40 and 110 miles out of central London. Table 7 shows that while in 1951–61, 63 per cent of the total increase of population in the South East occurred within 40 miles of Piccadilly Circus, it is tentatively hoped to cut this to 54 per cent during 1961–81.

Table III / South east England: population growth 1951–81

	1951–61		1961–81	
	annual increase millions per cent		estimated increase millions per cent	
South east England	1.3	100	3.5	100
London Region	0.8	63	1.9	54
Fringe Zone	0.5	37	1.6	46

This will be achieved by some of the largest and most imaginative planning proposals ever put forward by a modern democratic government. All are concentrated outside the London Region, most well outside. Three new cities are proposed: one in the Southampton–Portsmouth area, 80 miles south west of London, to take 250,000 people [here the existing cities already have big populations and the ultimate population of the area will be 1,150,000]; one in the Newbury area 50 miles west of London, to take 150,000; and one in the Bletchley district 50 miles north west of London, to take 150,000. A new town for 100,000 people is proposed next to London's third international airport, to be built thirty miles north east of London at Stansted in Essex. Many of the biggest towns of the "Fringe Zone" have been listed as candidates for drastic expansion: Ashford from 28,000 to 100,000, Ipswich from 120,000 to over 180,000, Northampton from 100,000 to 200,000, Peterborough from 60,000 to over 110,000, Swindon from 90,000 to 140–165,000. Smaller expansions are proposed for a dozen other towns, half of them outside the London Region. The net result will be that of the big increase of 1.6 millions projected for the "Fringe Zone," a majority—850,000—will be housed in fully planned, government-sponsored expansions.

But within the 40-mile radius of London, the London Planning Region, matters will be very different: here there must be no big government initiative which might make the area more attractive than it already is. So out of the total estimated increase of 1.9 millions, 1.4 millions will be housed through the normal workings of the land market; no further government New Towns will be started in addition to the eight existing ones, and most of the population increase will be housed, as in the 1950s, in outgrowths of the existing towns. The prospect of housing nearly 1.5 million extra people in this way, within twenty years in a ring only some 25 miles wide round London, is a daunting one; and it is a question whether the existing machinery of local planning authorities is capable of doing the job adequately.

The *South East Study* was widely attacked in the British press for accepting the pattern of growth in the South East as a *fait accompli*. This criticism is based on a fundamental misunderstanding of the strategy of the Study and diverts attention from what is perhaps a more telling point. Suppose the basic strategy did not succeed? It depends, after all, on the attempt to divert the growth of employment. Strong regional policies in other parts of Britain will reduce the rate of migration into the South East; strong policies within the South East will divert much migration, as well as overspill from the London Conurbation, out of the London Region altogether. These are the assumptions, and they are somewhat heroic ones. In the first place, migration into the South East may increase, as it did between 1959 and 1962; if the rate of those years were to be maintained, the prospect is an increase, not of 3.5 million but of 6 million. In the second place, the projections of employment indicate that most of the jobs to be diverted out of the London Region into the Fringe Zone will be office jobs. The *South East Study* recognises this fact, and suggests that some of the biggest expansion schemes may serve as "prestige office centres"; but it nowhere explains why it thinks offices in London should be inspired to migrate over such long distances, up to 80 miles from London, for the sake of "prestige." If the attempt to decentralise fails, then office employment will go up in the conurbation and even in the centre, whatever limitations are put on the development of new offices, and the commuter problem will get worse. The *South East Study* itself is relatively sanguine about the increase in long-distance commuting to the centre; it puts it as perhaps 200,000 up to 1971, against the theoretical maximum of 375,000 suggested by the Standing Conference planners. The real answer to the question of London's future, then, hinges on the economics of office location; and about that too little is still known, in Britain and elsewhere.

PLACE VILLA MARIE, MONTREAL, CANADA
An Underground City as an Approach to Severe Climate Problems

Montreal, where winter temperatures register lows of —30° and a season's accumulation of snow may reach ten feet, is the site of North America's largest underground downtown. As such, it offers a prototype for northern cities similarly afflicted by severe climatic conditions.

Background

The Canadian National Railways purchased the land in 1912 and began boring a tunnel through Mount Royal to provide access for its trains. In 1923 a terminal was built and the decision was made to develop the entire area of which the terminal was a part. Many plans to cover the massive railway cut were proposed and rejected over the years. The basic plan for the area hinged on two fundamental precepts: (1) that the development of the three blocks of CNR property was to proceed within the framework of a single master plan, and (2) that the plan was to provide for the needs of a growing metropolis.

A detailed study was conducted of pedestrian and vehicular traffic flows, office, retail and parking accommodation, and the inter-relationships of many facets of Montreal's downtown life. This resulted in "Master Plan, Ville Marie, Montreal" which was prepared by I. M. Pei & Associates. The initial construction contract was let in July, 1958 and excavation was begun on the site. Place Ville Marie was officially opened to the public in September, 1962 and all buildings were finally completed by the spring of 1969.

Features

Location—A 7-acre site in downtown Montreal

Owners of the land—The Royal Bank of Canada

Owners and Developers—Trizec Corporation Ltd.

Total Net Rentable Area—2,590,000 square feet

The Shopping Promenade—160,000 square feet

Parking—350,000 square feet (on two levels)

Number of storeys in buildings:
The Royal Bank of Canada—45
The IBM Building—14
The Esso Building—6
The Greenshields Building—6

Shops and Boutiques—more than 70

Restaurants—11, including one on the top of the Royal Bank

Cinemas—2

Theatre—1

Connections from Place Ville Marie:
Central Station of the CNR
International Aviation Building
Place Bonaventure
(Canada's largest merchandise mart)
Place du Canada and Chateau Champlain Hotel
Windsor Station on the Canadian Pacific Railways
Montreal and Canadian Stock Exchange Tower and underground shopping system of Place Victoria

All weather shopping area in downtown Montreal, a photograph of Underground Concorde, Place Ville Marie, Montreal.

Cruciform building marking Place Ville Marie, a photograph of the IBM
Building, Place Ville Marie, Montreal.

Photo credit: Arnott Rogers Batten, Ltd.

14. Land Reserves and Teamwork
in Planning Stockholm

SHIRLEY S. PASSOW

Sweden's municipal land reserves have long impressed American urban planners.[1] Thanks to the single-minded "spacemen" who accumulated the real estate inventory, some twenty new planned districts have come to life—at little or no tax bite for contemporary Stockholmers—on land acquired twenty, thirty, and even fifty years ago.[2] From 1904 to 1967, the city spent more than $110 million on approximately 134,000 acres of open and underutilized space.

What a painful contrast between those supplies of ready land—assembled, publicly owned and controlled, often amortized—and the site shortages that frustrate nearly all American metropolitan planners. Officials in New York City, for instance, rack their ingenuity to capture space. They explore the hidden potentials in "creative" (special) zoning, in air rights utilization, in bonuses for builders willing to produce such amenities as plazas, arcades, or legitimate theatres in Times Square office towers. As scarce land soars to $100 to $500 per square foot in choice central locations, city officials must dredge for government funds to write-down constructions costs of housing, public institutions, parks, and transportation. Too often, dislocation of established homes, groups, and businesses is the bitter trade-off for civic progress.

Swedish planners, meanwhile, are confident their plans will be carried out, producing transit links to the metropolis, high- and low-rise apartment blocks, shopping centers, office buildings, schools, hospital and health complexes, industrial estates, and recreation green belts. Underlying this assurance are several factors, including fiscal autonomy, but the chief element is the realty reserve. To Swedish

Shirley S. Passow, "Land Reserves and Teamwork in Planning Stockholm," in the *Journal of the American Institute of Planners*, Vol. XXXVI, No. 3 (May, 1970), pp. 179–188. Copyright 1970 by American Institute of Planners.

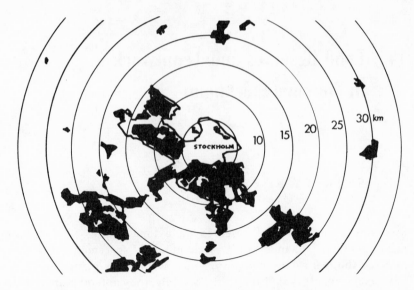

FIGURE 1   Stockholm's municipally owned real estate, both within and
beyond present city boundaries. Distances from the CBD are
shown by the five-kilometer concentric rings.

officials, public ownership of reserve land is so ordinary that even
their own publications treat the topic casually. However, within the
American context, these land reservoirs deserve a close look.[3]

History of Land Acquisition

Because Stockholm's records are so complete and her public officials
so accessible, most of this report focuses on Sweden's capital. Yet, the
land reserve story actually began in Gothenburg, Sweden's second
city, which in 1878 pioneered in purchasing municipal land reserves
and today is more active than ever in land acquisition.[4] The city
reports having spent $96 million for land between 1960 and 1967.[5]
This is nearly two million dollars more than Stockholm reports for
the same eight-year period.[6] However, since expenditures are not
itemized (contract price, administration, site preparation costs), it is
not fair to compare the two cities' outlays.

Land costs in Swedish cities are still low, by American standards.
An average construction budget for 1967 set land costs at a minimal
10 percent of total building costs.[7] However, land costs in the central
business districts of Sweden's three big cities (Malmö is the third)
have risen steadily. In areas adjacent to Stockholm's CBD, ground
rents ranged from $34 per square meter of floor area for housing to
$70 for office space to $200 per square meter for shop space.[8] Thus,

Table I / Selected Purchases and Development Dates, City of Stockholm

| | | | Development | |
| | | | --- | --- |
Location	Year	Hectares [a]	Purpose	Year
Traneberg	1904	28	Multifamily	1934
Farsta	1912	645	New Community	1950's
Hässelby	1931	973	New Community	1950's
Skärholmen	1945	110	New Community	1968
Varby	1931	1,020	New Community	1969

[a] One hectare = 2.4 acres.

Source: Stockholm's Statistics Office, *1964 Statistical Yearbook for Stockholm,* p. 225, Table 213, showing the municipal land acquisitions.

in the 1960's, pressures mounted to buy land in the outlying fringes.

Although two smaller cities, Malmö and Orebro, have also compiled outstanding records in land reservation, Stockholm is the best prototype. This is not only because of its accessible and complete records but also because the capital has had enough experience to yield stuning (if imprecise) returns on its investment in real property. With a touch of alchemy, the largest metropolis has turned farmland into the magnetic districts of Farsta, Vällingby, Skärholmen, and Bredäng, to name only four of some twenty self-contained new centers.

As a sample of the ripening process for municipal realty, Table 1 suggests the overall timing for Stockholm. Records dating from 1883 show Stockholm acquiring land for prompt development (not advance acquisition as a reserve) for water service, stone quarrying, sewerage, recreation, and health and welfare institutions.[9] Most of this land lay outside city boundaries; eventually, most of it was incorporated. In addition, the city bought, either through negotiation or by condemnation (processed in the city's so-called *expropriation* courts), large parcels within its limits. These were primarily for the tunnelbana lines and urban renewal areas. By 1966, Stockholm owned 74 percent of the ground within the city proper.[10]

The year 1904 is the landmark for the municipal reserve, because the city council voted then to purchase and save Enskede, a 1,500 acre estate in the parish of Brännkyrka. Publicly, advocates urged that the land be taken for outdoor recreation; privately, it was understood that an extensive housing estate for workingmen would be created as soon as possible.[11] When the supporters won, the municipal land reserve came into being.

One of the oddities about the new asset was that its godfather was a conservative aristocrat serving on the city council. Knut A. Wallen-

berg of the famous Enskilda Bank family persuaded the city fathers
that it made just as good sense for government as for business to plan
for growth. One knowledgeable observer believes that the city's chief
engineer greatly influenced Wallenberg.[12] Like other planners and
architects of turn-of-the-century Europe, the chief engineer had been
impressed by Ebenezer Howard's Garden City vision. As he tried to
cope with the influx of his fellow Swedes from the povery dried
hinterlands, he realized the city's housing shortage called for open
land—land in the surrounding region. The capital's population tripled
(up from about 140,000 to 420,000) between 1870 and 1920.[13] Mass
pressures of this type, plus the emerging socialism of the day and
Wallenberg's leadership combined to overcome opposition to investing
in land that would yield no immediate revenue.

There were many complaints: Enskede was too remote—five kilometers from the city center; the cost was wildly extravagant—two
million kronor, or $400,000 in unadjusted dollars. At current rates,
this would be roughly seven cents a square meter.[14] Today, Enskede
is a fifteen-minute ride on the subway from T-Central, the main
station on the tunnelbana line. It is a convenient location for thousands of modest owner-occupied, one-family "villas" and moderate
income apartments.

In 1904, shortly after purchasing Enskede, the city took title to
four tracts in Bromma commune. Adding the 3,152 acres there to
Enskede's 1,500 acres meant that Stockholm more than doubled its
size (4,000 acres as of 1903) in a year.[15] This spectacular start sub-
sided into an erratic pattern. During wars and depressions, few if any
purchases were recorded. Sometimes, under stress of economics or
politics, land was sold; at times the city was forced to buy back some
of these same parcels, but at higher prices. There were also land
swaps. In 1932, for example, Stockholm exchanged prestigious real
estate in Gärdet, the wooded area in the eastern sector of the city,
for a strip of land bordering Lake Mälar in its western sector. This
permitted the construction of Norr Mälarstrand, a major connector
road to Bromma and the other populous western suburbs that have
since grown up, including Vällingby and Hägersten.[16]

Typically, however, Stockholm held on to the land it bought and
created a leasehold system, the so-called "new tomträtt" law, which
plugged the loopholes in the nineteenth century system of token fee
payments. Its purpose was to retain title and control by the municipality, while freeing the land for use by citizens. The increment in
land values was, thus, to benefit the city and not merely the private
developer or owner. A major advantage was that leases helped the

city to regulate growth and design; they ensured the city of the land it wanted, when and where it was wanted.

The city council adopted new leasehold rules in 1907, approving sixty-year terms with no raise in rents. Parliament modified this in 1953 to enable cities to renegotiate fees every twenty years. In 1967, when the national body reduced rent renegotiations to ten-year intervals, Stockholm extended the lessee's rights by lengthening the lease term.[17] While a lessee can convey his lease to his heirs or others, the

Table II / Expenditures for Stockholm's Municipal Land Reserve
(Totals and Averages by Decades)[a]

Period	Total area of purchases (in hectares)	Total land expenditures[b] (000)	Average price per hectare[b]	Cumulative total land expenditures[b] (000)
1967–60	30,815	473,376	15,361.9	551,874
1959–50	1,719	13,748	7,997.7	78,498
1949–40	7,373	21,634	2,934.2	64,750
1939–30	5,815	19,937	3,428.5	43,116
1929–20	1,462	4,981	3,406.9	23,179
1919–10	2,341	7,342	3,136.3	18,198
1909–00	3,846	8,832	2,296.4	10,856
1899–1883[c]	4,273	2,024	473.7	2,024

Source: Stockholm municipal records. See note 9.
[a] All prices are current for the year of purchase and have not been corrected in terms of a base index.
[b] All values in this table are in Swedish kronor. One dollar equals five kronor.
[c] This period precedes establishment of the municipal land reserve. It is included for comparison.

property normally reverts to the municipality at the end of the term.

Aside from municipal purchases within city boundaries, Stockholm has generally bought suburban properties outside its limits. Some of these were thirty-five or more kilometers from the city center. (See Figure 1.) These extraterritorial properties were gradually incorporated, extending the city lines south, west, and southwest. In recent years, the northwest suburbs have attracted municipal agents, lying as they do along excellent suburban rail connections and with easy access to Arlanda Airport. Regional projections indicate major growth in this direction, with Stockholm and Uppsala (over sixty kilometers apart) tending to flow toward each other into a new metropolitan complex.

The Recent Land Boom

The 1960's were the great land-buying era in Stockholm's history. Records for 1960 to 1967 show that the city acquired 77,500 acres.[18] This eight-year tally is 21,500 acres more than all the real estate the city reports having bought during the preceding fifty-five years! From the birth of the municipal land "bank" in 1904, through 1959, the Stockholm Real Estate Board had acquired some 56,000 acres— or less than half the total reported, by January 1, 1968, of 133,500 acres. If the substantial accumulation of municipal land during 1968 and 1969 had been included in the study, the surge in muncipal title-closings for the 1960's would have been even more dramatic.

Directly correlated is the skyward profile of the municipal spending for land. (See Table 2.) From 1904 through 1959, under the aegis of the city Real Estate Board, Stockholm appropriated seventy-nine million kronor (about $16 million) for land. But in the last eight-year period studied (1960 to 1967), the city allocated nearly six times that amount for land: 473 million kronor (about $94.3 million). In short, of all the funds Stockholm had spent during the first sixty-three years of the land reserve, fully 85 percent were allocated during the last eight years of the study period.

What made the 1960's the great land-buying era for Stockholm? Political attitudes counted to some degree. Social Democrats have been consistently enthusiastic—while the Liberals (Folkparti) and Rightists (Högerparti) have been more ambivalent—about reserving land. Still, the power shifts of the century have not effected a clear impact on land policies. Rather, the swing factors appear to have been:

1. Passage of the 1967 tax on land-sales profits (*Realisationsvinst*).[19]

2. Implementation of the 1958 Regional Plan.

3. Creation and activation, late in the fifties, of STRADA, a municipal land-buying corporation.

The Capital Gains Tax   This was a one-shot catalyst for a flurry of land sales, which now have slowed down considerably. Historically and up to midnight of December 31, 1967, Sweden had sought to restrain speculation by exempting profits from sales of land held for ten or more years. But the *Realisationsvinst* levy removed this loophole by establishing a new schedule of taxes on capital gains, regardless of duration of possession. The tax was computed through a fairly complex formula which calculated profit, rates geared to duration of ownership, depreciation credits for improvements, cost-of-living index rates, and the like. When January 1, 1968 was set as the date for raising taxes on capital gains, property owners (especially long-time owners) flooded municipal real estate officials with land offerings. Stockholm, Gothenburg, and Malmö all benefited from owners' eagerness to dump their parcels before taxes guillotined their profits. Thus, the feverish land sale of 1967.[20]

The Regional Plan   In theory, a regional proposal should structure community planning decisions. This is what really happened in Greater Stockholm, a metropolitan network of forty-six member communities.[21] While the quasi-public Regional Planning Office was preparing base studies and preliminary projections for the 1958 Plan, Stockholm's municipal landbuyers were quietly assembling sites pinpointed for population and economic expansion. Before the regional plan surfaced publicly, the city had managed to purchase parcels at predevelopment price levels.

Could an American arm of government do the same? Or would the private sector exert pressures too great for public officials to counter? Here is one of the sensitive problems American supporters of land reserves must consider in any attempt to transpose Stockholm's success.

Underlying the municipal acquisition of land was the working relationship between local and regional staff and politicos. Both echelons interchanged their agency analyses and critiques of population, housing, transit routes, and employment clusters. Many elected municipal leaders served on the executive and operating committees of the regional body. Gradually, the communes began to share joint responsibilities for health, transportation, hospital, and other public facilities. The tradition of coalition among Sweden's parties facilitated these interactions. It permitted adjustment and rewriting at the working staff level, rather than the adversary debate on the political stage that we consider normal. Here is one example of how interagency criticism operates:

> Stockholm's reaction (not yet in) will be the most important. . . . We've gotten a look at a very big new study of Stockholm City and we're altering our projection to 2.5 millions instead of 2.2 by the year 2000. . . . I think we'll be making some compromises on development of land 'between the fingers' in the finger plan. Stockholm favors this and is powerful enough to carry the day.[22]

The benefits of plugging land purchases into a preliminary regional plan are manifest: the city can assemble large sites to meet its planning goals, can attempt to outflank realty speculators, and can increase its inventory of reserve land.

The dangers of this tactic are more subtle: planners can misjudge and stockpile land whose value declines with time. Growth may actually occur in an area that today's planners overlook. Yet, neither danger is so serious as failure to save any land for future city expansion. Tensions from competing citizen groups, pressures on obsolete and wornout public facilities, frustrations of thinly stretched municipal budgets—all these testify to the real cost of neglecting to provide land for tomorrow's generations.

Besides predicting metropolitan growth, Stockholm's Regional Plan Office guides land acquisitions by passing judgment on certain transactions. At the request of a county board, the regional body will indicate whether, for example, a developer's bid for farmland may conflict with the regional projection for green-belt conservation areas.[23] Though the regional office serves only in an advisory capacity, it generally influences the county board's decision.

The tri-level structure of the regional group is somewhat academic, because years of regional cooperation have brought the forty-six communities to the verge of metropolitan government. In September 1970, according to parliamentary directive, the constituent members of the regional planning group will elect 149 delegates to the first official metropolitan agency, the Greater Stockholm Council.[24] The metropolitan council, which becomes operative January 1, 1971, replaces the present eighty-five member assembly and its executive board (nine members and nine deputies appointed by the assembly). Its initial powers will be extensive: taxation of individual and corporate income; jurisdiction over transportation, schools, hospitals, and, to an undetermined degree, land acquisition and development.[25] Although the existing county council has some of these powers now, the creation of Stor Stockholmslandsting is a step toward major amalgamation of nearly four dozen small local governments—a nationwide process that Parliament has been encouraging in recent years. Planning for regional government has gone on for several years under the auspices of KSL, the Communal Council for Stockholm City and Council. Members of KSL include staff and elected officials of the region's towns.

One of the fascinating, unresolved issues is the whole scope of land policy: how will the emergence of the Greater Stockholm Council affect local control of land-buying, planning, developing? The answer is not yet predictable.

Closed Door Planning or Community Control

American planners, resigned to the goldfish bowl that is American government, are struck by the privacy that insulates Swedish planners.

For three reasons, government employees (planners, real estate agents, administrators, even elected representatives) enjoy a seclusion that is virtually unattainable in the United States:

1. As noted above, Swedish law reserves a planning monopoly for local government, with confidentiality built into the process.

2. There are no public hearings on pending matters. Instead, a proposed plan debuts through the so-called *Remiss* system, which circulates copies of preliminary drafts to selected organizations, individuals, and public libraries. Citizens are invited to comment by letter, or possibly by a visit to the office of the proper authorities. Citizen participation in American terms—especially open discussion and cross-questions in open meetings—is rare. So rare, indeed, it raises questions about the interpretations of democracy in Sweden and the U.S.[26]

3. The use of "straws" or decoy agents to buy land for the city has been mentioned earlier. Before purchase contracts are finalized, they are aired before the city council, which must approve major projcts and appropriations for land acquisition. However, legislative approval is almost ensured by backstage committees, including both elected and appointed policymakers. Land matters are the province of Fastighetsnämnd, the real estate board, a seven-member coalition drawn from all parties represented on the city council.[27] If the dominant members of the board, the commissioners of finance and real estate, approve a project, passage by the council is routine.

Naturally, Stockholm's penchant for privacy has its critics. Private developers resent government's competition in the realty market.[28] Suburban officials report their surprise at discovering that somehow Stockholm has become a new landlord of properties within the suburb's boundaries.[29] The moment of truth is often when Stockholm's representatives apply to the local building committee for a construction permit. However, as one suburban councilman explained wryly,

> It's true that a community through its *planmonopol* can control standards and theoretically could disapprove a plan. But they seldom do. Stockholm can promise or withhold various favors and thus force communities to cooperate, even if a development threatens the milieu of the locality. Vallentuna would like to keep its present 50–50 ratio of apartments and villas. But the Regional Plan wants to increase this figure to 70 percent apartments and only 30 percent villas.[30]

Two strong bargaining points enable Stockholm to overcome the small town's potential objections: first, residents pay income tax to the commune (town) in which they reside. Thus, the prospect of new revenue generally counterbalances fears of changing the character of the town—a familiar refrain in Sweden as in America. Second, Stockholm can extend, or delay extending, mass transit service to the affected suburb. And, finally, outside pressure for the commune to accept Stockholm's proposal to build apartments rises out of Sweden's oppressive backlog of housing applications. Postwar construction, at one of the highest rates in the world in 1968 (about twelve per thousand), has not been equal to the task of shrinking the ten-year waiting lists for housing.[31] The national government establishes annual, regional housing quotas, which are then filtered down to local building committees. Between the planning monopoly and the construction quotas, these local committees exercise power considerably beyond their American counterparts.

STRADA   This municipal land-buying company is the most effective tool Stockholm has shaped to give form to the city's faith in public ownership of land. Official Stockholm believes that ownership is the key to success in planning; that it enables the city to at least partially restrain price speculation; and that it channels increments in land value into the municipal treasury. When, in 1954, the council transformed a small building company into the prime agency for land acquisition, Stockholm's real estate inventory soared. The figures from 1904 through 1959, when contrasted with purchase and expenditures for 1960 to 1967, are the keenest evaluation of STRADA. As noted above, Stockholm bought 35 percent more land in those eight years than in the preceding fifty-five years; at the same time, the capital allocated was almost six times as much in the 1960's as during the previous half century. The agency's official summary of purchases and financial outlays leaves no doubt that the rate of land-buying rocketed when STRADA supplanted the real estate department as primary land-buyer.[32]

One point should be stressed: except for land acquisition, the real estate board dominates land policy and development. Its five major responsibilities are far-reaching:[33]

1. Approving land prices proposed by the staff of the real estate division, in accordance with national government guidelines. These must be ratified by the city council.

2. Coordinating national housing quotas for Stockholm.

3. Approving builders for long-range projects.

4. Supervising preparation of raw land for construction, including installation of streets and utilities by the city's roads division or by private contractors.

5. Securing financing for real estate purchases and related costs. The financial arrangements must be approved by the city's central finance commission.

Why then was the new agency formed?

Early in the fifties, Seth Höglund, Social Democratic Commissioner of Finance, persuaded the council to create STRADA as a stock company with a capitalization of between $20,000 and $60,000. Its charter bestowed autonomy designed to bypass bureaucratic webs. In the words of a descriptive memo,

> The main reason for the creation of a special purchasing company was that the City wanted to provide opportunities for rapid acquisitions in order to strengthen the municipal ability to compete with private buyers. Another reason was that, contrary to a public authority, a company must not make public the deliberations and statements that have been made before and acquisition takes place.[34]

The paper corporation was staffed and launched by Stockholm's present Commissioner of Real Estate, Hjalmar Mehr. Its policies are evolved by a prestige board whose members rank high in official Stockholm—a combination of political, legislative, technical, and administrative leaders. Interestingly, the finance and real estate commissioners are elected members of the city council; salaried, full-time heads of administrative staffs; and liaison officers with the technical staffs in their areas. The city corporation counsel, the managing director, and the two vice-managing directors of STRADA also serve on the board.[35] Since these experts represent the several parties in the city government, the feat of winning agreement on planning seems all the more impressive.

Dedication to municipal pursuit of real estate is the fuel that powers STRADA. The best symbol of it is probably Commissioner Mehr, who speaks of his assignment in these terms:

> Greater Stockholm is increasing by 25,000 people per year, one-quarter of a million per decade. By 2000 the prognosis is for 2.25 million to 2.5 million people. The census warns that space is needed for one-half to one million more in the next 35 years.

> Thus, we buy earth. That's one of the biggest political tricks that's been done. We don't say what and where. We talk about recreation uses and we've bought land at recreation prices.[36]

While this enthusiasm for real estate is not universal, neither is it partisan. An important Liberal figure, City Councilman Nils Hallerby, serving in 1968 as Commissioner for Greater Stockholm and (there-

fore) one of the architects of metropolitan government, revealed attitudes that paralleled the Social Democrats':

> We bought last year Brandalsund, below Södertälje, a large, beautifully
> situated farm on the Baltic Sea. Some people opposed this because it is
> too far from the city and wouldn't be suitable for building. For instance,
> the Center Party (the old Agrarian Party) opposed it on financial grounds.
> But we said we need it now for recreation. In fact, in the regional plan we
> recognize the need for a new road to replace the E4. Should this occur,
> we could foresee a new industrial center at Brandalsund.[37]

By now, the habit of thinking regionally probably outweights political ideology in the matter of advance land acquisition. Cost and
distance arguments against this or that parcel mean even less today
than they did against Enskede sixty-five years ago. Stockholm's
affluence and superior mass transit readily demolish these arguments.
However, some American planners lift their eyebrows at the readiness
with which Swedish officials justify a land acquisition in terms of
recreational needs, and then blandly shift the land use to industry or
housing, when the time is ripe. Considering the sacrosanct quality of
parkland in our own cities, there seems to be something faintly
evasive about this tactic. A closer look shows that the Swedes are
not outraging their customary standard of high public integrity in
this matter. Sweden, a lightly populated nation (eight million scattered
over 411,000 square kilometer),[38] is so respectful of her natural resources that vast tracts both in or near the cities, as well as a thousand
miles north of Stockholm, have been reserved through public ownership for public use. Thus, when a relatively small fraction of the land
inventory is converted to urbanization, for recognized public purposes
(as Sweden's courts interpret them), the voters generally acquiesce.

Medieval Genesis of Public Land Ownership

What, besides the rationalism that is a national trait, underlies
Swedish endorsement of municipal land ownership?

Any analysis should begin with the medieval tradition of crown
lands. King and Church were the chief landlords in sixteenth century
Sweden; for that matter, they still are. But in 1530, as part of the
Reformation, Gustav I Vasa seized vast church holdings and donated
them to the budding towns for common pasturage or other public
uses. Forbidden to sell off "the King's lands," towns evolved a system
of leasing, the so-called Old Tomträtt. To this day, crown land cannot
be sold, but must be leased or swapped for equivalent sites to meet
city planning goals.[39] The largest beneficiaries of royal donations were

Stockholm, Uppsala, Malmö, and Orebro. By royal decree, Gothenburg was established as a large crown town in 1619.[40] Swedes still feel free to walk across property—even the backyard of somebody's home—because of the embracing concept of the King's land.

Before leases were recognized as a source of valuable revenue for the city, they represented the ultimate royal title to real property. Thus, the supremacy of public ownership of land was built into a society that in other areas holds surprisingly fast to private ownership rights.

Stockholm bolsters her land reserves with more than tradition, planning rationalism, and laws: tax autonomy has given her fiscal independence and prosperity. The city council needs no higher approval to set the annual rate of income tax. In 1968, this percentage, applied equally to individuals and corporations, was 17.5 percent, a 3 percent rise over the 1964 rate.[41] At this rate (among the lowest in Sweden), the tax yielded about half the municipal revenues for 1968. The municipal income tax supplements the national income tax. The central government acts as the sole collection agency for all taxes, which it then recycles back to the municipalities in predetermined shares.

There is a ceiling on income tax: 80 percent, when income is more than one million kronor.[42] Swedes grumble, but there are no signs of a taxpayers' revolt. If anything, the recent resounding victories for the Social Democrats indicate public approval of the government's management of revenue, resources, and policies.

For land acquisition, Stockholm taps four major sources:

1. *Municipal revenues* including income tax, earnings from municipally owned corporations, rents and leasehold fees from publicly owned housing and other properties, and state grants.

2. *National government loans,* primarily from the giant National Pension Insurance Fund (Allmänna Pensionsfonden), which was projected at $7.4 billions by 1970.[43] Also, two infant loan funds to stimulate towns to acquire and reserve land were created by Parliament in 1965 and 1967.

3. *Bank loans* on the open market, most often from Kommunkredit AB, the municipal lending arm of Sparbankernas Bank AB, the central bank for the country's 350 savings banks.[44]

4. *Long-term bonds* issued with permission and under debt limitations of the National Bank of Sweden.

In a breakdown of fiscal support systems, Commissioner Mehr allocates the follow roles: an average of one-third of the funds for land-buying in 1968 came from bank loans, amortized on an annual schedule; one-third derived from municipal cash revenues; and one-third constituted debt paper. The latter consists of bonds or promissory notes (*revers*), repayable to banks such as Kommunkredit AB in annual installments over five to fifteen years.[45] Stockholm borrowed about 40 million kronor ($8 million) for "prepared ground" in 1967.[46]

Thanks to fiscal autonomy, Swedish cities can project realistic budgets. Their five-year investment budgets, which include reserve land, are partnered with annual review and amendment. Since the 1950's, Stockholm has cooperated with national officials in these annual budget reevaluations.

Has Public Ownership Captured Land Increments?

An important question at this point concerns the extent to which rising land values have accrued to Stockholm through public ownership of reserve real estate. Unfortunately, to answer this question fully would take a complete economic analysis, beginning with an effort to clarify empirical data documenting land value. But some clues exist. It is possible—by comparing original purchase prices with present-day costs of land in certain areas—to show that Stockholm bought many land bargains. As one example, the capital took title to Varby in 1931, an expanse of 2,550 acres lying twelve kilometers southwest of the city center and just outside the city limits.[47] At a cost roughly one cent per square meter, the entire property carried a price tag of $120,000. (This is an unadjusted price based on the present exchange rate of five kronor to one dollar.) Late in the sixties, when Stockholm began to develop Varby, a certain 9.6-acre tract was needed. The price for this small tract in 1967 was $47,000—or 39 percent of the price paid for the original 2,550 acres.[48] Obviously, land values have soared in the Greater Stockholm region, though they still do not match American levels except perhaps in the CBD's of the biggest cities.

Real estate prices held relatively firm from 1930 through 1960.[49] The trend has been attributed to two factors: first, by buying large parcels cheaply, Stockholm effectively restrained prices in nearby areas; second, to qualify for government mortgage loans, public and private developers had to keep land prices within the established ceilings, figured as a percentage of construction costs. Stockholm virtually dictated prices for most new housing construction, 80 percent of which was in multi-family structures.[50] Considering that the city not only issues building permits but also helps enforce the national housing quota assigned to the region (20,000 units in 1968), it is obvious that builders will make every effort to conform to price ceilings.

From 1960 on, land prices began to move upwards. In a study of the Swedish real estate market in twelve counties (1957–1963), Carlegrim noted that the price index for land had risen from 100 in 1957 to 117 in 1963.[51] Though this was higher than the general price index for the same period, land prices were still low by American standards. Average prices in 1968 were pegged at six to nine kronor per square meter.[52] This would translate into $4,800 to $7,200 per acre—perhaps half the average for metropolitan real estate in American suburbs.

Bargains in real estate are a significant plus for Stockholm. It was noted above that many self-contained communities were constructed on long-held municipal land without necessitating a tax boost for contemporary Stockholmers. But critics point out one lost opportunity in this scene: by setting leasehold fees too low and freezing them, the city missed out on significant revenues. Long-term land leases in Applevik, for instance, one of the earliest developments on municipal real estate, are reportedly so cheap that some officials suspect sellers must be getting under-the-counter bonuses for the buildings on their plots.

Under the non-profit philosophy of Swedish government, Stockholm pegs its lease fees just high enough to amortize short-term loans that finance acquisition of raw land and its preparation, prior to leasing it. A breakdown of the leasehold fee (tomträtt avgeld) would show that 10 to 15 percent covers raw land costs, while 85 to 90 percent covers preparation costs.[53]

As the supply of developable land continues to shrink, prices and leasehold fees are expected to rise proportionately. Along with the vertical spurt in land-buying from 1960 on, Stockholm recorded a sudden rise in leaseholds granted. Industrial leases are written for indefinite terms, while housing leases extend for eighty years. The 1966 yield from housing (ground rents) was twenty-three million kronor, of which 4 percent constituted new leaseholds for that year.[54] The industrial section of the real estate department reports that acreage leased for industrial uses rose from just under 180 acres in 1960 to 420 acres in 1967, showing a 230 percent increase. Revenue shot up from more than $600,000 in 1960 to $2,000,000 in 1967, a 233 percent gain from industrial fees in only seven years.[55]

What is land value? How can government manipulate it—assuming it should? To these basic problems the answers are tentative. Milgram suggests the scope of work to be done before flat judgments can be offered on land value:

One of the surprising gaps in economic knowledge is the absence of a well-developed body of theory and inventory of empirical data relating to urban land . . . when the effort is made to quantify the rate at which land is used, to determine the relative strength of various factors in promoting or retarding the amount of land which is moved from rural to urban use and the associated effects on land prices . . . the meager body of theory provides little guidance and empirical data are rarely obtainable in any readily accessible form.[56]

Transferability of Sweden's Experience

Finally, is there anything in the Swedish experience that speaks to American urban problems? No report on European achievements—especially Sweden's—is immune from the charge: "That's all right for a small homogeneous country, but it wouldn't work here." No thoughtful person suggests that ideas can cross national boundaries without undergoing some changes, but if advance land acquisition is basically valuable, then American planners, leigslators, and politicians might consider a serious effort to design land reservoirs to serve our cities.

If a study commission were appointed to evaluate and conquer the obstacles to municipal land reservation, what would it face?

1. *The imminent bankruptcy* that threatens most large American cities today. Without state and federal subsidies, cities cannot now meet their citizens' needs for housing, accessible jobs, clean transportation, waste removal, recreation, and the like. Tax reform is probably the key to the revenues that will rescue cities from their fiscal quagmires. Tax autonomy for city government is one missing piece of the puzzle. Other sources, such as municipal lease fees, should be explored to estimate potential yield.

2. *Tied-up capital.* Investing in land to be held for future development means sinking capital without immediate returns. For this reason, most cities (in Sweden as well as elsewhere) have been reluctant to follow the example of Stockholm, Gothenburg, Malmö and Orebro. Yet, here, the Swedish practice seems transferable: initially, land should be bought through borrowing (within debt limits, groaning though they are). Perhaps the two billion dollar life insurance fund would seed the early municipal programs. Commercial bank loans, underwritten by the government, could be a second source. Federal and state loans and grants could usefully stimulate municipal land reservoirs. Burgeoning municipal employee pension funds are untapped. Eventually, cities should allocate capital investment budget funds for reserve realty. Through lease-

holds, funds for repaying these loans could be gathered. Leasing would also permit interim use of the land, for selected activities, until the city is ready to contract for new housing enclaves, coordinated communities, or whatever its future population requires.

3. *The public purpose test.* When a municipality contemplates taking property through eminent domain, it must prove a public purpose.[57] Would the courts treat condemnation of property to be set aside as a municipal land reserve as a public purpose? The question is urgent since open space is generally a mirage in New York City and other agglomerations. The courts have broadened their construction of "public purpose" since the urban renewal era, but what are the legal precedents? A recent study for the Douglas Commission series reviews the legal bases for advance land acquisition in the United States.[58] Its summary of case law could guide those who want to clear away litigative barriers.

4. *Extraterritoriality.* There is plenty of open land outside city limits, in the hinterlands of suburbia. Could cities buy and contract with developers to build housing outside their jurisdictional lines? The law on extraterritoriality is complex. Will suburbs consent to negotiate with city governments on such housing proposals? One can hear the muted howls. Could cities offer bonuses to cooperative suburbs? Or, if resistance mounts, might state legislatures produce interstate compacts creating regional land boards, empowered like the awesome young Urban Development Corporation of New York state to acquire land and to develop it outside the restraints of local ordinances? The perils of such direct action are evident. But the alternative—the blistering rage of central city populations, now fully awake to their condition—requires from public officials something more than timidity toward suburban exclusionary devices.

The focus in any consideration of public land reserves must be the realization that these are not luxuries. They are a first step toward breathing space for metropolitan citizens. From the public viewpoint, advance land acquisition is the essential key to public implementation of planning.

The time of uncontrolled privatism, which has submerged public beneath personal goals, should yield now to the public imperative. In this stage, municipal ownership of reserve land will be the foundation of realty planning. The inherent promise for effective municipal planning more than justifies whatever legal and administrative innovation is needed.

NOTES

[1] Myres S. McDougal and David Haber, "Public Ownership as an Instrument of Planning and Development Policies," in *Property, Wealth, Land*, p. 896.

For a more recent view, see, Hans Calmfors, Francine F. Rabinovitz, and Daniel J. Alesch, *Urban Government for Greater Stockholm* (New York: The International Urban Studies of the Institute of Public Administration, Frederick A. Praeger, 1968).

[2] Yngve Larsson, "Building a City and a Metropolis: The Planned Development of Stockholm." *Journal of the American Institute of Planners*, XXVIII, No. 4, (November 1962), 220–8.

[3] The data in this article are (for the most part) drawn from my unpublished Master's thesis, "Municipal Land Reserves in Sweden: Key to Planning Success," Columbia University, New York City, May 1969.

[4] Memorandum dated May 3, 1968, from C. F. Bissmarck, Director of Gothenburg's Real Estate Division. For its translation, I am indebted to Miss Eva Hamrin, a consultant planner of Stockholm.

[5] *Ibid*. Gothenburg actually reported 481.4 million kronor. Five kronor equalled one American dollar in 1968 values.

[6] In Swedish terms, 473.4 million kronor. See Table 2.

[7] Memo from Carl-Olof Abelson, Managing Director, Stadsbyggnadbyran AB, Stockholm, February 1968. The organization is a consulting body composed of private builders, bankers, and other businessmen.

[8] Letter dated February 1, 1967 from Ake Pahlman, Director, Housing-Land Acquisition Division, Stockholm Real Estate Board.

[9] This statement, as well as figures in Table 2, were drawn from Table 213, *1964 Statistical Yearbook for Stockholm*, p. 225, Stockholm's Statistics Office.

[10] Letter of January 12, 1968 from J. H. Martin, Supervisor of Industrial Land, Stockholm Real Estate Board.

[11] Sweden's attitude toward assigning new uses to park land or open space is markedly different from the American counterpart. This may well be due to the overall stewardship by the Swedes of their outstanding natural resources. A body of law, such as the 1964 Naturvardslag passed by Parliament, ensures conservation of the shoreline and of vast areas adjacent to the archipelago, lakes, and seas that account for so much beauty in Sweden. Thus, when property is removed from the reserve and developed as a new urban area, little hostility appears to be generated toward public officials.

[12] Yngve Larsson, elder statesman and planner, who served in Stockholm's city government for forty years. He was interviewed in his office in the Municipal Archives—where, at 80-plus, he was finishing the second volume of his political history of Stockholm—on December 12, 1967.

[13] Municipal data are from *The 1966 Outline Regional Plan of the Stockholm Area*, issued by the Stockholm Regional Planning Office (Stockholm: N. O. Mauritzons Boktryckeri AB, 1968), p. 5.

[14] Table 213 in *1964 Statistical Yearbook for Stockholm.*

[15] Stockholm Real Estate Department, "Land Acquisition and Leasehold System in Stockholm," December 1967, p. 1. (Mimeographed.)

[16] Larsson, personal interview.

[17] Interview with Curt Berg, Supervisor of Housing Land, Stockholm Real Estate Board, at his office, May 3, 1968.

[18] Sweden measures land in hectares. One hectare equals 2.4 acres. For easier comparisons, I have translated the hectare figures in Table 2 into the American acre. As for figures covering 1904 to 1959, I computed these from the data in Table 213. See note 9.

[19] Text of the law appears in *Svensk Författningssamling,* Law 1967, Nos. 748–755. In an interview April 29, 1968, C. O. Sandström, division head in the National Finance Department, estimated that average annual revenue from the tax would be about 80 million kronor ($16 millions).

[20] A journalist, Nils Andersson, summarized the national scene in an article, "Dramatic Billion-Kronor Business," in *Arbetet,* Malmö, February 4, 1968, p. 8.

[21] Sven Jönsson, Vice-Managing Director of STRADA, interview, February 21, 1968.

[22] Interview with Josef Stäck, Assistant to the Director, Stockholm Regional Planning Office, May 8, 1968. After six months or so of reviewing the regional proposal, the staff of Stockholm's planning, real estate, and other departments held a two-day meeting in May 1968, to determine policy toward the plan. Curt Berg (See note 17.) says a report of the meeting was then forwarded to the regional office.

[23] *Ibid.*

[24] Storlandstingskommittén (Greater Stockholm Council Committee), *Storlandstinget* (Stockholm: N. O. Mauritzons Boktrckeri AB, January 1, 1968), describes the committee program for creating the metropolitan council.

[25] Interview with City Councilman Nils Hallerby in his office in Stockholm City Hall, June 7, 1968. As Commissioner for Greater Stockholm, Hallerby served on various committees of the Regional Planning Office and helped design Storlandstinget.

[26] For a dissection of one such episode, see Professor Thomas Anton's case study, "Politics and Planning in a Swedish Suburb," *Journal of the American Institute of Planners,* XXXV, No. 4. (July 1969), 253, ff.

[27] Berg, personal interview.

[28] Sten Källenius, Managing Director of Svenska Byggnadsentreprenörföreningen (Swedish Association of Builders and Contractors), spoke to this view point during an interview in February 1968.

[29] Professor Erik Carlegrim, Economics Department, Tekniska Högskola, Stockholm, views the problem from two viewpoints: as a member of the Vallentuna town council, a suburban group that resented the urban impact on their area when Stockholm moved in, and as a consultant to numerous government investigating commissions studying land policies. Interviewed in September 1967.

[30] Ivan Lidskog, member of both the local counsil in Vallentuna (*kommunalfullmäktige*) and the Stockholm County Council. Interview in Professor Carlegrim's office, Stockholm, October 1967.

[31] Interview February 1968 with Arne Carlsson, housing expert in the Department of Domestic Affairs (Inrikesdepartementet).

[32] AB STRADA, "Egendomar, förvarvade av staden genom AB Strada fr. o. m. dec. 1967," ("Properties acquired by the city through AB Strada from and including 1959 to and including December 1967,"), Stockholm, January 2, 1968. (Mimeographed.) Actually, no acquisitions were shown for 1959 or 1960.

[33] Berg, personal interview.

[34] Stockholm Real Estate Department, Public Information section, "Some Facts about Strada," Stockholm, December 1967, p. 1. (Mimeographed.)

[35] Jönsson, personal interview.

[36] Councilman-Commissioner Mehr was interviewed in his City Hall office April 23, 1968.

[37] Hallerby, personal interview.

[38] *Statistisk Arsbok 1967 (Statistical Yearbook of Sweden, 1967)*, Table 9, "Population, Area, Density of Population in Stockholm (City and County) and other Major Counties, January 1, 1965 and 1966." The kilometers are the equivalent of 173,000 square miles, with a population density of forty-six persons per square mile.

[39] Stadsjurist Erik G. Westman, Corporation Counsel of Stockholm, cites 1789 as the year of the royal decree forbidding the sale of crown lands donated to the towns. Interviews with Westman at City Hall May 14 and 22, 1968.

[40] Lennart Améen develops the theory that the origins of land ownership set the pattern for urban development, in his book, *Stadsbebyggelse och domanstruktur (Urban Settlement and Domain Structure)* (Lund: C. W. K. Gleerup, 1964), p. 235.

[41] Calmfors, Rabinovitz, Alesch, *Urban Government for Greater Stockholm*, p. 50.

[42] Martin, letter of 29 July 1969.

[43] Borje Kragh, "Sweden's National Pension Insurance Fund," *The OECD Observer*, No. 33 (Paris: The Organisation for Economic Co-operation and Development, April 1968), p. 5.

[44] Ragnar Ivestedt, Director of Kommunkredit, interview at his office in Stockholm, May 13, 1968.

[45] *Ibid.*

[46] Letter dated 30th August 1968 from Mrs. Carin Lindén, Stockholm Real Estate Department, Public Information section.

[47] Table 213. See note 9.

[48] Mimeographed summary of city-owned properties shown on city's official map. Varby is number 90 on the city map.

[49] Berg interview. See note 21.

[50] *Ibid.*

[51] Carlegrim, *Fastighetsmarknad 1957–1963 (Real Estate Market 1957–1963)*, Report to the National Institute for Building Research, Report 10: 1966, Stockholm, p. 9.

[52] Jönsson, personal interview.

[53] Berg, personal interview.

[54] Letter from Mrs. Lindén. See note 46.

[55] Graph, "Total area and leasehold yield of industrial areas, yearly (1935–1980)," prepared by the Industrial Section, Stockholm Real Estate Board. No. F 357. From Martin—see note 10.

[56] Grace Milgram, *Land Prices in the United States 1945–1967*, A Study prepared for the National Commission on Urban Problems (New York: Institute of Urban Environment, Columbia University, June, 1968), p. 1.

[57] Eminent domain by the Swedish municipality is authorized by Paragraph 44 of the basic Law of Expropriation, 1917 laws of Sweden. A taking must be in accordance with defined public purposes.

[58] Fred P. Bosselman, *Alternatives to Urban Sprawl: Legal Guidelines for Governmental Action*. See, "Public Land Assembly," Chapter IV, page 41. National Commission on Urban Problems, Research Report No. 15, Washington, D.C., 1968.

15. Hawaii's Experience with Its State Land Use Law

SHELLEY M. MARK

Hawaii has been and continues to be a real laboratory in the development of state and local planning. It has firmly adopted a simplified governmental structure and divided up the functions of state and local government in a fairly efficient manner; it produced the nation's first statewide general plan in 1961; it has adopted state zoning for all public and private lands through the vehicle of land use districts; it has been using a statewide capital improvements program which includes all state agencies, as well as aid to counties; it has uniform statewide property assessment and tax collection; it developed a Planning-Programming-Budgeting mechanism as a guide to its biennial operating and capital budgets—an outgrowth of its General Plan Revision of 1967; and it has embarked strongly on statewide environmental planning.

We can expect that Hawaii will embark on other policy planning matters; these might include population stabilization (Hawaii gives its citizens freedom to choose contraception and abortion, with the state neutral in these delicate matters of conscience related to religion); redistribution of the population among the counties in accordance with a state urban growth policy-integration of social and economic planning policies, and completion of the first statewide open space plan.

During the preparation of Hawaii's State General Plan of 1961, certain land use issues were clarified. It became evident that:

1. Development of land for urban uses, in many cases, tended to

Shelley M. Mark, "Hawaii's Experience with Its State Land Use Law," in *State Planning Issues*, ed. by Richard H. Slavin and Robert M. Cornett (Lexington, Kentucky: The Council of State Planning Agencies and the Council of State Governments, 1971), pp. 44–47.

occur in areas where it was uneconomical for public agencies to provide proper and adequate service facilities; consequently, there was a lag in the provision of such facilities, to the detriment of the general welfare and convenience;

2. Development of land for urban uses, in many cases, occurred on the state's limited prime agricultural land, which has a greater capacity for contributing to the long-term basic economic stability of the state by remaining in agricultural use;

3. There was adequate land on all the islands of the state for full development of the urban uses forecast for the next 20 years without using lands with high capacity for intensive cultivation;

4. Development of urban areas should be encouraged in an orderly and relatively compact manner in order to provide for economy and efficiency in public services and utilities;

5. Land not required at any given time for urban or intensive agricultural uses should receive special attention regarding land management practices and use.

Subsequently, the 1961 legislature passed the Land Use Law establishing the State Land Use Commission, calling for classification of all lands in the state and authorizing the adoption of rules of practice and procedure, and regulations for land use within the various districts.

The law, as amended in 1963 by addition of the Rural District, and in 1965 to shorten petition processing time, provides for four districts: Urban, Rural, Agriculture and Conservation, to be determined by a nine-member Land Use Commission appointed by the Governor and confirmed by the Senate.

The law stipulates: "Irrespective of changes and adjustments that may have been made, the Commission shall make a comprehensive review of the classification and districting of all lands and of the regulations at the end of each five years following the adoption thereof."

The original District Boundaries, Rules of Practice and Procedure and State Land Use District Regulations were established in 1964. The first mandatory boundary review was completed in 1969; it reviewed all related facets of land use in Hawaii within the five-year time period.

Of the four districts provided, urban districts are generally defined as lands in urban use with sufficient reserve to accommodate foreseeable growth. Agriculture districts include land with a high capacity for intensive cultivation, with a minimum lot size of one acre. Conservation districts comprise primarily lands in the existing forest and water reserve zones. Rural districts are defined as lands composed primarily of small farms mixed with low density residential lots with a minimum lot size of one-half acre.

Land uses within urban districts are administered solely by the counties. In the agriculture and rural districts the Land Use Commission establishes the land use regulations, and the counties are responsible for their administration. In the conservation districts, land uses are administered solely by the State Department of Land and Natural Resources.

Once established, district boundaries can be changed by the Land Use Commission through a petition and public hearing process. The procedure includes a County Planning Commission recommendation, a public hearing and action by the Land Use Commission requiring six affirmative votes for approval. In agriculture and rural districts, certain uses are permitted without a change in district designation. Unusual and reasonable uses may be permitted through special permits requiring a public hearing and both county and Land Use Commission approval.

One of the intentions of the Law is that property tax assessments are meant to encourage the best use of land. The Land Use Commission informs the Department of Taxation of changes in district boundaries and special permits so that the department can give consideration to the existing and permitted uses of land in making its assessments.

During the 1970 session, the state legislature in another precedent-setting measure amended the Land Use Law to require the State Land Use Commission to establish, throughout the state, shoreline setback lines between twenty and forty feet from the shoreline. The shoreline —always difficult to find—is, the Law says, defined by "the upper reaches of the wash of waves, other than storm and tidal waves, usually evidenced by the edge of vegetation growth." County planning commissions were mandated to promulgate and enforce shoreline setback rules and regulations.

Additionally, the Land Use Commission was given the authority to impose additional restrictions on special permits in agriculture and rural districts. In its 1969 boundary review, the Commission also altered its rules and regulations with the intent of strengthening its hand in dealing with development proposals, particularly those of large scope and requiring many years for fruition. Under its revised rules, the Commission can approve a total scheme, in concept, grant initial rezoning to initiate the developmental process, and approve future rezoning on the basis of performance as represented by the developer and agreed upon by the Commission. The club it holds is in its power to down-zone any property if evidence is obtained that the development has not occurred within the time period indicated in the manner originally represented. This is believed to be the first comprehensive use of the down-zoning authority by a state or local body.

Perhaps the best measure of the efficacy of the Hawaiian land use law is in terms of its basic underlying legislative intent—namely, the attempt to preserve prime agricultural lands. The records show that from the time the Land Use Commission drew up its first district boundaries in 1964 up to the latter part of 1970, it received requests for more than 100,000 acres to be reclassified into the urban district, where economic valuations are obviously the highest. Of that 100,000 acres, only 30,000 acres were given urban classification by the Commission. Of the 30,000 acres reclassified into the urban district, only 3,500 acres were considered prime agricultural lands. And even these prime lands included two pockets in the midst of an already heavily urbanized area, while the remainder of the reclassified agricultural lands were devoted to immediate housing needs. There is also evidence that as a result of the state's strong land use law, its plantation management has been given incentive and assurance to plan for long-term stability and growth in agriculture operations. This, together with Hawaii's traditionally strong conservation interests, promises to preserve its greenery and scenery, and provide other benefits—new income from sugar production, a better urban-rural balance, green belts between and within communities, and a largely pollution-free Island environment.

However, this is not to underestimate or understate the formidable problems that remain in the way of full and effective implementation of the Land Use Law, nor does it obviate further changes in the Law itself. In the absence of a clearly articulated and widely acceptable population stabilization and distribution policy, state or local zoning powers represent rear-guard or holding actions at best. Planning boards or commissions throughout the country have no doubt found the most irresistible arguments put forth by developers or property owners to be the provision of new housing or the assurance of a new or more stable employment base. Then, too, the Hawaiian experience has brought out quite clearly the predominant role of the tax assessor in constraining or even formulating planning decisions, often to the benefit of the individual property owner and contrary to the so-called public interest. While the Land Use Law does have the intent of requiring tax assessment to take cognizance of state and local zoning decisions, it is evident that the "highest and best use" market dictates can actually accelerate urbanization pressures and cause premature rezoning or redistricting. Much closer coordination of state land use planning and tax assessment policies, whether administratively or throuh legislative change, will be required so that the two authorities complement rather than contradict each other in the attempt to attain rational land use policies and practices at the state and local levels.

Some Conclusions Based on the Hawaii's Program

1. Although Hawaii's pioneering approach to comprehensive state-level zoning (within which local government is guided in its planning and zoning of specific uses) has now survived 10 years of sometimes turbulent experience and can point to a number of positive achievements, the necessary pre-conditions and divergent sectional influences seem to preclude wholesale adoption of such a control device, except on a crisis basis. Much can be learned from the Hawaiian experience and some states are experimenting with their first steps toward land use regulation. However, it is highly improbable that the conditions leading to passage of Hawaii's Land Use Law will be replicated elsewhere at another time. Nevertheless, these statewide attempts, together with current state planning efforts in such functional areas as open space, shoreline and beach access, flood plain zoning, and coastal zone management, could result ultimately in the creation of the mechanisms and testing of interrelationships necessary for the comprehensive planning process. In all of this, Hawaii has undertaken its share of innovative activity and stands to benefit from accomplishments and successes achieved elsewhere.

2. The realities of current state and local affairs suggest that an adaptation of the Hawaiian land use control experience might best be applied at a regional or metropolitan district level within a state. This proposal does not underestimate the many vexing questions and actualities which stand in the way of rational land use policies, such as: the feasibility of inter-state compacts, the fact that most regional and metropolitan planning agencies are politically amorphous and ostensibly advisory bodies, and the very remote possibility that the rival and parochial attitudes common to the local units of government will suddenly disappear en masse to allow regional, metropolitan, or county-level land use commissions to determine the "public interest" in land use disputes. Yet the very vesting of statutory authority, the appearance of action, and the outcries of those affected by

decisions made may be the persuasive influences needed in these cases.

3. Two emerging influences may make the Hawaiian scheme more assimilable at the state and local levels. These influences are the threat of judicial intervention and the growing federal interest and impact on state and local planning directions. Without a doubt, Senator Jackson's National Land Use Policy Act of 1970 is the strongest force to emerge in years at the federal level in this regard. While the Jackson proposal is noble in intent and holds promise for a concerted national effort, its present exclusion of existing incorporated areas, which exercise planning and zoning powers, will seriously limit its impact. A national land policy must look to the optimum use of the community's resources to attain agreed-upon social and economic goals. As such, it must be long range in concept and application and comprehensive in scope and jurisdiction. Lands which are not subject to its direction, and whose use is not integrated with other productive resources, can pose a serious constraint on the productive efficiency of the economy, as well as on the environment and patterns of development within local communities.

   More importantly, the bill's preoccupation with the development of "Statewide Environmental, Recreational, and Industrial Land Use Plans" seems to ignore the evolving philosophy of urban and regional planning which, put simply, places the emphasis on process over product.

4. At the very least, the Hawaiian experiment with a statewide land use control system vindicates in a small way Justice Oliver Wendell Holmes' observation that "one of the most significant contributions of the federal system to the art of self-government was the opportunity for a state to serve as a laboratory in which new ideas in government could be tested."

At its very best, Hawaii's approach establishes a prototype for the reform of the substantive chaos in our nation's land use laws through the imaginative invention of a viable framework which provides a modicum of order while respecting the disorder, complexity, and spontaneity of men's aspirations. In addition it demonstrates that our state legislatures, spurred on and supported by able and visionary professional planners, are capable of functioning as the harbingers of progress.

Government is an intense experience that makes a deep impression on the minds engaged in it, usually resulting in firm habits of thought difficult to break. This does not mean, however, that experience need take precedence over imagination, that our elected representatives should be guided by hindsight rather than foresight, or that our state legislatures must always view a clarion call to action as a plea to preserve the status quo.

16. Conservation Commissions in Massachusetts

ANDREW J. W. SCHEFFEY

OVERVIEW

Stages of Growth

Conservation Commissions have started in several ways, but usually the early beginnings can be traced to the efforts of a single individual. More often than not the origins have been undramatic. The idea arose in a meeting of a local garden club, was discussed in the Grange, or was developed as a special project by the League of Women Voters or by a service organization. In some cases the appointment of a study committee was suggested by a town official or member of a planning board. Frequently, a local newspaper brought the concept to the attention of the community.

Regardless of the initial point of departure, the intent in each case was to place in the town warrant an article structured along the following lines:

> To see if the town of _____ will vote to accept the provisions General Laws Chapter 40, Sec. 8C amended, and direct the Board of Selectmen (Mayor or City Council) to appoint a conservation commission for the promotion and development of the natural resources and for the protection of the watershed resources of said town.

Upon favorable action, and frequently at the same time, similar articles concerning the establishment of a Conservation Fund and the appropriation of monies to this fund were inserted.

From *Conservation Commissions in Massachusetts* by Andrew J. W. Scheffey, with a supplementary report on the emergence of Conservation Commissions in six other Northeast States by William J. Duddleson. Copyright © 1969 by the Conservation Foundation. Copies available from the Foundation's office, 1717 Massachusetts Avenue, N.W., Washington, D.C. 20036. Each copy $3, prepaid.

To see if the town of   will vote to accept the provisions
of G. L. Ch. 4, Sec. 5, Clause (53), as amended, to establish a Conservation
Fund in said town.

To see if the town will vote to appropriate the sum of $.......... to
the Conservation Fund.

The 23 towns responding to the 1960 questionnaire consisted
mainly of old and established residential communities located in
eastern Massachusetts, well within commuting range of Boston and
with an average population of 5,000. More than half had a population
density below that of the state as a whole, despite their location in
the densely settled eastern counties. These low ratios were maintained
by the presence of relatively extensive open areas still held privately
in the form of rural estates or "weekend farms," but becoming increasingly vulnerable to mounting demands for house lots, shopping
centers and industrial parks. A sohisticated and high-income citizenry
was cognizant of these trends and anxious to preserve the natural
amenities that remained. The Conservation Commission appeared as
an obvious answer. A few of the post-war "bedroom communities"
were included among these forerunners, but almost none of the larger
urban centers.

This suggests generally that the first Conservation Commissions
represented a fairly homogeneous clientele and that the purposes of
their programs were well defined. Part of the 1960 questionnaire was
devoted to Commission objectives. Answers focused primarily upon
the question of open space preservation.

> . . . The town itself owns only 18 acres of land which can be used for
> recreation, all of which is currently being used for such purposes. . . . Our
> Planning Board is strongly opposed to Master Planning. If just six land-
> owners should decide to sell their property today, more than one-half of
> the town would be developed without any regard to the vital natural
> resources thereon or the setting-aside of any areas for future recreational
> uses of the town.
>
> . . . we get our water supply from wells driven into various parts of an
> extensive swamp. Any plan to drain, ditch or fill in parts of this swamp
> for mosquito control or development might be a tragic mistake and we
> want to insure that this does not happen.
>
> We are experiencing a terrific growth in population and development.
> Two major interstate highways are bisecting the town. . . . Due to these
> factors a number of groups thought it was very important to establish
> the Commission. We do hope to have a member of the Planning Board
> appointed to the Commission . . . to tie the two groups together.
>
> Rapid housing developments in recent years have threatened recreation
> areas, lands about ponds, etc.

To hold and better our Town owned property.

The need for protection for our shellfish; to preserve our coastline from the encroachment of developers.

We thought it would help to preserve open spaces in this one square mile town.

. . . we wish to perpetuate open areas, preserve our natural water supply, wildlife, and save the old town from uncontrolled building activities.

Our problem seems to be to conserve the scenery and the natural and historic objects and the wildlife therein.

Housing development was viewed as the dominant threat to existing values, and the goals were to preserve land as a means of maintaining natural amenities. When a second questionnaire was distributed among 200 Commissions four years later, 179 were returned. Unlike the earlier respondents, these contained a striking diversity of program objectives and Commission goals. In part this was due to the larger "mix" of towns and municipalities involved, but it also reflected a natural learning process. The eastern part of the state still accounted for two-thirds of all Commissions, and they existed in clusters spreading outward from the pioneering Commission towns. A demonstration effect had taken place, drawing in communities with varying social structures, development problems and conservation needs. The idea had started to move westward in a spotty fashion, following major highway systems and population centers. The location of Commissions was conforming increasingly to the settlement patterns of people. In the three counties of the Connecticut Valley, the major agricultural area of the state, Commission towns accounted for 70% of the population but only 15% of the land area. But in the more suburbanized counties surrounding metropolitan Boston, the towns that had established Commissions accounted for 80% of the land area and two-thirds of the population living outside of the city of Boston. In scenic but sparsely populated Berkshire County, Commissions had been created in the communities where over 80% of the population lived, but their jurisdiction affected only 40% of the land area.

In the early years, the Commissions seemed to have rather clearly defined ideas of needs and procedures. For the most part, they enjoyed the support of a major segment of a voting population which tended to share their views. Few signs of overt hostility were noted in the 1960 questionnaires, and such opposition as existed was attributed to "outside" development forces. But if these first Commissions were largely the children of a staid and confident suburbia, the picture began to change even in the early sixties. The "average" town was becoming involved, and after passage of the Self-Help Program with its lure of financial assistance, even urban conservationists were able to persuade city councils and mayors of the worth of Commissions. The average Commission town had a population of 5,000 before 1960. By 1964, nearly one-half of all Commissions were in the 5,000 to 20,000 category, 20 were in cities from 20,000 to 50,000, and three in metropolitan centers of over 100,000.

This infusion of new people, places, and problems had a profound impact upon the thinking of Commissions and their self-defined roles. Many of the same single-purpose, straight-line obectives were repeated in the returns from the 1964 questionnaire, but a number of new needs were included. More than 40 different goals were discussed, including the need for improved coordination among the town agencies and at the local-state level, and the promotion of unified thinking regarding land use. The concept of flood plain zoning was discussed frequently, together with the idea of promoting the "steady planned growth" of the community. The term "environment" began to appear. A number of specific problems were defined: improving access to public areas; air and water pollution; zoning changes to permit cluster housing development; the planning and location of highways; billboards and the underground placement of utility lines. Conservation education in the local school system was noted as an important concern. Some of the more active of the older Commissions had become highly professional in their approach, engaging in programs of resources mapping and evaluation, initiating research in ecological problems, experimenting with new patterns of land use control. In the process their conception of earlier issues had become less clear-cut, their statement of objectives more comprehensive and abstract.

In 1960, the bulk of Commission programs seemed to center around land acquisition, preservation of open areas, the development of specific projects. By 1964, these activities had broadened appreciably while at the same time becoming more realistically attuned to political and economic reality. Conservation Commissions were found to be working more closely and frequently with planning boards. Greater attention was being directed towards research to justify Commission claims, and towards the necessity of relating Commission projects to the larger process of public planning and private development as it affected the total landscape and environment. This resulted in a growing recognition of the need to promote more widespread involvement of people and institutions.

If a mail questionnaire were conducted among Commissions today, it would probably show that the majority of plans and activities are still clustered around these two general themes—securing land and starting projects, involving institutions and people. But it is likely that the gradual formulation of a new set of goals would be discernible on the part of established, pace-setting Commissions, as well as some new ones that have capitalized on the experience of others. While not abandoning the practical necessity for prompt and effective action while opportunities still exist, these measures would be directed towards the broader goal of building a more satisfactory environment.

Recognizing that the environment represents different things to different people, and that its qualities are not always measurable in traditional terms, Commissions are starting to provide new insights for understanding local and regional environments. A dialogue has been started among citizens and their governmental representatives, and from this could emerge new perspectives for planning. This seems to be the third stage of development within individual Commissions and for the movement as a whole.

Any classification is hazardous, particularly so when dealing with organizations demonstrating the spontaneity and individuality that has been so characteristic of the Commission movement. The three stages of growth delineated represent trends and general orientation more than categories. They reflect the degree to which Commission programs have become articulated with the forces of growth within their community. Aggregate data on Commission growth and project activity during the last 10 years, together with field studies, point to these successive levels of involvement, which correspond in a loose way to the growth patterns of individual Commissions.

Membership and Organization

The 1957 act provided for the appointment of from three to seven persons by the selectmen, mayor or town manager to serve as Conservation Commission members for staggered terms of one to three years. In 1960 an average of five members had been appointed to each Commission; by 1964, the average was six, and today most Commissions have the full complement. Housewives, businessmen, and professional persons made up the bulk of this membership in 1960, with the individuals frequently selected on the basis of their association with other conservation-oriented groups. By 1964 the proportion of businessmen had increased to about one-third of the total. Twenty percent were professional people, including a generous proportion of lawyers, 10% were housewives, and among the remainder were technical persons from resource agencies, office and factory workers, retired persons and farmers. In 1960 about 30% of the Commissions reported cases of membership overlapping with other town agencies—

the planning board, recreation board, town forest committee or finance committee. The trend toward joint membership on two or more town agencies became stronger, and in 1964 some 150 Commissions reported that this was the case.

In communities with a long-standing tradition of private conservation action appropriate candidates for Commission membership were readily found. As already noted, these towns had little difficulty in deciding where to begin, since a well-indoctrinated membership had firm ideas about what needed to be done.

But in towns without such a history of active conservation concern, without private land trusts, forest committees, or even planning boards, there frequently were no *natural* candidates for Commission membership. The task of drawing up a balanced slate of five to seven persons was not easy, and often a process of trial and error was necessary before the proper combination was obtained. In limited cases, where powerful interests opposed the whole idea of taking land out of circulation, or where outspoken citizens resented the notion of "taking land off the tax roles," or where established agencies were fearful of a "power grab" on the part of the new agency, members clearly unsympathetic to conservation objectives were named. This was especially true where the opposition was unsuccessful in smothering the idea before it was accepted by town meeting. But these cases appear to be the exception, found usually in larger urban centers or small rural towns.

As Commissions become more deeply involved in the institutional, planning and political aspects of the job, qualities other than conservation experience are sought. Some put leadership abilities at the top of the list, on the grounds that any leader can learn conservation while not all conservationists can become leaders. Others maintain that a Commission should not become overloaded with professional resource persons and others from the technical staff of public and private resource agencies. Although knowledgeable in their fields, such individuals sometimes lack the fresh approach found in lay persons looking at problems for the first time. As Commission programs become more involved and far-reaching, certain professional skills are demanded, including experience in legal affairs, planning and design, sociology and finance.

The relationship of a Commission membership to its community is critical. Time and again reference is made in questionnaire returns to the need for balanced representation from different groups and interests—women's organizations, youth groups, business, the land and housing development industry, and the traditional resource interests—

hunters and fishermen, agriculturists, wilderness enthusiasts and naturalists, local historians and recreation leaders. Also noted has been the need for someone on the Commission who knows his or her way around city hall, either as a regular employee or elected official. One of the most useful Commission members is seen as the long-time resident familiar with the landscape and landowners. A final and perennial need noted is good relationships with the press, either through direct membership or some other arrangement.

While each of these criteria is important, all cannot be accommodated within a membership of seven. For this reason, Commissions tend to secure wider participation as their programs develop. This is accomplished through the appointment of associate members who meet regularly and take on particular assignments, the use of subcommittees to work with individual members, the establishment of ad hoc study groups or citizen advisory committees. The town of Wayland, in carrying out a comprehensive resource mapping project, was able to secure the volunteer services of more than 70 persons over a sustained period of time through these various devices.

Most new Commissions are best described as loose confederations of interests and abilities and, even among the most experienced Commissions, there are not necessarily firm correlations between the success achieved and the degree of organization imposed. Some of the most dynamic and imaginative groups call their membership together only sporadically, preferring to conserve time and energy by making specific assignments to individual members and allowing them to work alone. Coordination rests with the chairman, and the success of the Commission depends upon his skills. If this leads to designation of a "one-man commission," it does not denote under-utilization of Commission resources, but merely underscores the critical role that a chairman can play.

For the most part those Commissions that have carried out consistently effective operations have developed thoughtful organizational systems and procedural arrangements. Joint meetings with other town agencies may be scheduled throughout the year to insure continuity of information flow. Regular newsletters are distributed among key citizens, organizations and officials of the community. Members are assigned to represent the Commission regularly on other boards, regional organizations, or associations. Formal methods of reporting to the full Commission are developed for those members with definite areas of responsibility—conservation education in the schools, public relations and the press, financing and fund-raising, the management and supervision of Commission lands.

Whether a Commission leans toward a freewheeling association of individuals or a deliberately managed machine, it is clear that the key to success lies most frequently in the person of the chairman. The backgrounds of the outstanding chairmen are as varied as the problems they attack—a retired school teacher, a corporate attorney, a small town banker, a civil engineer, a fisheries biologist, a chemist, an active physician. Some maintain that a housewife with grown children should be selected because of the time demands of the job, or that it should be given to a professional in the field, or an expert in public relations or group dynamics.

In the absence of a resourceful person in this position—and this is perhaps the answer—the collective ambitions of the most enterprising memberships have been stifled. On the other hand, those with able chairmen can point to amazing achievements under the most unlikely circumstances. The well-timed and properly-chosen word, the knowledge of when to press forward and when to stand back, intuition, foresight and imagination—these are the elements that time and again have made the difference between fulfillment and failure.

Activities and Conflicts

Each Commission emerges from a distinct complex of causes and these factors, together with the composition of its membership, influence its early forms of development and the general direction of its program. A Commission must design its program in part to accommodate the competencies of its members. While initial goals may be ill-defined, it soon becomes evident that public support cannot be generated around general concerns and vague statements of intent. Issues have to be highlighted or created in order to gain momentum, build support, and show tangible program accomplishment. An alert chairman quickly realizes this, and rather than dispersing the energies and talents of a half dozen members into as many projects, attempts in most cases to concentrate upon one major problem, to channel Commission activities towards a common goal.

An important factor in deciding upon initial projects is a reasonable expectation of success in a relatively short period of time. This is important for the morale of the Commission members and for its future status within the community. In the majority of cases these early activities fall under the heading of land acquisition. This can be a very specific venture, but it soon leads the Commission into far broader areas of involvement.

A Commission has the option of acquiring a tract of land by various means: donations from individual owners, funds of a private land trust, special appropriations by the town, or participation in the state Self-Help Program. Some communities have used all of these, but in the majority of cases early contact has been made with the Department of Natural Resources for preliminary planning assistance and ultimate benefit from state financial aid. Once this move is made the Commission is committed to land planning activities in association with the town planning board, conferences with wildlife experts, recreation site designers, foresters and landscape architects. Meetings must take place with the town council, private landowners, lawyers, and town officials. On the suggestion that other lands already owned by the town would be equally satisfactory for Commission purposes, a project to locate, map, and evaluate all town-owned lands and tax delinquent properties may be initiated. If someone asks why the Commission has elected to purchase one specific site as opposed to alternative areas, an overall inventory of all land and water resources in the community may be undertaken. This may lead to the preparation of a comprehensive land use and open space plan for the community, requiring a period of years and the participation of other state and local agencies.

Even if such planning ramifications do not develop at once, the purchase of a site necessitates various levels of working relationships with other community interests. The public works department may be asked to assist in building a parking area or access road, constructing a bridge or impoundment. Cooperation may be sought from a local garden club in the identification of plant species and the design of nature trails. Boy Scout troops have participated in the construction of camping sites and clearing underbrush. Sportsmen's organizations may assume responsibility for stocking streams or for game management. The support of the chamber of commerce may be sought for fund-raising purposes.

The public education phase begins with the need to gain support and financing for land acquisition, to deal with a particular resource issue in the community, or simply to increase levels of general understanding. Few land acquisition projects have succeeded without some degree of public relations activity, whether a series of articles in the local newspaper, or a full-fledged campaign for a municipal bond issue. If the case in point is a particular resource conflict, such as a highway plan that would bisect an existing park, a particularly offensive subdivision proposal, a high tension utility line, or the draining of a valued area of marsh, energetic and aggressive campaigns may be launched that involve door-to-door canvassing, public opinion polls, radio and newspaper coverage, organized trips to the problem area in question. These issue-oriented public relations projects frequently lead to sustained research by the Commission which may enlist public assistance and volunteer support. The need to "get the facts," marshal evidence and present alternatives has become recognized as the most effective means of overcoming opposition and gaining public support. Time and again, such issue-oriented investigations have stimulated broadly-based programs of resource analysis and research.

Whether the first stab at public relations and education takes place to raise funds for a meadow, create support for master planning, or to fight water pollution, this activity, like the superficially simple act of purchasing the first piece of land, tends to broaden the Commission's program by building new working relationships with other agencies and new lines of communication between the community and its citizens. This transition marks the beginning of the Commission's potential role as community spokesman for general resource concerns and as arbiter in resolving resource-use conflicts.

Relatively few Commissions face overt hostility at the beginning. Most come into existence either in the atmosphere of goodwill and generosity that tends to pervade the word "conservation," or they are regarded as a harmless assemblage of "bubble-headed bird watchers" and "do-gooders." But with the intent on making an impact, the Commission soon finds itself embroiled in an increasingly seething atmosphere of interagency strife, economic discord, and local-regional stress. As the community focal point for a range of questions regarding the physical environment, the Commission is destined to become involved in a continuing discourse with planners and operating agencies, developers and preservationists, scientists and citizens. There are no consistent relationships between the conflict generated and success enjoyed, but it is clear that no significant degree of accomplishment can be realized in the absence of discussion and debate. To the degree that a Commission becomes constructively engaged in current issues, providing a platform for the airing of differences and a framework for compromise, it is fulfilling a new and vital role.

The type of conflict varies with the community in question. In the older communities on the immediate edge of metropolis, much of the land has already been committed to urban uses, and only narrow margins of maneuverability exist for dramatic open space ventures. Here a major objective of Commissions is to keep existing public open spaces intact, to protect them from the inroads of both private and public development. In seaboard communities estuary areas and marshes are particularly vulnerable. In larger urban centers, the Conservation Commission is frequently viewed with suspicion and hostility by established municipal agencies. This may be attributed to inter-agency rivalry for limited public funds, or simply to the fact that demonstrated public support for the new body would reflect unfavorably upon another agency's past record of performance.

In communities within a 20 to 50-mile radius of urban centers a different situation exists. While already experiencing the full onslaught of urban expansion, many physical amenities of the rural countryside still remain in these towns: meadows, winding roads, and commercial farms. Here the first impulse is to attempt to maintain things the way they are through stringent zoning controls, conservation easements, and the acquisition of extensive land areas serving as greenbelts, buffer zones and natural areas. For the most part Commissions have the full-fledged support and understanding of the voters, many of whom share the same goals. The major battle lines are drawn first with private development interests, rather than with other agencies of local government. The charge of removing land from the tax rolls, often leveled against Commission proposals, tends to be outweighed by strong public support for acquisition. Another issue is local versus regional use of Commission lands. If financed through the Self-Help Program, Commission properties must be made available to the general public. Whether motivated by fear of overcrowding or the prospect of undisciplined urban gangs moving in with their litter on weekends, many of these communities prefer to forego state aid to insure exclusive use.

The last broad category of Commission towns, described most imaginatively as the "sleeping beauties," are those in the metropolitan hinterland regions. Lying beyond effective commuting range by today's standards, and with extensive areas of open land, most are unprepared for urban pressures already at play just beneath the surface. The major conflicts in these towns exist between the Commission itself and the town's populace. Little awareness, a basic conservatism and almost no sense of urgency characterize the outlook of longtime residents, and proposals for open space planning and land use controls are usually met with indifference or scorn. While signs of urban pressures are increasingly evident, traditional forms of urban land use controls are absent, and planning is looked upon as a newfangled idea. Participation in the Self-Help Program is frequently rejected, not on the grounds of retaining exclusive use for local residents, but because of the loss of hometown sovereignty. Under these conditions a new Commission must proceed gingerly, promoting more traditional tree-planting and habitat-improvement projects while gaining general acceptance.

These are starting points. Whether to advance slowly or to move ahead aggressively when open conflicts arise is a question each Commission faces. Most Commission members contacted in the course of this study agreed that the best way to avoid the debilitating effects of conflicts was by increasing the flow and content of information within the community—among the interests involved, local officials, and citizens. One chairman stated that a duplicating machine has been the Commission's most productive investment. Some provide weekly columns for the local newspapers, send copies of reports of special studies on research findings to town agencies and prominent citizens, or sponsor conferences and open meetings on controversial issues, drawing upon outside counsel and making full use of all available professional talent within the community and region. Commissions have sponsored the preparation of lecture kits and slide programs depicting both sides of a given issue and setting forth alternative solutions. At the Commission's urging, special subcommittees have been appointed by town officials to study problems and make policy recommendations for community action.

The purpose of all these efforts is to have controversial issues openly discussed before the boiling point is reached. Bring groups together, provide the facts, show the alternatives and weigh the pros and cons, keep the town informed—these are elementary tools of conflict resolution being employed by Conservation Commissions in communities throughout the state.

An Evolving Concept

In its broadest perspective, the Conservation Commission must be viewed as a mechanism for promoting change in the minds of people. Few Commissions start with such grandiose vision, but it is the direction in which most are headed. This applies to the growth within individual Commissions, and it characterizes the movement as a whole. While both are moving steadily towards more pervasive and fundamental levels of involvement, the subtle evolution of individual values and public scales of priority into a demonstrated commitment towards the environment is most clearly visible at the community level.

The Commission experiences discussed in the following chapters were selected to illustrate this process of growth. Each represents a somewhat different approach at three successive levels of involvement: *securing the land and starting projects; involving institutions and people; providing new perspectives for planning.* Every Commission must function within the context of its own community, facing different constraints and exploiting different opportunities. Overlap among these broad groupings of activity is great and any attempt to classify Commission programs must be largely arbitrary. The purpose is not to render judgment on performance but to illuminate the processes involved.

SOME EXAMPLES

1. Longmeadow: On an Upward Curve

"Our Commission was five years too late in getting started," the chairman of the year-old Longmeadow Conservation Commission reported in the summer of 1963. Much of the Commission's success in moving ahead since then might be attributed to the constant reminder that it had worked against time. Located on the Connecticut River between the spreading metropolitan centers of Springfield and Hartford, Longmeadow already had a population of 12,000 when, in 1962, the Future Planning Commission recommended establishment of a Conservation Commission. A Commission was approved by a large majority vote in March of that year, and an appropriation of $500 was granted for operating expenses. The appropriation was increased to $2,500 in the second year, and since that time an annual operating budget of $15,000 has been approved. In 1966 the Commission received a supplementary appropriation of $42,000, and a private gift of $18,500, to purchase two tracts of 42 acres, with total acquisitions of nearly 100 acres during a four-year period. The Commission was instrumental in obtaining purchase by the Park Department of 88 acres in the center of town for park purposes. It has sponsored an effective program of conservation education in the local school system.

When asked in 1966 to explain its success, the chairman pointed to the Commission membership and replied, "We want no fancy names." He explained that influential people and respected names are no special asset to a Commission unless there is also a demonstrated commitment to hard and time-consuming work. The Longmeadow Commission has been able to secure committed members, and its achievements are due to their efforts alone.

During its first two years the Commission scheduled regular meetings every other Tuesday night, and successfully called upon its members to take part in field trips and special discussions. A Commission philosophy was developed and a plan of action decided upon. The results of these deliberations were published at year end in an attractive and effective brochure entitled *A Message to Longmeadow Landowners: Facts from Your Conservation Commission with a Proposal for You.* The pamphlet discussed urban sprawl and outlined arguments favoring timely action to preserve open space areas.

Copies of the publication were mailed to every taxpayer in the community. While some established agencies were alarmed by possible Commission encroachment, initial reservations were gradually overcome during the following year as Commission members discussed their objectives at public meetings and informal gatherings. The publication helped to create a more accurate image of the Commission in the eyes of townspeople, and established understanding that its purposes were broader than nature study and preservation for the sake of preservation.

After two years of planning, the Commission was able to proceed with its land acquiring objectives, focused in the initial stages upon a broad stretch of marsh and lowlands between the Connecticut River and Interstate 91. More than half a dozen separate tracts were acquired through gifts and purchase, and the Planning Board is cooperating in developing flood plain zoning ordinances for those lands not directly under Commission jurisdiction.

In 1964 the Commission joined with the Parks Department and the Future Planning Committee in developing a proposal for a 10-year municipal acquisition of 83 acres of centrally located land about to be purchased privately for subdivision. A series of slides were prepared for presentation at town meeting, showing that non-subdivision land had been reduced from 2,400 acres in 1958 almost to the vanishing point in 1964. As a representative from the Park Board explained, "It's not a case of whether we can afford to do it, but can we afford not to?" Following the presentation, some 400 members of the town meeting voted unanimously to appropriate $39,700 for the first stage of a 10-year acquisition program.

Longmeadow's work illustrates how a Conservation Commission can function as an informal community educational force. The Commission has sponsored a pilot program of conservation education in cooperation with the Biology Department of nearby Springfield College. Each spring and fall for four consecutive Saturday mornings, a group of selected fifth-grade pupils—two from each of the town's 11 fifth-grade classes—has participated in an outdoor education program directed by Springfield College staff volunteers and conducted on Commission land. The success of the program is leading the Commission to more direct involvement in conservation education programs throughout the school system.

The Commission's plans include a town arboretum, beautification projects in cooperation with filling station operators, tree planting projects for elementary school classes, and a program of public forums on conservation issues. Unlike many eastern Massachusetts communities, Longmeadow cannot point to a tradition of conservation concern. The Commission got off to a good start because of the hard work and enthusiasm of its early members, and now seems to be riding the crest of a wave. The present chairman recently compared the development of the Longmeadow Commission to learning how to water ski: "After a few false starts on the water, our Commission is now up on those skis and actually being cheered on by our fellow townspeople. We love it, and although we're not complacent, we're happy."

2. Springfield: An Uphill Fight in the City

Unless the city has people with guts enough to do what has to be done, the city is lost. Most of the problems facing us today are not the result of external forces over which we have no control. It would be nice to delude ourselves into believing that this was the case but closer to the truth is that we have had people in the past with no vision, no resolution and perhaps no courage when it became a little difficult to do the right thing.

You've got to fight. My advice to conservation leaders is to be dynamic. It is far simpler to learn how to become a good conservationist than it is to learn how to become a good leader. If those individuals responsible for appointments to Conservation Commissions would spend less time trying to convert well-meaning but inept conservationists into leaders and more time in converting interested leaders into conservationists, the entire field of conservation would progress much faster.

These are the words of Benedict Brietung, chairman of the Springfield Conservation Commission, which today stands out as one of the most aggressive in the Commonwealth. They express a Commission strategy that has gradually emerged over the course of six years of struggle against public apathy, special interests and bureaucratic maneuverings, a strategy that differs substantially from methods used in the typical suburban community. Tracing this development provides useful insight into the "political ecology" of a Conservation Commission functioning within an urban environment.

Early Years

Springfield is a city of over 175,000 and is the major industrial and commercial center of western Massachusetts. In 1958 several individuals active in the city's sportsmen's organizations, in a prepared statement, urged the City Council and mayor to establish a Conservation

Commission. The mayor became enthusiastic and began to push, and a Commission was authorized by the City Council in 1959. Members were appointed the following year, and reflected the interests of the early proponents of the idea. The first chairman was closely associated with the Massachusetts Council of Sportmen's Clubs, a major state-wide organization, another member was proprietor of a sporting goods store, and most of the others were avid hunters and fishermen. There were no joint appointments with other municipal agencies.

It was quite natural that initial attention of the Commission should focus on the Connecticut River, perhaps the most prominent natural resource of the city. Specifically, attention was directed toward pro-viding greater access for boating and fishing. During the first several years the Commission devoted much of its time and energy to obtain-ing a public boat launching facility that would also include a picnic area on the riverbank. The first site proposed was on land already owned by the city, and an attempt was made to have this turned over to the Commission. However, other municipal agencies had interests in the area in question, and conflict developed. Eventually, the land was set aside for a municipal incinerator installation, and the Com-mission began to look elsewhere.

The Commission started to work with a community across the river to secure another site. Arrangements were finally made for the city to acquire some three acres of riverfront land, which it leased to the Department of Natural Resources. Working through the Public Access Board, the Department assumed responsibility for installing the boat launching facilities. More than three years of Commission effort were required and there was considerable strife before this contractual arrangement between the city and the Department was developed, but the launching service is now operating smoothly and an important need has been met.

The Commission's first attempt to secure open space land ended in political defeat. A 60-acre tract parallel to Interstate 91, at the south-ern boundary of the city, was proposed for acquisition as the basis of a future greenbelt system. Commission members worked for several years to prepare a project application to the Open Space Land Branch of the Federal Housing and Home Finance Administration (now HUD) and to the State Self-Help Program. The owners of that and adjacent land were contacted, prices established, statements of justification prepared and land use plans drawn up. The project was submitted and just as final approval was about to be granted, the city Park Department took the area over by power of eminent domain.

Approximately the same thing took place in connection with a property that was up for a change in zoning from residential to industrial. This involved 60 acres of land, and the owner had offered to give the city $175,000 to buy an additional tract if the proposed zoning change was permitted. The Conservation Commission worked very hard to prevent this change of use. Finally the mayor had the area taken over by eminent domain through the Park Department, rather than have the zoning classification changed.

To obtain an index of open spaces, the Conservation Commission made use of a master plan which had been prepared by the city planner in 1950, but never accepted by the city. The plan designated certain areas as permanent open space. Each member of the Commission was given a portion of the plan and a corresponding zoning map for his area, and proceeded to cross-reference the information. The purpose was to provide in one document all possible information concerning the use of private open space areas and public lands. This process required approximately two years. When completed, the open space data was consolidated on one map and turned over to the city Planning Department.

These examples illustrate the nature of problems encountered. From 1960 through 1965, members of the Commission worked diligently to get conservation action started, facilities constructed, land acquired, open space planned. While certain of their objectives were ultimately realized, none of them were accomplished in the name of the Commission itself. The Commission was able to point to things that it had promoted in the first instance, but in each case these projects were taken over by other agencies. This was not a deliberate policy of working behind the scenes, but the result of inadequate muscle in the political hurly-burly of a large city. It was not that the people of Springfield were against conservation, but simply that they did not even know the Commission existed. Annual appropriations to the Conservation Commission by the city of Springfield never exceeded $25, and at the end of the first five years the Commission had no land or resources under its control.

No one was more cognizant of these facts than the chairman himself. In 1965 he spoke freely of the things that had been learned regarding the ingredients of an effective Commission:

One weakness in the early years was to stick too closely to the narrow interpretation of the enabling legislation, to play primarily an advisory role, and to avoid political infighting. At the same time the Commission was insufficiently aggressive in securing proper funding. It did not provide sufficient publicity concerning its objectives and needs. The make-up of the Commission was originally too conservative, the members did not make themselves heard. One of the most important needs on a Commission is to have someone who can speak effectively, selling the idea to various parts of the town structure.

A Watchdog Role

The first chairman resigned in 1965, and the mayor selected Benedict Breitung, an active member of a private conservation organization in Springfield, the Allen Bird Club, to complete the vacated term. Breitung had been an outspoken critic of the Conservation Commission for several years.

Breitung has viewed the central role of the Commission as that of *attacking any attack upon natural resources* in the city, and considers publicity its major weapon. He does not believe that conservation accomplishments can be realized through high ideals, but only by becoming deeply involved in the political arena. He has stated emphatically that in a large metropolitan situation, where many existing agencies have deeply vested interests in all aspects of future land use, a rough and tumble approach is essential. He is opposed to overcommitment to specific projects on the ground that it can dilute the effectiveness of an urban Commission.

Breitung's first step was to make several new appointments and to revise its organization. Each member was given a definite area of responsibility—the protection of existing outdoor areas, the operation of city government as it affects all aspects of the natural environment, trouble shooting on a problem-by-problem basis, liaison with the Planning Board, and conservation education in the schools.

Great reliance was placed on press coverage and reporters have been invited to all meeting of the Commission. Controversial issues have been sought out rather than skirted. Stories for the press have been prepared whenever an issue developed.

Individual citizens have been asked to contact the chairman directly regarding developments of which they disapprove and the Commission takes it from there.

The Commission has cultivated the support of radio and television in its efforts to prevent the needless destruction of shade trees, to reduce spraying with DDT and pesticides, to exert greater control over the erection of billboards and the proliferation of used car lots and junkyards, to resist the rezoning of existing residential areas, to fight the draining of wetlands. A mailing list of some 100 key persons—councilmen, Planning Board members, department heads and influential citizens—have been developed and information is sent to the list whenever an important issue comes up. An average of three or four newspaper articles are prepared each month, describing critical issues or explaining the long-term plans of the Commission.

Although the Commission is operating "across the board" in its efforts to educate people and influence decisions, it has also begun to experience the satisfaction of tangible accomplishment. An initial achievement came in 1965, when four acres of city land were turned over to the Commission, the first area received in its name. In that year the Commission asked for an operating budget of $500, which was granted with the understanding that separate appropriation requests would be made for special project activities or land acquisitions. The Commission has since developed a five-year plan of land acquisition that will involve purchase of some 250 acres of land throughout the city. The support of the City Council and mayor has been won, and steps are under way to acquire 12 of the 36 sites proposed, at a cost of approximately $250,000. State or federal matching funds will be used wherever possible.

The Commission's first dramatic project achievement involved a clash with the powerful Board of Public Works and the outcome served to establish the organization as a force to be reckoned with in the agency hierarchy of Springfield. The issue centered on Schneelock Brook, a stream that flows through a seven-acre marsh before starting a meandering course through a residential area. Disturbed by mosquitoes, certain of the residents requested the Board of Public Works to straighten the brook and drain the adjacent upland area. The Board was about to proceed with such action when the Conservation Commission intervened. A strong presentation was made against the proposal before an open meeting of the City Council. The councilmen ordered the project stopped temporarily, and requested the Commission to make its own study and file a counter proposal.

The Hampshire County Conservation District assisted the Commission in developing an overall land use plan for the area, including limited drainage of parts of the marsh, but leaving the meanders intact. The Commission plan reflected ecological considerations that had been overlooked in the former proposal, and was documented by detailed hydrological and soil investigations sponsored by the Conservation District. It constituted not only a workable compromise, but a more sophisticated analysis of the problem than the "bulldozer approach" of the earlier proposal. The Commission plan was accepted by the City Council, and as a result of the agitation that the controversy had stimulated over the general loss of wetland resources in the Springfield region, the mayor directed the Planning Board to prepare a wetlands map for the city. After review by the Conservation Commission and other agencies, this will be incorporated into the master plan now in development.

This experience gave the Commission added confidence, and it has continued to play an active role in wetland protection.

A permanent billboard watchdog group was established within the Commission to deal with this aspect of landscape disfigurement. When it was first created there was no formalized procedure for reviewing permit requests for the construction of new billboards, and most were being granted without any particular consideration. The Commission prepared a formal statement to the mayor asking that the job of reviewing requests for billboard permits be permanently assigned either to the Planning Board, or the Commission itself. This has since been accomplished, and the Conservation Commission now has the authority for preliminary review of all permit requests. Since that time, the Commission has opposed six specific permit requests and on five of these its judgment has been upheld by the state Outdoor Advertising Board.

A similar oversight function has been exercised with regard to the care and removal of shade trees. Although laws have been on the books for many years, few departments of city government paid much attention until the Commission stepped in. Throughout the city, trees were destroyed at will to facilitate sewer construction, road widening, sidewalk repair, utility line construction. The Commission became alarmed at this incremental process of frequently needless destruction, studied the laws, made their content known, and took steps to see that they were observed.

Not all of the Commission's activities have been of such a regulatory nature. One member has been particularly active in work with the local school system. In May 1966 an extensive report on conservation education was prepared, designed specifically to meet the needs of urban children in the Springfield system, and outlining subject matter that could be incorporated into existing curriculums from primary grades through high school. Professional talents from the Springfield area were enlisted in this project, and the proposal was well received by school administrators. Contact has since been made with the educational office of the Massachusetts Audubon Society, which will assist the schools in implementing this program of curriculum reform.

THE FUTURE

"You've got to fight. You've got to educate the public. Conservation in most communities is affected by many municipal departments—engineering, parks and recreation, health and public works. Many of the officials in these departments must be educated too," Breitung says.

While the Springfield Commission cannot lay claim to extensive areas of permanently reserved open space, its chairman feels that it is building respect and helping to promote improved channels of cooperation among other groups and organizations. The mayor has become one of the Commission's strongest supporters. "City officials," according to the mayor, "are open to suggestions; all they need is to be presented with the facts." Views of the Commission gradually are being accepted by other agencies.

The greatest victory came early in 1967 when the Springfield City Council approved the appointment of a full-time planner to staff the day-to-day work of the Conservation Commission. Breitung regards this as a milestone, an indispensable measure in the Commission's efforts to incorporate conservation perspectives into the framework of city government. While this administrative development will present questions and create new conflicts, it represents a first step towards this goal. For despite the noise and clamor that the Commission has created, far out of proportion to its size, legal authority and budget, Breitung has no illusions concerning the abilities of a small group of volunteers to affect major change in the functioning of a massive urban bureaucracy.

"We advise loudly. That's our only weapon. It's nice to try to win friends, but in some matters we don't care if some people don't like us," the chairman adds. Evidence suggests that conservation interests in Springfield are winning more friends each day.

3. Concord: Participation by Design

It has been said that Concord was spared burning by the Indians in King Philip's War because it was looked upon favorably by the gods. Anyone viewing the accomplishments of its Conservation Commission over the past eight years would attribute equally benevolent attitudes to its present-day citizens. Few communities in the Commonwealth have achieved a greater sense of responsible resource stewardship. While this might be attributed in part to historical carry-over—Thoreau, Walden Pond, the Transcendentalists—more direct credit must be given to the good sense, deliberate planning and pragmatic wisdom of the original members of the Commission, and particularly to its first chairman, Thomas Flint.

If much of Concord's success reflects the man himself, the same must be said about the Conservation Commission development as a whole. As one of the small group of early proponents, Flint was instrumental in getting the movement off to a sound start. In 1960 he was elected as the first president of the Association of Conservation Commissions, and held this position for the next five years.

Conservation was not Flint's first foray into the art of local government, and he came fortified with more than theory. A resident of Concord for over 30 years and a professional engineer, he had held a series of elected town offices: chairman of the Finance Committee, chairman of the Public Works Department, chairman of the Water Department, and chairman of the Long Range Comprehensive Town Planning Commission. It was from this latter group that the idea of creating a Conservation Commission first emerged. This first important step is thus described by Flint:

> Some five or six years ago our Planning Board found itself too heavily burdened by the problems of subdivision control to do any real long-range planning. It is not practical to require volunteer servants of the town to carry on the laborious detail of everyday control with the heavy added burden of long-range planning. Faced with this problem, the Board requested that a special committee be established and charged with presenting the town with a comprehensive long-range plan. Members of this committee included representatives of the Selectment, Finance Committee, Planning Board, School Committee, Recreation Commission, Forest Committee, as well as leaders representing the town in most of its important aspects. We tried to represent the group of people who made their living in Boston and the group of people who made their living locally. We had a large and unwieldy group and I must say that the early parts of our work were extremely frustrating and tiring. There was a great deal of talk and no progress.
>
> I want to emphasize here that this is one of the practical aspects of town political life. If you wish to live in a nation governed by consent, you must be able to deal with a lot of people who want to talk without thinking and who have to get this out of their systems. This process is painful but it is the price of providing leadership and leadership is essential to good democracy. If issues are to be resolved in clear factual terms without emotional content, those concerned must be permitted to air their ideas.

The dialogue started. Flint had noted: "We spent one whole year on this, apparently achieving nothing, but it is my conviction that it was the most valuable of the three years spent, for when we finally got down to work we were able to proceed without serious interference." This first year of discussion resulted in a proposal to the town for the preparation of a long-range plan using funds from a federal program. The Committee worked closely with the professional planning consultants, established a Citizens' Advisory Council of unlimited numbers to enable all interested persons to become involved in the planning process. The final plan was unanimously accepted three years later, and each of its major recommendations has been approved and implemented in the years since.

The Citizens' Council became an educational force in the community as well as an advisory mechanism. More than 250 took part. Everyone was asked to come and present his views of town needs. "For a while they found it difficult to think coherently and many preferred to give snap answers which were meaningless," Flint observed, "so we circulated a carefully prepared questionnaire which was slanted in such a way as to require responsible answers." The questionnaire brought a 70% response and initiated a process of citizen thought and participation that continues today.

It became apparent to all who were concerned with the program that long-range planning and conservation were inextricably related. The questionnaire clearly demonstrated that townspeople not only wanted to maintain the rural residential qualities of the community, but that they were prepared to pay the costs involved.

A Conservation Commission was proposed in 1959 and approved without a dissenting vote. Each year it requested the maximum appropriation for matching funds, then limited to $\frac{1}{20}$ of 1% of assessed valuation, and again these requests were approved unanimously—$10,800 the first year, increasing gradually to $13,350 in 1963. When the percentage limitation was removed in 1964, annual appropriations increased and in 1966 the town approved a single land acquisition commitment of nearly $200,000.

The Commission included two attorneys, one housewife and a farmer, but official members had access to the voluntary support and assistance of many capable individuals in the community who were not only aware of the problems and needs but willing to do something about them. The Commission soon formalized its relationship with citizens by establishing the Concord Land Conservation Trust, a private organization empowered to accept gifts of land and rights to land and money to be held in trust for the town, and whose membership advises the Conservation Commission.

Operating funds of the Trust are raised through membership dues and contributions, and it provides an alternative mechanism for dealing with donations of land rights other than those of outright ownership, conservation easements and zoning restrictions controlling the future use of property. The Land Trust is able to regulate the use of its lands more rigorously than a Commission, and can act promptly in an emergency. Gifts to a trust can be in the form of a "memorial." By introducing a degree of flexibility not otherwise available, this non-governmental agency has cooperated actively with the Commission and broadened the base of public participation.

During the first year careful consideration was given to the formation of basic operating policy, defining the objectives of the Commission and clearly delineating its responsibilities and areas of jurisdiction. This initial effort has brought good relationships with other town agencies, since it was decided that the Commission would take action only when conservation was determined to be a primary objective. While it interpreted the term "natural resources" very broadly, action (but not necessarily consideration) would be confined to preserving open spaces, marshes, rivers and river meadows, ponds and forest areas. It was also decided that property would not be taken by eminent domain. In cases where conservation was deemed subordinate to other affairs entrusted to other town boards, the Commission agreed to act only in an advisory capacity. The cooperation of interested agencies was to be sought at all times and the public was to be fully informed on conservation issues. Properties under Commission jurisdiction were to be maintained essentially in their natural state for conservation purposes and quiet enjoyment. While its interests might be "across the board," a deliberate attempt was made to avoid being all things to all people. All this was to prevent infringement on the duties and prerogatives assigned to others.

During the first years several cases arose which illustrate the difficulties of making such distinctions, but which also demonstrate the wisdom of following such a course. The town Recreation Committee suggested that the Commission initiate action to enlarge and develop a rifle range. The Commission was interested in the general objective, but determined that it was not within its province to acquire land for this type of recreation. Arrangements were developed for the Commission to acquire surrounding lands to serve as a natural buffer, while the Recreation Commission raised the funds through town meeting and assumed management responsibilities for the rifle range itself.

In another instance, a group of private citizens asked the Commission to acquire some 50 acres of river bottom land, partially marsh, for a playground. About half of this area was below the flood plain contour. The Commission eventually acquired this section, under the

Self-Help Program, and assisted the Recreation Commission in acquiring the upland portion for playground purposes.

In 1962 the Commission clashed with the Public Works Department, which wanted a small portion of Conservation Commission land for new bridge construction. It was determined that this *was* Conservation Commission business, on the grounds of principle if nothing else. The proposed taking was contested in town meeting, and assurance was received that the Commission would be reimbursed by the town with an equivalent piece of land, and also paid for the land taken.

Concord was one of the first towns to apply for financial reimbursement under the Self-Help Program, and its land acquisitions during the first several years are typical of those that have followed. An 86-acre lake in the western part of the town at a cost of $5,000; 17 acres of meadow land along the Sudbury River, together with five additional acres purchased cooperatively with the Recreation Commission at a total cost of $16,200; an 11-acre area containing a small skating pond and a wooded hill, for $3,300; eight acres of woodland adjacent to the Town Forest and a municipal recreation area, costing $5,000, serving as a buffer zone; a 20-acre knoll surrounded by flood plains; a six-acre marsh; and a 250-acre purchase now pending. The Trust, meanwhile, has secured gifts of land and restrictive covenants in deeds that together make up almost one square mile of wetland. During this time, the town has transferred certain tax title lands to the Conservation Commission.

In 1966 the Commission undertook a bold scheme of private open land preservation by purchasing a farm that was about to be sold for development purposes. While the owner was no longer able to continue farming in the face of increased real estate taxes, he and the community were anxious that this land be maintained in agricultural production, for its contribution to permanent open space values and because of the ready supply of fresh produce that it provided each summer. The selling price was $160,000. The town appropriated $80,000 to the Conservation Fund, and floated a bond issue for another $80,000 enabling the Commission to purchase the entire property and arrange a long-term lease with the present owner contingent upon continuation of farming. Known as the Millbrook Valley project, plans are now underway to acquire adjacent areas under similar conditions, at an estimated cost of over $1.5 million.

These are some of the bits and pieces, the microcosm aspects of the Commission's work. It has supported many kinds of land acquisition and open space preservation. Today, nearly one-fourth of the 16,000 acres of the community is under some form of conservation control—local, state, federal, and private, outright ownership or easements. In 1967 the Commission was instrumental in raising funds to purchase 1,000 acres for use as an Ecological Study Area by Harvard University. The Nature Conservancy and various private interests participated in this most recent accomplishment. The Commission played a major role in establishing another "first" in Concord—the creation of a Department of Natural Resources, combining other agencies to promote more effective resource administration and management in the community.

Concord is surrounded by Conservation Commission towns, and has taken the lead in promoting the regional watershed planning and conservation program in the Sudbury Valley. When the state Legislature passed a wetlands preservation bill for the Sudbury Valley several years ago, statutory support was provided for implementing the conservation plans that Concord had already drawn up.

In the judgment of Flint, the most significant accomplishment lies in the sustained public interest that has been created and that continues today. He has observed:

> Our town is now an educated and wise one. It has been made wise because we have enlisted, at great pain for a while, the support and participation of all the people at the local level in the work of official, unofficial and private groups. This is, I believe, the key to the success of any venture of this sort.

Flint believes that a Conservation Commission has the potential for becoming a powerful influence in any community. Because of its breadth of diversity and concern—economic, ecological, esthetic and cultural—he feels that a Conservation Commission has the capacity to engage the energies of virtually every citizen. He has pointed out that since it has no executive powers, the only way in which a Commission can affect change is through the gathering of factual information and interpreting and applying this knowledge to meet the demonstrated wants and needs of people. This process must inevitably start at the community level, but can go on to shape policies at the state and regional level. Proceeding upward, it can result not only in a more liveable physical landscape but in a more rewarding political environment.

Massachusetts Conservation Act

Ch. 40, Sec. 8-C, as amended by Acts. of 1961, Ch. 258, Acts of 1965, Ch. 769, and Ch. 885, Acts of 1967 reads as follows:

A city or town which accepts this section may establish a conservation commission, hereinafter called the commission, for the promotion and development of the natural resources and for the protection of the watershed resources of said city or town. Such commission shall conduct researches into its local land areas and shall seek to coordinate the activities of unofficial bodies organized for similar purposes, and may advertise, prepare, print and distribute books, maps, charts, plans and pamphlets which in its judgment it deems necessary for its work. It shall keep an index of all open areas within the city or town, as the case may be, with the plan of obtaining information pertinent to proper utilization of such open areas, including lands owned by the Commonwealth or lands owned by a city or town. It shall keep an index of all open marsh lands, swamps and all other wet lands in a like manner, and may recommend to the city council or selectmen and, subject to the approval of the city council or selectmen, to the department of natural resources and to the state reclamation board, a program for the better promotion, development or utilization of all such areas. It shall keep accurate records of its meetings and actions and shall file an annual report which shall be printed in the case of towns in the annual town report. The Commission may appoint such clerks and other employees as it may from time to time require. The Commission shall consist of not less than three nor more than seven members. In cities the members shall be appointed by the mayor, subject to the provisions of the city charter, except that in cities having or operating under a Plan D or Plan E form of city charter, said appointments shall be by the city manager, subject to the provisions of the charter; and in towns they shall be appointed by the selectmen, excepting towns having a manager form of government, in which town appointments shall be made by the town manager, subject to the approval of the selectmen. When a Commission is first established, terms of the members shall be for one, two or three years, and so arranged that the terms of approximately one-third of the members will expire each year, and their successors shall be appointed for terms of three years each. Any member of a commission so appointed may, after a public hearing, if requested, be removed for cause by the appointing authority. A vacancy occurring otherwise than by expiration of a term shall in a city be filled for the unexpired term in the same manner as an original appointment and in a town in the manner provided in section eleven of chapter forty-one. Said commission may receive gifts of property, both real and personal, in the name of the city or town, subject to the approval of the city council in a city or the selectmen in a town, such gifts to be managed and controlled by the commission for the purposes of this section.

Said commission may acquire by gift, purchase, grant, bequest, devise, lease or otherwise the fee in such land or water rights, or any lesser interest, development right, easement, covenant, or other contractual right including conveyances on conditions or with limitations or reversions, as may be necessary to acquire, maintain, improve, protect, limit the future use of or otherwise conserve and properly utilize open spaces and other land and water areas within their city or town and shall manage and control the same. For the purpose of this section a city or town may, upon the written request of the commission, take by eminent domain under chapter seventy-nine, the fee or any lesser interest in any land or waters located in such city or town, provided such taking has first been approved by a two-thirds vote of the city council or a two-thirds vote of an annual or special town meeting, which land and waters shall thereupon be under the jurisdiction and control of the commission. The commission may adopt rules and regulations governing the use of land and waters under its control, and prescribe penalties not exceeding a fine of one hundred dollars, for any violation thereof. No action taken under this section shall affect the power and duties of the state reclamation board or any mosquito control or other project operating under or authorized by chapter two hundred and fifty-two, or restrict any established public access. Lands used for farming or agriculture, as defined in section one A of Ch. 128, shall not be taken by eminent domain under the authority of this section. Upon a like vote, a city or town may expend monies in the fund, if any, established under the provisions of clause (51) of section five for the purpose of paying, in whole or in part, any damages for which such city or town may be liable by reason of any such taking.

Conservation Fund Act

G.L. Ch. 40, Sec. 5 Cities and towns may expend money:

(51) For the establishment and maintenance of a conservation commission. In addition a city or town may appropriate money in any year to a conservation fund of which the treasurer shall be custodian. He may deposit or invest the proceeds of said fund in savings banks, trust companies incorporated under the laws of the Commonwealth, banking companies incorporated under the laws of the Commonwealth which are members of the Federal Deposit Corporation, or National banks, or invest it in paid-up shares and accounts of and in co-operative banks or in shares of savings and loan associations or in shares of federal savings and loan associations doing business in the Commonwealth, and any income therefrom shall be credited to the fund. Monies in the fund may be expended by said Commission for any purpose, other than a taking by eminent domain, authorized by Sec. 8C.

Massachusetts "Self-Help" Act

G.L. Ch. 132-A, Sec. 11

The Commissioner shall establish a program to assist the cities and towns, which have established conservation commissions under section 8C of Ch. 40, in acquiring land and in planning or designing suitable public outdoor facilities as described in Secs. 2B and 2D. He may, from funds appropriated to carry out the provisions of Sec. 3, reimburse any such city or town for any money expended by it in establishing an approved project under said program in such amount as he shall determine to be equitable in consideration of anticipated benefits from such project, but in no event shall the amount of such reimbursement exceed fifty percent of the cost of such project. No reimbursement shall be made hereunder to a city or town unless a project application is filed by such city or town with the Commissioner setting forth such plans and information as the Commissioner may require and approved by him, nor until such city or town shall have appropriated, transferred from available funds or have voted to expend from its conservation fund, under clause of Sec. 5 of Ch. 40, an amount equal to the total cost of the project, nor until the project has been completed to the satisfaction of the Commissioner, in accordance with said approved plans. Any reimbursement received by a city or town under this section shall be applied to the payment of indebtedness, if any, incurred in acquiring land for such conservation project.

Section 2B. It is hereby declared to be the policy of the Commonwealth that all such sites acquired or developed by the Commissioner shall in so far as practicable be preserved in their natural state; that they shall be in so far as possible collectively self-supporting; and that no commercial activities except those essential to the quiet enjoyment of the facilities by the people shall be permitted.

Section 2D. (1) to acquire, plan, construct, maintain and operate public recreational facilities, including roads, areas for parking, picnicking and camping, provisions for swimming, wading, boating, outdoor games, winter sports, horseback riding, bicycling and hiking trails, nature study, rest areas, outlooks, comfort stations, food accommodations and such other facilities as the commissioner deems necessary and desirable and consistent with the policy of the Commonwealth, as set forth in Sec. 2B.

NEW YORK'S URBAN DEVELOPMENT CORPORATION

The State of New York's Urban Development Corporation represents a seemingly successful attempt to cut through the maze of fragmented jurisdictions which has frustrated urban reconstruction throughout the nation. Designed and currently headed by Edward Logue, former redevelopment director in Boston and New Haven, the UDC builds on past experience by converting massive state funding via bond issues into viable local projects of all shapes and sizes which have attracted large scale private investment. The UDC model appears to be popular; similar corporations are in the planning or development stages in other parts of the nation.

ORIGIN

The New York State Urban Development Corporation Act was signed into law on April 10, 1968. The UDC is a corporate governmental agency constituting a political subdivision of the state of New York and a public benefit corporation.

PURPOSE

UDC's basic purpose is to deal more effectively than state and local government have been able to in the past with a broad range of urban problems including physical deterioration, economic stagnation, unemployment, shortage of housing, and lack of civic facilities that confront urban areas throughout the state.

It is a fundamental principal of UDC, enunciated in the act, to encourage the maximum participation of the private sector of the economy and to make maximum use of private financing in developments it sponsors.

PROGRAMS / RESPONSIBILITIES

UDC can plan and carry out projects to supply housing for low-, moderate-, and middle-income families (about 70 percent is for middle-income families, 2(percent for low-income families, and 1(percent for the elderly); to redevelop blighted areas through land use improvement projects; to assist industrial and commercial development in areas of unemployment and blight; to provide needed educational, cultural, community and other civic facilities; and, through combination of these activities, to develop new communities.

UDC may identify and plan projects commission architectural plans for project construction; and acquire, by purchase, lease or condemnation, land on which projects are to be developed. I may secure financing and other assistance for projects from other governmental sources, arrange equity and debt financing for projects from private sources, and directly provide financing from the proceeds of sale of UDC' bonds and notes. When the projects are ready for construction, or at any other time during the course of project development.

UDC may transfer projects to its subsidiary corporations or to unaffiliated private owners to build and operate in accordance with agreed arrangements; or UDC may, directly or by contract, construct projects on its own behalf. It may sell or lease completed projects, or it may operate and manage projects which it owns or has leased back.

POWERS
UDC is empowered
—to acquire real property by purchase, lease or condemnation;
—to develop projects without conforming to local zoning ordinances, building codes, or other local laws or regulations when compliance is not feasible or practicable;
—to create subsidiary corporations to carry out UDC's purposes;

FINANCING
UDC is authorized to issue notes and bonds in the aggregate principal amount of $1 billion. UDC also has received appropriations from the state of New York. In addition, UDC draws on and uses other public and private sources of financing for its projects.

UDC projects are exempt from local real property taxes except assessments for local improvements, and broad exemptions are made for UDC, its subsidiaries and their activities, projects, or properties from other local taxes and state taxes.

DESIGN APPROACH
Aside from standards of safety, special needs of large families and of the elderly must be met with design solutions. Whenever possible, family housing is built in low buildings—with up to five bedrooms. Children's play yards must be in full view of kitchens and laundry rooms. The small amenities that turn "housing" into homes—landscaping, attractive site plans, handsome and functional lobbies or individual unit entrances, off-street parking, splash pools, sitting and play areas—are seen as an integral part of each development, not as frills.

PROJECT STATUS

CITY/Project	Dwelling Units		Cost (in millions)	Date Started
Binghamton, Ely Park	202	(of 414)	$ 5.6	9/24/70
Buffalo, Waterfront (Stage I, Phase 1)	142	(of 2400)	$ 4.4	6/ 8/70
Buffalo, Waterfront (Stage 1, Phase 2)	476		$14.1	10/29/70
Buffalo, Ellicott	180		$ 4.4	10/29/70
Ithaca, Scattered Housing	100	(of 300)	$ 2.6	10/ 6/70
New York City, Coney Island (sites 5 & 6)	332	(of 1031)	$14.2	9/11/70
New York City, Coney Island (sites 7 & 10)	484		$19.8	10/29/70
New York City, Twin Parks (NE)	275	(of 1853)	$11.2	9/21/70
New York City, Twin Parks (NW)	334		$13.8	10/20/70
Newburgh, Lake Street	375		$ 9.7	10/29/69
Niagara Falls, Unity Park	204	(of 400)	$ 5.5	10/26/70
Pittsford, Gleason Estates	300		$ 6.8	10/ 5/70
Rome, Wright Park	200	(of 300)	$ 4.2	9/25/70

PROJECT STATUS (continued)

City/Project	Dwelling Units	Cost (in millions)	Date Started
Syracuse, Townsend Tower	200	$ 5.3	10/ 8/7
Syracuse, Clinton Square			
1.2 million sq. ft.	commercial	$27.0	10/30/7
Utica, State Street	300	$ 8.5	9/15/7

In addition, demolition work started October 2 for the four-block Ten Eyck commercial complex in downtown Albany, which is estimated to cost nearly 40 million dollars.

About 20 projects in 11 localities are included in UDC's 1970 scheduled construction starts, which will provide nearly 7500 units of new housing.

Since its inception in 1968, UDC has signed agreements with 24 cities and three counties throughout the state for project activities in areas where 75 percent of the state's population lives. From the start, UDC has followed a policy of only going into a city when invited by local officials.

To date, 43,000 housing units in 2 different localities have been committe by UDC.

The 43,000 units include about 18,50 for three planned new communities. On new community is in Amherst, outsid Buffalo, where 8500 housing units ar included on 2400 acres around the Stat University Campus being built there The second is in Lysander, 12 mile northwest of Syracuse, where 5000 unit are part of a 2700-acre site. The thir new community is a joint city-state ven ture on Welfare Island, in the middle o the East River, New York City, wher 5000 units for all income levels will b built.

Source: Journal of Housing, No. 11 (December, 1970), p. 589.

VI

NEW TOWNS

A truism of urban growth in the United States seems to be that where many people live, more people will live. This trend is not unique to the United States, nor are its problems unique. One finds congestion, slums and deteriorating environment in many other nations. What is becoming painfully clear to all concerned, both professionals and citizens, is that the quality of life that has emerged in urban areas in many parts of the world fails to satisfy the desires and requirements of the people who live in them. And the problem is most apparent in the older urban areas, particularly the central cities.

As America's central cities have become increasingly dilapidated, residents with sufficient financial resources have fled to the more pleasant suburban or rural areas. Many programs have attempted to rescue the core communities from seemingly inevitable collapse, and there have been some noteworthy, albeit limited, successes. Urban renewal and rehabilitation programs have triumphed over tremendous odds to rejuvenate rundown business and a few residential areas, but the decay of the slums continues and in some cases seems to be accelerating. By the late 1960's, it became clear that neither planned nor spontaneous renovation programs were able to achieve success on anything approaching an appropriate scale. Demands simply outpaced even the best attempts. Furthermore, we now know that some solutions merely spread the disease; for instance, suburbs that have reached a certain age seem to replicate central city troubles—creating their own slums, developing their own history of racial tensions, all to be followed by a new middle class exodus to a newer suburb.

One alternative approach to dealing with the urban dilemma is to bypass them; to set aside the central cities as an essentially insoluble complex of problems suitable at best for a holding action while attention focuses on outlying areas. For example, sweeping proposals have been advanced to create over 100 new towns in the United States with a total planned population of about 10 million. In combination with the 70 new towns existing in 1969 (planned population 3.5 million) this would mean that by the year 2000 one American in twenty could be living in a planned new community. If it is assumed that conditions in our cities cannot be substantially improved at reasonable cost, it follows that the simplest solution is to abandon them and concentrate on small and medium sized cities, on suburbs and on building new towns. A frontal assault on central city problems clearly has significant political and racial overtones. It is equally clear that the strategy of suburban new towns appeals to quite specific political constituencies and exclude others. Perhaps there will be a fatal confrontation of constituencies, but at present the United States is committed to both strategies, although new town development has a growing political edge.

New towns have, of course, been under development in various areas of the world for hundreds of years, and yet the term has not been clearly defined. Here and abroad the term has been applied to a wide range of urban developments having a number of different objectives. The leading modern prototypes of the new town concept are found in Europe, particularly in the United Kingdom. The British experience is significant in light of its impact on the development of new towns in America and elsewhere.

In Britain, a new town is defined as an independent, relatively self-contained, planned community of a size large enough to support a range of housing types and to provide economic opportunity within its borders for the employment of its residents. It is large enough to support a balanced range of public facilities and social and cultural opportunities. In addition, it is surrounded by a green belt which serves the dual purpose of relating the town to the surrounding countryside and limiting its growth to a predetermined size both in population and area. Through this process the population density can be determined in advance. In the same way the desired proportion of industrial, commercial, residential, public facilities, and open space can be specified during the planning process.

The British turned to new towns as a way of alleviating population pressures in heavily built-up metropolitan areas. New towns allowed the British to work on several urban fronts simultaneously, hence solving several urban problems at the same time: reducing the concentration of population, de-centralizing employment, and rebuilding older central cities. In the readings which follow, the essay, "The New Towns of Britain," explores the history of the British new

*town experience. It includes a discussion of development corpora-
tions, finances, housing, employment, transportation, and the provision of services and amenities. By the end of 1968, thirty new
towns had been designed in Britain with a current combined population of 950,000—less than two percent of the United Kingdom total.
However, plans call for an ultimate expansion to a total of 3 million
people living in new towns.*

*Although Great Britain has had the longest and most extensive
experience with new towns, other European countries have also had
some noteworthy successes. The most interesting examples include
the Netherlands, Sweden and Finland. Each has followed a different
approach. In Sweden a large role was played by private enterprise
operating within a national plan and policy. In the Netherlands, new
town development is part of a highly centralized national urban
development and land-use control program. Finland's Tapiola is the
work of a nonprofit organization created during the post-war housing
shortage by a group of welfare and labor organizations who sub-
scribed its initial capital.*

*American planners studied the European record and developed an
approach that incorporates some of the same features, while at the
same time adapts to the realities of the American political, economic
and social condition. For example, new towns in the United States
are not independent entities in the same sense as the British new
towns. At times they include some retail and light industry, but not
necessarily a substantial, diversified economic base. Moreover, with
few exceptions, they are located within commuting distance of existing employment centers. As a result, new towns in the United States
are sometimes called new communities rather than new towns.*

*"New Communities in America and Their Objectives" describes
the early history of the new town experience in the United States
and portrays the new towns presently under development. It
includes also a discussion of various aspects of planning for new
towns including location, financing, governmental framework, planning, land-use and development regulations, public facilities and services, federal and state programs available for new community facilities. Finally, it examines the opportunities for experimentation in
new towns and the problems facing potential developers.*

*Some social aspects of new town experience in the United States
are explored by Wolf Von Eckardt in his essay, "A Fresh Scene in
the Clean Dream." Eckardt concentrates primarily on Columbia,
Maryland, with additional references to Reston, Virginia, and Jonathan, Minnesota. Columbia was designed to be economically and*

*socially inclusive rather than exclusive, unlike those class-angled sub-
urban communities that often try to bar entrance to low and moderate
income groups. As one Columbia official said, "If Columbia is to be
an experiment in building for the Next America, then it must be
workable for all Americans."*

*Although Columbia and the other American new towns are as yet
too new to permit a fair evaluation, it would appear that they have
been able to solve many of the practical problems which have arisen
during the early growth stages. They offer pleasant, safe environments for their residents including considerably more open space
than is found in traditional subdivisions. (However, many seem to
suffer from the same malaise that grips American suburbs and British
new towns—an after-dark dullness repellent to the young.) But this
progress has not been accomplished without extraordinary effort and
tolerance on the part of both developers and residents. Perhaps this
is the ingredient missing from many of our urban community renewal
programs: the will to succeed and the enormous energy required to
achieve the goals.*

*Provisions of the 1968 Housing Act have to a limited degree elimi-
nated some of the financial risks which earlier new town developments were forced to assume. The federal government now guarantees aid to support the initial heavy fixed cost in land acquisition and
planning, helping the developer wait out the slow return of his investment. The developers of Reston and other early new towns paid a
high penalty for pioneering. This risk will not be as great for the
developments which follow.*

*The new towns concept provides an attractive approach to two
problems: the desperate need for new housing and the equally
desperate desire for pleasant living environments. Although this approach has been badly neglected in the United States until recently,
now faced with apparently hopeless conditions in its central cities,
the United States seems to be moving rapidly in this field. Foreign
nations have taken the lead in new towns, but if current plans
materialize the United States may catch up.*

17. The New Towns of Britain

INTRODUCTION

The new towns are one of the most striking developments of the last two decades in Britain. They are comprehensively planned communities—pioneering examples of modern urban planning—providing opportunities for people to live and work in pleasant surroundings and in conditions that favour industrial expansion.

The new towns attract large numbers of overseas visitors every year: although there are new towns in many other countries, nowhere have they been built in such substantial numbers as a matter of policy as in Britain. In 1967 an international prize for community architecture was awarded to Cumbernauld, one of Scotland's five new towns— the citation said that the town although incomplete "has already a real sense of community . . . that will endear it to residents and visitors alike." The degree of success achieved by the new towns is suggested by the results of a number of surveys which show that at least four-fifths of new town residents are pleased that they moved there; movement away is very small.

"Garden cities"—the forerunners of new towns—were originally conceived as an antidote to the over-crowded living and working conditions prevailing in the industrial towns of Britain at the end of the nineteenth century. In the hundred years between 1800 and 1900 the proportion of the population living in the large towns rose from about 20 to 80 per cent as a result of the labour demands of the industrial revolution. In these towns, conditions for the mass of the working people were so crowded and unhealthy that a number of enlightened, wealthy individuals turned to the solution of planning entirely new settlements such as Saltaire (1853), Bournville (1878) and Port Sunlight (1887). Among those most convinced of the benefits of

Great Britain, Central Office of Information, Reference Division. *The New Towns of Great Britain*. London: Her Majesty's Stationery Office, 1969.

New towns of Britain.

establishing new settlements was Ebenezer Howard, who saw them as a means of combining the advantages of town and country life. In his book *Tomorrow: A Peaceful Path to Real Reform*,[1] published in 1888, he put forward detailed plans for the layout of complete new "cities" in which factories, houses, schools, shops and other facilities could be provided. The "cities" would be surrounded by open country for recreational purposes and urban sprawl would be prevented by separating the "cities" from existing large towns. In 1899 the Garden Cities Association (which later developed into the Town and Country Planning Association) was founded to promote these aims. By 1903 Ebenezer Howard's ideas had been put into practice with the establishment of Letchworth (some 35 miles north of London) and in 1920 Welwyn Garden City—a similar distance from the capital—was founded. Although there were no further garden cities, the idea gathered considerable support in the following years, and became the basis of official policy in plans prepared during the early 1940s.

In a report on the *Distribution of the Industrial Population*[2] published in 1940, the Barlow Commission urged that urban growth be restrained by the adoption of a positive policy of developing new and expanding towns. In 1944 Sir Patrick Abercrombie's *Greater London Plan* proposed that a series of new towns should be established, each accommodating 60,000–80,000 people and industry from the overcrowded capital. He recommended sites about 25–30 miles from London, well outside the suburban areas where a speculative and unplanned housing boom had taken place during the 1920s and 1930s. As a result of these proposals the Government set up a committee in 1945 under the chairmanship of Lord Reith

'to consider the general questions of the establishment, development, organisation and administration that will arise in the promotion of new towns in furtherance of a policy of decentralization from congested urban areas; and in accordance therewith to suggest guiding principles on which such towns should be established and developed as self-contained and balanced communities for work and living.'

A year later the Reith committee issued three reports[3] which contained a blueprint for the administrative and financial machinery needed for the creation of new towns and recommendations concerning their size, lay-out and economic and social structure. These reports were generally accepted by the Government as the basis of its policy.

Statutory provision for the establishment of new towns in Great Britain was first made in the New Towns Act of 1946; similar provision was made for Northern Ireland in 1965.

Achievements

The new towns construction programme was launched with the designation of Stevenage in November 1946. By the end of 1968 30 new towns had been designated in Britain—20 in England, 2 in Wales, 5 in Scotland and 3 in Northern Ireland.[4] Some of these towns are virtually complete, in others building is well advanced and a number are only in the planning stage.

Eleven of the new towns situated in the south-east of England around London are designed to help to solve the capital's housing problem: they are Basildon, Bracknell, Crawley, Harlow Hatfield, Hemel Hempstead, Milton Keynes, Northampton, Peterborough, Stevenage and Welwyn. Telford[5] and Redditch were designated to serve a similar purpose for Birmingham and the congested Midlands, while Skelmersdale and Runcorn are helping to relieve population pressure in Liverpool and on Merseyside. Warrington is to be expanded to accommodate people from Manchester. The Scottish new towns—Cumbernauld, East Kilbride, Glenrothes, Irvine and Livingston—are being developed primarily to take overspill population from Glasgow. Irvine and Livingston are also designed to be areas of industrial growth in central Scotland. Washington is planned to take overspill from the Newcastle area and to be a centre of economic growth. Peterlee was designated to provide homes and alternative employment for miners in the area. Cwmbran in south Wales is fulfilling a special function in providing housing for workers, many of whom used to travel considerable distances to work there. Aycliffe and Corby were designated to play a similar role: they are also areas where industry is expanding further. Newtown in mid-Wales is to be expanded primarily to encourage economic growth in the region.

In Northern Ireland a new city is being established at Craigavon and the existing towns of Antrim and Ballymena are to be rapidly expanded in an effort to reduce the concentration of people who live and work in the Belfast urban area. In addition they are expected to attract new industry, thereby discouraging further migration from Northern Ireland.

Since the late 1940s more than half a million people have moved into the new towns, which now have a total population of some 950,000. By the end of 1968 some 186,500 new houses, flats and maisonettes, more than 950 new factories, some 620 new offices, nearly 3,000 news shops and about 370 new schools had been built. The necessary services and facilities such as water, gas and electricity supplies, roads, footpaths and public transport were also provided.

Most of the new towns are planned to consist of groups of residential communities, known variously as neighbourhoods, districts or villages, providing homes and facilities such as a primary school, welfare clinic, shops, a community centre, a public house and a church within some ten minutes' walking distance, for some 4,000 to 5,000 people. The town centres provide the focal point for the major commercial, administrative and social activities. The new towns have provided an opportunity for developing and experimenting with new concepts for the design and planning of urban centres, such as the development of traffic-free residential and shopping areas (see p. 308) which have become generally accepted elsewhere. The industrial sections of the towns are sited in planned relationship to transport services and the residential areas.

Trends

Throughout the period of new town development, planning policies have evolved in the light of growing experience. Over the years, increasing provision has been made for car ownership (see p. 308). The new towns' contribution to regional development has been increasingly recognised and has led to the location of larger new towns well away from the conurbations, particularly London, to help to generate economic activity elsewhere. Often they help to renew the economic base of an area where existing industry is in decline, as a number of comprehensive studies of the various regions of Britain, undertaken over the past few years, have advocated.[6]

Another important influence encouraging the development of larger new towns is the continuing problem of alleviating congestion in the older big cities. Whereas in the 1940s planners believed that the population would remain fairly stable, official estimates now indicate a rise of nearly 20 million over the next 33 years to a total of some 74.5 million in the year 2000. In addition to the need to provide dwellings for this growing population, there is the problem of replacing large numbers of old, unfit dwellings—a legacy left by the rapid growth of the industrial towns in the nineteenth century. According to a government survey carried out in 1967[7] there are some 1.8 million slum dwellings in England and Wales, most of which are to be cleared from the congested inner areas of the large towns. Rehousing the occupants to modern standards requires far more space than is available within the towns; in Birmingham, for example, it is calculated that there will be a net loss of some 45 per cent of the dwellings in the course of comprehensive redevelopment. An estimated one million Londoners will need to be rehoused outside the conurbation by 1981.

The earlier new towns had target populations of under 100,000; with the designation of Milton Keynes in 1967 a major new city accommodating some 250,000 by the end of the century is being planned for the first time. A faster and more economic rate of building is expected as the result of planning on a bigger scale. Additional advantages are that a larger new town can offer a greater variety of employment to its inhabitants, and it will become economic to provide a wider range of urban facilities at an earlier stage in the town's growth. With the rise in car ownership, the increased mobility of the average family in Britain has made it possible to envisage larger new towns without loss of the sense of community.

A further development of the new towns concept, designed to combine the advantages of large-scale new building with the benefits of a continuing urban tradition, is the construction of big new towns based on large existing communities. The first example was the designation in 1968 of Peterborough, which has a population of some 81,000, where planned expansion as a new town is to be undertaken to accommodate an additional 70,000 people, mainly from London, by 1981. Similar proposals have been made for the existing towns of Northampton[8] and Ipswich[9]—each has a population of some 120,000 and is expected to provide accommodation for an additional 70,000 Londoners by 1981—and also Warrington (in the north-west region) where the population of 125,000 is to be increased by 40,000 by 1981, helping to ease congestion in the Manchester area. A large new town in the Preston-Leyland-Chorley area of Lancashire is under consideration as a further measure to help to relieve the congestion in Manchester and to provide a focal point for industrial growth; it is expected that a new town in the area could grow to accommodate about 500,000 people by the end of the century—double its present population.

The advantages of using established towns as a nucleus for large-scale expansion include the existence of an experienced administrative organisation to work alongside and in co-operation with the development corporation; the public services, shopping centres and other facilities are already available—and greater emphasis can therefore be placed on the house building programme; and established industry in the town can take the opportunity to expand. At the same time the existing towns can undertake the renewal of outworn areas, particularly the replacement of low-standard housing.

ADMINISTRATION

The New Towns Act of 1946 and subsequent legislation [now consolidated for England and Wales in the New Towns Act of 1965 and for

Scotland in the New Towns (Scotland) Act of 1968] gives the Minister of Housing and Local Government and the Secretaries of State for Scotland and Wales power to designate any area of land, including an existing town or village, as the site of a new town and to appoint a development corporation to be responsible for its planning and development. The Minister of Development in Northern Ireland has similar powers under the New Towns Act (Northern Ireland) 1965, and appoints development commissions. The local authorities concerned, interested government departments and other bodies are consulted about proposals: public local enquiries are held by an independent Inspector (who reports to the appropriate Minister) to consider objections to proposed development from interested parties such as farmers, whose land would be required for development. Most objections concern the amount and quality of agricultural land involved. One result of such protests—made at an enquiry about the designation of Milton Keynes—was that the Minister of Housing and Local Government decided to accept a reduction in the proposed area of some 3,300 acres (1,320 hectares).

Development Corporation

Development corporations (or commissions) consist of a chairman, deputy chairman and not more than seven members, who are appointed for their experience and knowledge—not as representatives of particular bodies or interests. The aim is to gather together a balanced team of people, capable of directing the development of the town. The recently appointed development corporation for Milton Keynes, for example, consists of a leading businessman, an industrialist, a chief general manager of a large building society, the deputy leader of the Greater London Council and chairman of its housing committee, an academic concerned with the development of the social services in Britain and four members of local councils. Membership is part-time and initially for two years, except for chairmen who have three-year appointments.

The development corporation prepares a "master plan" for the new town, sometimes commissioning private consultants for the purpose. The plan shows the location of industrial, residential and service areas, the town centre, parkland, recreational areas and other open spaces and provides for transport systems and all the necessary amenities which the corporation thinks will offer the best possible conditions of life, work and recreation for the inhabitants. The plan is flexible enough to allow for growth and change. In recent years this has proved particularly important with the rapid growth in car ownership (see p. 308), for example. The master plan is submitted to the Minister for his approval. He again consults in detail with the local authorities and other interested bodies and considers representations from the public, after which he may agree on certain modifications with the development corporation, and then development proceeds in accordance with the approved plan.

The corporation has powers to acquire (by agreement or compulsory purchase), manage and dispose of land and other property; to carry out building, including that of houses, factories, schools, offices and shops; and to make provision for public services such as water, sewerage and electricity. Each corporation has a staff of executive officers including architects, engineers and finance officers, which may number as many as 300 in an established town like Stevenage.

The development corporations do not replace, but work with, the existing local statutory authorities in the designated area of the new town. These locally elected councils—they range from county boroughs (the largest, mostly with populations of over 75,000) to parishes (the smallest)—already have powers according to their status to provide many facilities including schools and health and welfare services.[10] In planning the large-scale additional provision needed for the new town, the corporation consults with the appropriate local council on the most effective division of work between itself and the council. (See also p. 301 on costs.) Particular attention is given to the establishment of a good working relationship between the new town development corporation and the local authorities: most of the new towns have joint advisory committees to discuss such subjects as the provision of amenities and common management services for housing. The local councillors who are members of a development corporation do not, however, act as representatives of their councils. In the recently designated new towns based on large existing communities the local authorities and development corporations have jointly commissioned consultants to do the fundamental planning and the formal responsibility for the basic development plan will be a joint one. Two or three members of the development corporation are to be drawn from the local council and as far as possible both authorities will share the same executive staff.

The development corporations make annual reports, including a statement of account, to Parliament: their work is financed by the Government (see p. 312).

The Commission for the New Towns

Under the New Towns Act 1959 a Commission for the New Towns in England and Wales was set up to take over the property from the development corporations and to manage it when the period of rapid population growth has been substantially completed. By 1968 the assets in four new towns, Crawley, Hatfield, Hemel Hempstead, and Welwyn had passed from their development corporations to the commission.

The commission may consist of not more than 15 members appointed by the appropriate Ministers. Its headquarters is in London. When the commission takes over from the development corporation continuity is ensured by the fact that the executive staff in the towns remains substantially the same.

The functions of the commission are those of estate management, primarily to maintain and improve the substantial assets of land and property that have been built up by the development corporation, while paying attention to the purpose for which the town was developed and to the needs and wishes of the people living there. The commission delegates a range of its responsibilities to local committees composed of people who live in or have detailed knowledge of the towns, including local councillors. These committees are responsible for the local management of commission property, including such functions as the planning of housing layouts and the design and construction of further building. They select tenants and fix rents for dwellings and also sell dwellings for owner occupation (advancing the mortgages in some cases). They co-operate with the local authorities, particularly in housing management. In Crawley and Hemel Hempstead, for example, common housing lists are administered by the borough councils and the commission.

The Government has announced that it intends eventually to dissolve the commission and that local housing authorities (most councils) will be wholly responsible for managing all publicly owned housing when a town is fully developed. The problem of the ownership of the considerable commercial and industrial assets of the towns at that stage is being considered.

Finance

The capital works undertaken by new town development corporations and by the Commission for the New Towns are financed by advances made to them by the Ministers under the New Towns Acts. The original Act in 1946 fixed the limit of these advances at £ 50 million but this was increased by successive Acts until in 1968 it stood at £ 800 million.[11] Commitments were running at about £ 90 million a year in 1968 and over the following year or two were expected to rise to some £ 130 million a year as development proceeded in towns recently designated. The money is being repaid by the corporations over a period of 60 years out of the income from the property. Interest is paid at the rate determined by the Treasury for government credit when the advance is made. Income is derived mostly from housing, industrial and commercial rents.

In the initial stages of development, expenditure is inevitably far greater than income because of the need to provide basic services on a large scale before remunerative development takes place. A development corporation is compelled to carry forward any revenue deficit, and finance it out of working capital borrowed from the Exchequer. The cost of providing essential services in the new towns may be shared between the local authority and the development corporation if the development is likely to impose too great a strain on the technical or financial resources of the local authority. For example, with the approval of the appropriate Minister and the Treasury, the development corporations frequently take over from the local authorities responsibility for the construction of main drainage systems and sewage disposal works. They may also help by providing land at less than cost. The development corporation and the local authority usually share the expense of constructing principal roads.

In the long term the new towns are proving to be a profitable investment. The substantial profit gained from commercial income is shown in Crawley and Hemel Hempstead where the market value of commercial assets (excluding housing) was estimated at £27 million, some 20 years after designation—a capital appreciation of some 60 per cent.

Like the development corporations, the commission submits an annual report—with accounts—to Parliament.

CHARACTERISTICS OF NEW TOWNS

Housing

A variety of housing has been provided in new towns, including two-storey houses, bungalows, flats and maisonettes. The greatest demand is for houses with gardens. Livingston Development Corporation, for example, has decided that only 10 per cent of its housing will consist of flats. Many families moving to the new towns have previously lived in overcrowded conditions in flats or rooms in the centre of cities and want the space and freedom of a house and a garden, where children can play in safety. In view of this preference care is taken to provide houses of varied architectural types in a range of layouts to avoid monotony and ensure privacy. They may, for example, be built in courts, closes, terraces or other groupings and set at various distances from and angles to roads. A number of materials such as bricks and cements of different colours and panels of natural timber are also used. Landscaping with trees is considered to be particularly important. The houses usually have two or three bedrooms and one large or two smaller living rooms though a number of both larger and smaller dwellings are also provided; all have kitchens and bathrooms with hot and cold running water and inside lavatories. Many have central heating and wired radio and television.

Densities in the new towns vary—the average being about 15 persons an acre (0.4 hectare). The consultant planner for Welwyn, for example, believed it important to maintain existing trees and shrubs and to blend the new building in with them. In this way the town was developed at a low density. Cumbernauld and Skelmersdale, however, are examples of towns planned at a higher density as compact urban units with the emphasis on the town centre as the hub of the new town.

By the end of 1968 nearly 186,500 new dwellings had been built in the new towns and a further 17,500 were under construction. Expenditure on housing amounts to two-thirds of the total capital expenditure on new towns.

Industrialised Construction. The large continuing housing programmes undertaken by the development corporations on big sites are in some cases specially suitable for construction by systems of industrialised building. About half the dwellings are currently being built by these methods, which offer the advantages of very rapid construction on the site, greater independence of weather conditions and the use of fewer skilled workers than traditional building methods require. At present, however, it is in general cheaper to build two-storey houses by traditional methods. Economies are achieved by industrialised methods only if construction is on a sufficiently large scale and confined to a limited number of building systems. Skelmersdale and Runcorn, for example, are obtaining the benefits of these economies by building dwellings designed for certain local housing authorities which have grouped together to form housing consortia to achieve the necessary scale of operation. At Glenrothes, the National Building Agency[12] is to undertake experiments intended to show the conditions under which industrialised building can be competitive with traditional house building methods in price, productivity and standards of amenity.

Rents. More than two-thirds of new town dwellings in England and Wales are rented from the development corporation and are subsidised. However, the corporations are expected to allocate subsidies according to the needs of the tenants and are given guidance about rent rebate schemes by the central housing departments. Under such schemes standard rents are fixed for each dwelling according to its size, type, location and amenities: tenants are able to apply for rebates related to their income and family responsibilities. In English new towns, an average 20 per cent of income is paid in rent. A rather lower rate is paid at present in Scotland, largely for historical reasons, but a new rent scheme, designed on similar lines to that recommended for England and Wales, was introduced in 1967 in the Scottish new towns; by 1972 rents should be broadly equivalent to those payable in English new towns.

Owner-occupied Dwellings. The demand for houses for owner-occupation is increasing rapidly and it is intended that in the future about half the dwellings built in new towns (and in the country as a whole) should be available for home ownership. In some of the more established new towns around London nearly one-third of dwellings are owner-occupied. Development corporations may build houses expressly for sale, or make existing rented houses available for sale to tenants or provide land for houses to be built by private developers.

A number of dwellings are also being provided by non-profit-making housing associations and self-build groups. In 1962, for example, the Cockaigne Housing Group was founded in Hatfield to provide specially designed houses for sale to members of the group. The members elected a committee to run its affairs including the organisation of the house building and maintenance.

The importance of increasing opportunities for home ownership and expanding the work of housing associations and co-ownership societies has been underlined by a report undertaken by members of the Centre for Urban and Regional Studies at Birmingham University. Social surveys were undertaken in Crawley, Stevenage, Aycliffe and East Kilbride to get the opinions of new town residents.

Smaller Dwellings. As experience in new towns is built up the authorities are finding it necessary to provide a larger proportion of housing for groups such as the elderly, single people and second generation families, with differing housing needs.

Bungalows and flats are increasingly being provided for elderly people—often the parents of new town residents who wish to live near their families. The development corporations are encouraged by the Government to allocate some 15 per cent of their dwellings for the elderly so that the social structure of new town communities may become more balanced and family ties strengthened.

Architects at the Ministry of Housing and Local Government have designed some grouped flatlets[13] with a resident warden on call, for old people in Stevenage. A common room, laundering facilities and a television service are provided. The flatlets are situated close to shops, a school, public house and church so that the inhabitants feel themselves to be part of the community. In Harlow some of the larger houses have "granny" flats attached to provide accommodation for grandparents. The flats are completely independent from the house, having all their own facilities. A particular problem in housing old people is the type of heating system to be installed. The flatlets in Stevenage have electric underfloor heating, the adequacy and cost of which has been studied by the Building Research Station.[14] In Glenrothes research is being undertaken with the help of the Department of Geriatric Medicine, Glasgow University, to discover the most efficient and economic heating systems in houses for the elderly.

In well-established towns small dwellings are also valuable for parents whose children have left home on marriage, and for the young married couple. It is estimated that after 15 or 20 years provision must be made in a new town for increasing numbers of second generation families.

Residential clubs and hostels, run by voluntary organisations such as the Young Men's Christian Association, provide accommodation in some towns for young people employed or studying in the area. The Galaxy Centre in Harlow accommodates some 100 people. In Bracknell a tower block provides one- or two-bedroomed flats and bed-sitting rooms for couples without children and single people (often professional workers). In Basildon a fourteen-storey block provides a focal point in the town centre (see pp. 313–314).

Employment

It is a basic principle of the new towns that work as well as housing must be provided to ensure that new towns do not become merely dormitory suburbs of the cities whose "overspill" population they are designed to accommodate. One of the most important tasks of a development corporation, therefore, is to attract to its town a number of industrial and commercial companies. New towns are able to offer special advantages, such as the allocation of houses for a firm's employees, and the space for expansion.

Under the Government's policy for the location of industry in the country as a whole, industrial development is guided by the Board of Trade to areas where it is most needed in local and national interests: in carrying out this policy the board gives a high priority to the new towns.

Industry. Most new town plans provide for industry to be sited in several areas of the town and particularly on the periphery to avoid traffic congestion at peak travelling hours in the mornings and evenings—one firm in Crawley has estimated that more than 80 per cent of its employees travel to work by car or motorcycle.

A development corporation usually builds factories of varying sizes which are available for rent over long periods or leases sites for industrialists to develop themselves. In some cases special factories are built to a company's own requirements. Experience in Scotland has shown that firms going to new towns are glad to occupy corporation-built standard factories initially but generally move to purpose-built ones within a short time.

At the end of 1968 industrial development covered an area of some 36 million sq. ft. (more than 3.35 million sq. metres) in the new towns and provided employment of more than 143,000 people. The rate of unemployment is generally low. The proportion of skilled employment in new towns is generally higher than the average in the country as a whole, and often there are more vacancies than workers available.

Industrial selection registers are kept by some cities (in conjunction with the employment exchanges and the Department of Economic Affairs), to try to ensure that employment vacancies in new towns which carry the offer of a house with them, are filled by people from congested areas such as London, Glasgow, Birmingham and Liverpool. These registers record job qualifications, the degree of housing need and the geographical preference of people willing to move to new towns. Employers notify the authorities of vacancies: in the process of selection preference is given to existing local authority tenants, people on a council's housing waiting lists, families affected by slum clearance, and others in housing need.

Development corporations are aware of the importance of offering a diversity of employment opportunities to achieve a balanced community and to mitigate the effects of any future economic difficulties in particular industries which might affect the prosperity of the town. Companies operating in Skelmersdale, only five years after development had begun, included metal-working, engineering and electronics firms, and others manufacturing products such as rubber goods, polythene containers, household polishes, pharmaceutical goods, colour television tubes and clothing. This range of industrial activity is an indication of the contribution that can be made by a new town in the economic rejuvenation of an area such as the north-west of England, where traditional industries like textiles and coal-mining are contracting. Some of the Scottish new towns have been successful in attracting technologically based industries, such as electronic engineering, which are important to the expansion of the Scottish economy. An industrial area in East Kilbride, comprising about 70 acres (28 hectares) is occupied entirely by the Ministry of Technology. The National Engineering Laboratory has been established there and an Institute of Advanced Machine Tool Technology is to be set up. Overseas firms are also expanding in the new towns. An American and a German company are setting up plants in Craigavon, for example, where building began in 1967.

Offices. In well-established towns there is a growing demand for work by young people, who are usually leaving school in increasing numbers 10 or 15 years after a town's designation. A considerable proportion of them—particularly the girls—want to do office work; of recent school-leavers in Crawley, for example, some 35 per cent of the boys and 70 per cent of the girls wanted to do office work. To help to meet the demand, offices of several government departments have been set up in the new towns: the headquarters of the Meteorological Office, for instance, is at Bracknell and an Inland Revenue Computer Centre at East Kilbride. At the end of 1968 there were nearly 3 million sq. ft. (278,700 sq. metres) of office space in new towns in which some 16,500 people were employed. Offices are usually situated in the town centres—often over shops.

Women at Work. There is also an increasing demand for employment by married women in the more established new towns. In 1967 the Harlow development corporation reported that more than one-third of the total labour force in the town was female.

In the early 1950s the corporation had rejected development applications from firms employing substantial numbers of women because the population structure of the town—mostly families with young children—largely precluded the employment of women. However, recent research[15] has shown that as their children grow older, an increasing proportion of mothers go out to work. By 1966 in Bracknell (designated in 1949) nearly 72 per cent of all employed married women were mothers.

Transport

The assessment of public and private transport needs in a new town is a major influence determining the general shape of the master plan. In a variety of ways the planners have aimed at preventing the traffic congestion that causes growing problems in established towns.

Car Ownership. The rising level of car ownership has been one of the most important changes to take place in the twenty or so years during which new towns have developed. In 1967 there were about 10.3 million cars on the roads in Britain compared with 4.2 million ten years earlier and 1.9 million in 1947. In new towns the level of car ownership is, in general, higher than the national average: a survey carried out in Bracknell in 1966 showed that 64 per cent of households there had a car—a proportion nearly 20 per cent bigger than in Great Britain as a whole.

This growth has brought formidable problems for well-established new towns such as Crawley and Welwyn. When Crawley was designated in 1947 the appropriate ratio of garages to dwellings was estimated at 1 to 3, with the result that more than a third of cars there now are parked in the streets over night. In towns like Welwyn, which have become regional shopping centres, the Commission for the New Towns estimates that the number of parking spaces will have to be increased by up to three times within the next 20 years.

Cumbernauld, designated in 1955, was the first new town planned to cater for a high level of car ownership. Garage and parking facilities are ultimately to be provided for an estimated 140 per cent household car ownership. Other more recently designated new towns usually provide one garage for each dwelling and an additional parking space for every two dwellings.

A related problem is the need to adapt the road system of the earlier new towns to the increased volume of traffic, and to the larger ultimate populations which some of them are now planning to accommodate. East Kilbride, designated in 1947 and originally planned for a population of 45,000, will ultimately expand to 100,000; the authorities concerned, with the help of a team from Strathcylde University, Glasgow, are carrying out a comprehensive traffic survey to ensure that future road development follows the most economic pattern for a town of that size.

Traffic Segregation. The principle of segregating pedestrians and motor traffic has been adopted in many of the new towns, particularly to ensure freedom from the danger, noise and fumes of vehicles. Special attention is paid to shopping centres, which may include pedestrian precincts, and to housing estates, where children's play areas are provided well away from traffic and the housing lay-outs—often on Radburn principles[16]—allow separate access for motor vehicles. Pedestrian ways lead to the front doors of dwellings and motor access roads and garages are at the rear. The pedestrian ways are usually the shortest routes to shops, schools and open spaces. People cross the main vehicular routes by underpasses and footbridges. Cwmbran's development corporation reported that by 1966 all its housing layouts provided for the complete segregation of pedestrians and vehicles. This involved the construction of underpasses at an average cost of £4,250 each. In the town centre of Corby there are plans to close the main "spine" route to vehicles, and extend the centre on both sides of it by means of pedestrian courts and malls of shops. Offices and residential accommodation will be erected above the shops: a service area, including a bus station, will be situated below.

In Cumbernauld, where the separation of traffic and pedestrians has gone furthest, none of the main roads have footpaths alongside. The figures of road accidents indicate that Cumbernauld is the safest town in Britain— during the years 1962–66 nobody was killed on the roads there and the proportion of those injured per head of the population was lower than a quarter of the national average. The existence of a separate cycleway system in Stevenage (which runs beside main roads, underpassing major road junctions) is believed to be an important factor in keeping the town's road accident rate below that in the country as a whole.

Dispersal of Facilities. In the traditional lay-out of towns, many of the major buildings and activities are concentrated at the centre, with the pattern of communications radiating outwards. This leads to congestion at the centre, particularly when the level of car ownership is high. In order to minimise congestion, some of the more recent new town plans provide for a wider distribution of traditionally "central" functions.

The preliminary plan for the large new town in central Lancashire proposes that three linked existing towns—Preston, Leyland and Chorley—should have specialised roles as the administrative, industrial and social centres respectively as well as serving the needs of their immediate populations. A system of high speed internal traffic routes designed in a linear pattern would make it practicable for people to travel easily from one town to another.

In the plans for Washington and Livingston traffic routes do not all converge on the town centre. Washington is being laid out on a "grid mesh" pattern. Facilities generating traffic such as shopping areas, secondary schools, and the hospital are to be evenly distributed in the town, to make them easily accessible. For the same reason the industrial areas in Livingston are being widely spaced. In Cumbernauld the road transport system is divided into separate categories so that traffic in residential and industrial areas is limited to that generated by the particular area alone. The urban motorway forms the main communication network in the town: two-level interchanges link it with distributor roads from the residential areas, making it unnecessary to have traffic lights or policemen to control the traffic.

Plans which provide for the dispersal of activities encourage the use of private cars: public transport on a comprehensive scale would be uneconomic because of the need for complex routing to link all the separate buildings and activities.

Public Transport. As an alternative to encouraging even further the growth in car ownership some new town planners believe that increasing emphasis should be placed on the provision of efficient public transport services both as a solution to the congestion and expense engendered if all journeys were undertaken in private cars, and to cater for those, particularly school children and old people, who do not have the use of cars. The Government's view[17] is that "it is useless to devise a structure for a city on the basis that nearly all journeys will be made by car if this demands an investment in highways so huge that the resources of the country cannot provide it"; and furthermore, that the mobility which ownership of a private car provides should not be allowed to damage the environment in which people live.

The master-plan for Runcorn provides for a roughly equal distribution of journeys between public and private transport. A "rapid transit" public transport route, to be reserved for buses, is to be constructed to link the local communities, the town centre and the industrial areas. The separate track will enable the buses to maintain their time schedules, resulting in an efficient service for the public. Bus stops are to be located at intervals of 500 yds. (460 metres)—the estimated maximum distance that people may be expected to walk to use public transport rather than their private cars. Bus stops at the industrial estate are to be deliberately sited closer to factories than car-parks. The rapid transit buses are to be given priority over all other forms of transport to the central shopping area—which itself is traffic-free. In this way it is believed that the public transport service will be cheap, fast and frequent enough to compete on equal terms with private cars.

Provision of Services and Amenities

Development corporations aim to ensure that adequate facilities are available in their towns as the population increases and needs arise. They negotiate with the appropriate interest or authority whose responsibility it is to provide particular facilities, they make land available, and, in appropriate cases, give financial assistance (see p. 301). The provision of essential services such as water, gas and electricity is, throughout the country, the responsibility of special regional boards. The General Post Office provides telephone and postal facilities. British Rail and local bus companies provide the railway and bus services respectively. The building of schools, clinics and amenities such as community centres and swimming pools is the statutory responsibility of the appropriate local authority and is financed from the rates. Fire and police services are also provided by the local authorities. The financial contributions made by the development corporation are to ensure that provision is made when the revenue from rates is not high enough to finance it. Although a development corporation has wide powers, the Government does not expect it to build facilities such as churches, public houses, cinemas or other buildings for commercial amusement, which are normally provided by private interests.

Two studies undertaken by sub-committees of the Central Housing Advisory Committee, a statutory body, have considered the facilities and services required in new and expanding towns. Both reports stress the importance of appointing an official Social Relations Officer to superintend and co-ordinate the development of services as they are required. They suggest that a specific programme of social development should be drawn up, covering the provision of physical amenities and the staffing of services to meet the social needs of families living and working in a new environment. The planning consultants for the proposed new town in central Lancashire have surveyed the social facilities in the established new towns together with those in existing large towns in the north-west region of England and have produced a scale relating facilities to the size of population served.

It is considered particularly important that the provision of medical services, schools, shops and facilities for recreation and entertainment in the new towns should be co-ordinated with housing and industrial development. The predominantly young population makes particular demands on services and amenities. It is estimated that at present more than 80 per cent of people living in the new towns are under 45 (compared with the national average of 60 per cent) and some 4 per cent only are over 60 (the national average is 17 per cent). In the early years of a town's development there is usually a rapidly increasing birth-rate but in the long-term the population becomes more balanced. A survey undertaken in Bracknell in 1966 showed that the annual natural increase per 1,000 of the population was more than twice that in Britain as a whole. However, in the older "neighbourhoods" there was a trend towards the national average.

Health and Welfare. At the start of a new town's growth the development corporation gives priority to the establishment of good maternity and child welfare services among its general health and welfare facilities. These include specially designed health centres, sited near to shops and patients' homes and staffed by doctors, dentists and other health and welfare workers such as health visitors and midwives.

Harlow has pioneered a comprehensive community medical service, including a unique industrial health service. The Nuffield Provincial Hospitals Trust, a philanthropic organisation, financed the establishment of six health centres situated at strategic points in the town. Building and equipping the centres has cost more than a quarter of a million pounds. In one unit near the town centre special services such as speech therapy, marriage guidance and family planning advice are given. Industrialists in Harlow, with the help of the Trust, have also set up centres in the industrial areas to provide a medical service for their employees. An emergency casualty service is provided by nurses and general practitioners: specialist clinics are also held. Member firms are visited regularly by medical teams which give advice on such problems as special hazards to be found in factories and the training of first aid workers.

At Livingston, medical centres, to be built in pedestrian precincts, will each serve some 12,000 people: the main health centre will be situated in the grounds of a new district hospital. The Government believes that health centres help to engender close working relationships between the general practitioners and local health services such as those for expectant mothers and young children; and encourage higher standards of medical care as a result of the co-ordination of the various services and the use of better equipment. The Department of Health and Social Security guides local authorities on the design of health centres.[18]

The responsibility for providing hospitals in Britain rests with special regional boards. Hospitals have been built in some new towns such as Welwyn, where they serve the surrounding district, and for other new towns the existing regional hospital services are expanded as necessary.

Education. The rapid provision of educational services is also of special importance in the early stages of a new town's development. Some 370 new schools had been completed in new towns in Great Britain by the end of 1968, providing places for 178,000 pupils. In order to ensure that educational provision matches the changing population structure of the new towns in the future, the Scottish Education Department has commissioned a survey in Cumbernauld, East Kilbride and Livingston to forecast the school population over a period of 8 to 10 years and, in the long-term, over a 25-year period.

In Telford and Redditch the local education authorities are organising the schools in a three-tier comprehensive system, providing education for all children living there on a non-selective basis. The development plan for Telford shows that two "first" schools (for children aged between 5 and 9 years) and one "middle" schools (for children of 9 to 13 years) will be built in each residential area while a "senior" school (for young people aged 13 to 18 years) will be built in the district centre and have combined sports facilties for the use of the school and the general public (see p. 315).

Colleges of Further Education (for young people over 15) are being provided as the need for them arises. Each of the four towns administered by the New Towns Commission has a college of its own, together providing places for some 18,000 students. To help to cater for the increasing demand for higher education throughout Britain, Hatfield College of Technology is to be developed as a polytechnic,[19] offering a comprehensive range of full-time and part-time courses up to a high academic standard. In Corby, in 1966, the first student teachers were admitted to the newly established extension of Leicester College of Education. Additional facilities for training young people are provided in Harlow and Aycliffe, where engineering training centres have been set up by local industrialists with aid from the industrial training boards.[20]

Town Centers

The central areas of new towns have usually been designed as the focal point of the town. They contain public buildings, including a town hall and law courts, police and fire stations and the main post office; a comprehensive shopping area; and entertainment facilities, including restaurants and hotels. Blocks of flats and offices are often built there. Many of the areas are traffic-free: large car parks are provided.

Most new town residents, coming from large cities, are used to a wide range of shopping facilities. By the end of 1968 nearly 3,000 new shops had been completed in the new towns. Although a number of shops are situated in "neighbourhood" areas for convenience, the main shopping areas including multiple department stores are in the town centres. The New Towns Commission reports a trend towards the establishment of the supermarket type of shop in new towns and warns that the initial design should be flexible; space must be available for an extension of sites as a town develops. Some towns such as Welwyn and Cwmbran have become regional shopping centres, attracting a large proportion of their customers from 10 to 15 miles away.

The first phase of the multi-level town centre at Cumbernauld was opened in 1967. This contains, under one roof, some 120,000 sq. ft. (11,150 sq. metres) of shopping space on the first floor, including a supermarket and a department store, and 40,000 sq. ft. (3,700 sq. metres) for offices (more than half of which is occupied by the Scottish Office of the Land Commission), a health centre, library, public hall, hotel, public house, restaurant and skittle alley and flats at other levels. When complete, the town centre will provide access for traffic and parking space for 5,000 cars at the lowest level, from which lifts, escalators and ramps will rise to a series of pedestrian decks, enclosing shopping malls. Pedestrians enter directly into the shopping area using the footpath approaches from the housing estates.

The new town centre of Runcorn containing a large shopping area and blocks of offices is to be developed by a private company (in co-operation with the development corporation). The centre will be built on a raised platform, clear of all traffic. Multi-level car parks will be provided at the edges of the shopping decks.

In many town centres architects have planned features of visual interest such as attractive pieces of sculpture and fountains. A number have won national awards, for example, the water gardens in Hemel Hempstead, which won a Civic Trust award for good design. The planners of most towns are convinced of the importance of landscaping central areas and nursery gardens and "tree nurseries" have been set up to provide plants and shrubs for such purposes. Corby development corporation plans to transplant 200 mature trees annually to improve the general environment.

Social Activities

When new communities are first set up individuals and groups, with help from the development corporations, voluntarily combine to provide a network of social, political and specialist activities. Preschool play groups, rotary clubs and branches of the Women's Royal Voluntary Service and the Civic Trust, for example, have been established. Although many of the residents may be preoccupied with their homes and young children, others give much of their time and experience to community affairs. In Livingston new tenants who have worked with voluntary organisations elsewhere are especially encouraged to continue their work in the town.

Community centres situated in the "neighborhood" areas are valued by the elderly, young people, and mothers who cannot easily travel far from their homes; the Carnegie United Kingdom Trust, a philanthropic organisation, has given grants for the establishment of community social centres in Cumbernauld and Skelmersdale. Children's play areas, playing fields and parks are dispersed within every town.

In 1964 the Ministry of Housing and Local Government and the Department of Education and Science issued a circular recommending that in the planning of new facilities the needs of the community generally should be considered and suggesting the dual use of facilities such as schools' playing fields and athletic tracks, to meet local needs. At Telford and Skelmersdale plans have been made to establish social and recreational buildings around the schools so that they might be more easily available to the whole community at appropriate times. This will provide a greater range of activities for adults, and on a larger scale than is usual at an early stage in a town's development, and school-leavers will be able to continue recreational skills and pastimes learnt at school. In Skelmersdale several industrial firms are contributing towards the cost of public playing fields so that their employees might have facilities for football and other games.

It is a feature of new towns that large areas should be left relatively undeveloped for recreational purposes. In practice an average 20 per cent of land may be designated as "open space" in town plans. At Craigavon extensive recreational facilities are envisaged for an area on the shores of Lough Neagh. On the outskirts of many of the new towns, also, there are large tracts of open countryside; Bracknell is close by Ascot Heath, Windsor Great Park and Virginia Water, much of it Crown land available for public use.

As new towns become well-established and their populations grow large enough to give the necessary support, they can offer a greater variety of facilities for recreation and entertainment. The advantage of multi-purpose recreational centres like the Harlow Sports Centre—costing some £200,000—is that it can be used by a wide variety of sports bodies, youth clubs, charitable organisations and other enthusiasts to achieve economy in management, services and maintenance. Many activities can take place at the same time within the one structure and the available space—athletic track, arena, playing fields, courts, halls and small rooms—can be used for different purposes throughout the week and new interests can be accommodated as they develop. In addition, opportunities are available in such a centre for people to widen their interests and make contacts in the new community. Entertainment centres including dance halls, cinemas, restaurants and hotels are gradually being provided in the new town centres.

Several of the well-established towns are also encouraging interest in the arts. The Basildon Civic Arts Society has promoted an exhibition of contemporary art and a poetry competition, and a civic arts centre was opened in the town in 1968. Welwyn has an art gallery and an arts trust which provides living and working accommodation in the town for a group of young artists, to help to further their professional careers. Operatic societies flourish in some of the towns and Harlow has a professional string quartet, the Alberni. A junior orchestra has been formed in Bracknell. At Corby there is a civic theatre, and plans are in preparation for establishing theatres at Harlow and Glenrothes with support from the development corporations and local councils and with financial assistance from the Arts Council—a government agency. The Government fosters the development of the arts throughout the country in many ways[21] and has urged greater local support, for example, through the encouragement of local amateur dramatic or musical groups, so that a wide range of facilities are available to people outside, as well as in, the large towns.[22]

APPENDIX 1

Town Development Schemes

Some towns in Great Britain are being expanded by means of schemes undertaken under the Town Development Act 1952 and the Housing and Town Development (Scotland) Act 1957. The implementation of such schemes is an alternative method to the creation of new towns of relieving urban congestion, providing homes for a rapidly rising population and giving encouragement to industrial growth. Voluntary agreements are made between local authorities in big cities with "overspill" problems and those in country towns willing to accept people and industry from the cities in order to strengthen their economic base. Unlike the arrangement for towns to be developed under the New Towns Acts, when the Government takes the lead, the initiative for schemes under the Town Development Acts must be taken by the local authorities concerned. The movement of population is entirely voluntary; the "exporting" authority publicises its schemes to attract firms looking for space to establish themselves or expand, and people in need of homes.

Progress

Over 60 town expansion schemes have been agreed, of which about half are related to London: others are related to Birmingham, Bristol (completed, Liverpool, Manchester, Newcastle upon Tyne, Salford (completed), and Wolverhampton.

The provision for London includes development in Swindon, which is planned to accommodate 75,000 Londoners by 1981, and in Basingstoke, which will take 40,000 people from London. Nine other towns, including Aylesbury, Haverhill, and Thetford in the south-east and eastern regions of England (well away from London) will eventually accommodate more than 10,000 people each. By 1968 some 30,000 London families had moved away from the capital under such schemes and more than 15 million sq. ft. (1.4 million sq. metres) of factory space had been completed to provide employment for them.

Several towns are to be developed on a relatively small scale to take population from Birmingham: some 17,500 people will move to Daventry. Winsford is to provide accommodation for nearly 56,000 people from Liverpool. Two schemes being undertaken at Cramlington and Killingworth to relieve pressure on the Newcastle area have been agreed for 40,000 and 11,500 people respectively. Provision has been made for Glasgow overspill in the surrounding area. More than 20,000 families had moved from the city by the end of 1967. A planned balance of growth in population and employment is considered vital to the success of the schemes.

In some cases the implementation of a town development scheme completely changes the nature of an existing town. It may, for example, double or even treble the existing population. Apart from the erection of new houses and the development of factories, sewerage and water schemes need to be extended and other services including schools and public transport provided. The town centre is often redeveloped to accommodate larger shopping areas, public buildings and social facilities.

Prospective inhabitants are encouraged to visit the expanding town and to inspect, for example, the types of houses available, the transport services, and the shopping facilities.

Industries are attracted to the expanded towns since a sufficient labour force can be guaranteed, and costs are generally lower than they are in the larger cities. Industrial selection registers (see p. 306) are used for London and Glasgow schemes.

Finance and Administration

The exporting and receiving authorities directly concerned with town development contribute towards its cost. The county council in whose area the expanding district is located may subsidise the housing to be provided and pay for water and sewerage facilities and social amenities. The exporting authority usually contributes only towards the housing subsidies: its main concern is to house its "overspill" population. The Greater London Council (GLC) usually provides the initial finance for London schemes, the receiving authority reimbursing the GLC when houses and factories become profitable through the payment of rents and rates. Government grants and housing subsidies are also available. Private developers are playing an increasingly important role in town expansion schemes; at Cramlington, for example, they are providing a major proportion of the dwellings and developing one of the industrial estates.

In some cases the GLC offers towns special help in development. Technical services such as advising on contracts and supervising constructional work, are available on an agency basis so that schemes may progress more quickly. Lancashire County Council has established an estate development team to assist any developing district in its area.

APPENDIX 2 / SOME FACTS AND FIGURES

	Date of designation	Area designated (hectares) [1]	Distance from nearby city (kilometres) [2]	POPULATION		
				At designation	End 1967	Ultimate
Great Britain:						
Stevenage	November 1946	2,500	50 —London	7,000	61,700	100/105,000
Crawley	January 1947	2,420	48 —London	10,000	63,700	75,000
Hemel Hempstead	February 1947	2,400	47 —London	21,000	67,900	80,000
Harlow	March 1947	2,560	40 —London	4,500	75,800	80,000
Aycliffe	April 1947	1,000	19 —Durham	60	18,000	45,000
East Kilbride	May 1947	4,100	14.5 —Glasgow	2,400	57,000	100,000
Peterlee	March 1948	1,000	16 —Durham	200	20,000	30,000
Hatfield	May 1948	940	32 —London	8,500	24,700	29,000
Welwyn	May 1948	1,700	35 —London	18,500	44,300	50,000
Glenrothes	June 1948	2,300	50 —Edinburgh	1,100	23,700	75,000
Basildon	January 1949	3,120	48 —London	25,000	75,000	140,000
Bracknell	June 1949	1,320	45 —London	5,000	28,300	60,000
Cwmbran	November 1949	1,260	29 —Cardiff	12,000	41,700	55,000
Corby	April 1950	1,720	37 —Leicester	15,700	47,500	80,000
Cumbernauld	December 1955	1,660	24 —Glasgow	3,000	23,000	70,000
Skelmersdale	October 1961	1,615	21 —Liverpool	10,000	16,000	80,000
Livingston	April 1962	2,680	24 —Edinburgh	2,000	7,200	100,000
Dawley [3]	January 1963	3,660	48 —Birmingham	21,000	22,000	90,000
Redditch	April 1964	2,880	22.5 —Birmingham	29,000	29,000	90,000
Runcorn	April 1964	2,900	22.5 —Liverpool	28,500	28,800	90/100,000
Washington	July 1964	2,120	9.5 —Newcastle	20,000	21,400	80,000
Irvine	November 1966	5,000	42 —Glasgow	27,000	27,000	85,000
Milton Keynes	January 1967	8,800	80.5 —London	40,000	40,000	250,000
Peterborough	May 1967	6,400	133.5 —London	80,500	81,000	175,000
Newtown	December 1967	600	43.5 —Aberystwyth	5,000	5,000	13,000
Northampton	February 1968	8,000	106 —London	131,000	131,000	220,000
Warrington	April 1968	7,460	24 —Manchester	127,000	127,000	205,000
Northern Ireland:						
Craigavon	July 1965	2,480	48 —Belfast	40,000	41,000	150,000
Antrim	July 1966	1,500	24 —Belfast	5,000	7,000	30,000
Ballymena	August 1967	2,260	40 —Belfast	20,000	20,000	70,000

[1] One hectare = 2.5 acres. [2] One kilometre = 0.625 miles. [3] Re-named *Telford* in October 1968 when the area designated was doubled in size to take an ultimate population of 220,000.

APPENDIX 3

NEW TOWN ADDRESSES

Aycliffe Development Corporation,
 Churchill House, Newton Aycliffe, Nr. Darlington, Co. Durham.
Basildon Development Corporation,
 Gifford House, Basildon, Essex.
Bracknell Development Corporation,
 Farley Hall, Binfield, Bracknell, Berks.
Corby Development Corporation,
 Spencer House, Corporation Street, Corby, Northants.
Crawley Office,
 Commission for the New Towns, Broadfield, Crawley, Sussex.
Cumbernauld Development Corporation,
 Cumbernauld House, Cumbernauld, Glasgow.
Cwmbran Development Corporation,
 Victoria Street, Cwmbran, Monmouthshire.
East Kilbride Development Corporation,
 Norfolk House, East Kilbride, Glasgow.
Glenrothes Development Corporation,
 Glenrothes, Fife.
Harlow Development Corporation,
 Gate House, The High, Harlow, Essex.
Hatfield Office,
 Commission for the New Towns, Church Road, Welwyn Garden
 City, Herts.
Hemel Hempstead Office,
 Commission for the New Towns, Swan Court, Waterhouse Street,
 Hemel Hempstead, Herts.
Irvine Development Corporation,
 151 High Street, Irvine, Ayrshire.
Livingston Development Corporation,
 Livingston, West Lothian.
Mid-Wales New Town Development Corporation,
 Newtown, Montgomeryshire.
Milton Keynes Development Corporation,
 Wavendon Tower, Wavendon, Nr. Bletchley, Bucks.
Peterborough Development Corporation,
 Peterscourt, Peterborough, Northamptonshire.
Peterlee Development Corporation,
 Shotton Hall, Peterlee, Co. Durham.
Redditch Development Corporation,

Holmwood, Plymouth Road, Redditch, Worcs.
Runcorn Development Corporation,
    Chapel Street, Runcorn, Cheshire.
Skelmersdale Development Corporation,
    High Street, Skelmersdale, Lancs.
Stevenage Development Corporation,
    Daneshill House, Danestrete, Stevenage, Herts.
Telford Development Corporation,
    Priorslee Hall, Oakengates, Shropshire.
Washington Development Corporation,
    Usworth Hall, Washington, Co. Durham.
Welwyn Garden City Office,
    Commission for the New Towns, Church Road, Welwyn Garden City, Herts.
Antrim/Ballymena Development Commission,
    Thomas Street, Ballymena, Co. Antrim, Northern Ireland.
Craigavon Development Commission,
    Bachelor's Walk Portadown, Co. Armagh, Northern Ireland.

Commission for the New Towns,
    Glen House, Stag Place, London, S.W.1.

NOTES

[1] Re-issued under the title *Garden Cities of Tomorrow*.

[2] Cmd. 6153.

[3] Cmd. 6759; Cmd. 6794; Cmd. 6876.

[4] For dates of designation and other facts and figures see Appendix 2.

[5] Including Dawley.

[6] See COI reference pamphlet *Regional Development in Britain*, RF.P. 5804/67.

[7] See *Old Houses into New Homes*, Cmnd. 3602, HMSO, 1968.

[8] Designated February 1968.

[9] Still under consideration.

[10] See COI reference pamphlet *Local Government in Britain*, RF.P. 5505.

[11] A Bill is before Parliament to increase this amount by a further £300 million.

[12] Established by the Government to give technical advice on building methods. It is at present concerned with increasing the rate of house building.

[13] Design Bulletin, No. 11 *Old People's Flatlets at Stevenage*, HMSO, 1966.

[14] A government body concerned with the techniques of building design

and construction and the organisation, productivity and economics of building work.

[15] *Survey of Women's Employment*, Vol. 1. HMSO, 1968.

[16] A term derived from a system introduced in Radburn, New Jersey, USA where the arrangements for the movement of pedestrians and vehicles were planned as physically independent but related systems.

[17] *Public Transport and Traffic.* Cmnd. 3481, HMSO, 1967.

[18] *Local Authority Clinics.* HMSO, 1962.

[19] *A Plan for Polytechnics and other Colleges.* Cmnd. 3006, HMSO, 1966.

[20] Established under the Industrial Training Act 1964.

[21] See COI reference paper *The Promotion of the Arts in Britain,* R. 5647.

[22] *A Policy for the Arts: the First Steps.* Cmnd. 2601, HMSO, 1965.

18. New Communities in America and Their Objectives

THE AMERICAN EXPERIENCE

The first settlers at the beginning of the 17th Century were concerned primarily with establishing a foothold and with surviving. Considering the odds against which they fought, it is surprising how early their attention was drawn to establishing planned new towns, as distinguished from simple fortified settlements. By the end of the century a quite sophisticated plan was developed and implemented for Williamsburg to serve as the colonial capital of Virginia.

As colonization spread westward across the continent, new villages, towns, and cities followed in its wake. Yet only rarely was the gridiron street, strip commercial development pattern broken as it was in the early Ohio planned community of Tallmadge, which was laid out around a rectangular village square with radial streets reaching out from it. Since all of the early pioneer forest and prairie towns were new in the same sense that the colonial settlements had been, the exceptions stand out mainly because of the quality and imaginative nature of their planning and execution. The antecedents of today's new communities were generally called "planned communities."

Industrialization and Urbanization

The course of industrialization in the United States destroyed or rendered irrelevant many features of the agrarian ethic and created the framework of today's urban development. Between 1840 and 1900, the massive influx into the newly created great cities erased the rural population predominance over urban centers and helped establish an industrial economy. Simple forms of government and haphazard

Advisory Commission on Intergovernmental Relations, *Urban and Rural America: Policies for Future Growth*. Washington, D.C.: Government Printing Office, 1968, pp. 67–79, 89–93. Reprinted by permission.

community growth relevant to an agrarian economy, however, persisted well into the 20th Century, even though the problems of urbanization increasingly demanded attention.

Widespread recognition of the drawbacks of aimless urbanization and expansive growth has been slow in developing. The concept of a coordinated planning effort has been resisted by both private developers and government. American community planning generally has been characterized by unrelated efforts of individuals and groups.

Each attempt at urban planning, however, has provided its own responses to these problems. Lessons can be drawn from these experiences that should be considered by those who would propose a more thoroughgoing program of community planning in general and of new communities in particular. Despite the comparatively small number of community planning efforts, they constitute a vital part of urban development in the United States. In the following historical survey, attention is devoted to the main percursors of current new community development even though not all would meet a strict contemporary definition.

Private Development and Planning

Company Towns. In the evolution of planned communities in the United States, company towns stand out as the first major development, mainly because they were an initial outgrowth of the industrial revolution. The National Resources Committee's 1939 publication *Urban Planning and Land Policies* classified 52 of its 99 case studies of planned communities as company towns.[1]

Between 1830 and 1900 construction of these towns was at its height. However, as time went on, only a few could be considered well planned, largely because the promoting industries were concerned mainly with profits and the needs of the company rather than with experimental planning. Prior to the 1850's, this was not so much the case. For example, when obliged to employ female workers as a result of labor shortages, Francis Cabot Lowell's textile manufacturing company responded to New England social pressures by adopting a policy of company paternalism. In 1832, Lowell, Massachusetts, was constructed on a simple and functional plan that created a town of unique character admired by many foreign visitors. With the influx of cheap immigrant labor in the 1850's, Yankee millowners no longer felt the need to provide company town facilities.

The labor-management controversies following the Civil War industrial boom dampened any inclination favoring long-range planning considerations over short-run objectives in the construction of company towns. Developments such as Gary, Indiana, built by U. S. Steel on the south shore of Lake Michigan, are illustrative of company towns of this period. The development of Gary emphasized private incentive in home building, and included steel manufacturing facilities, railroad transportation, and public utilities. A. P. Melton, the chief planner, foresaw the development of a linear string of separate towns connected by railroad in the Gary region, but such development occurred rather less systematically than he expected and produced not a new community pattern, but a vast regional industrial sprawl.

Many industrial towns—Kohler, Wisconsin; Granite City, Illinois; and others—followed this pattern of unrestricted growth, with such resultant shortcomings as inadequate housing, street, and parking facilities. Yet, some company towns instituted important innovations in physical planning, financing, and services. The general faith of these industrialists in the economic viability of large-scale property operations encouraged later private developers to attempt similar projects.

Two of the most significant examples of company towns were Pullman, Illinois and Kingsport, Tennessee. Completed in 1884 as an "industrial park," Pullman featured cultural, educational, and athletic facilities provided by a large arcade and numerous playing fields. Housing varied with income and was above the general contemporary standards. All homes were on a rental basis, and all costs, including construction and maintenance, were charged against the generally high rents. The principal problem was the absence of democratic checks on the exercise of the authority of company agents and supervisors to conduct municipal affairs.

The development of Kingsport in 1915 marked perhaps the greatest advance in planning a company town. Its features included a diverse industrial base, an early planning body utilizing private zoning regulations, and initially a wholly democratic council-manager form of local government operating under a model city charter. However, the physical plan and the generally inadequate permanent zoning restrictions retarded the healthy, balanced development of Kingsport.

Generally, company towns have been a minor element in the American tradition of city planning. As John W. Reps has stated: "the history of these [industrial] communities provides few precedents that we would care to duplicate in the future. American industry, for all its success in production, singularly failed in its attempt to manufacture noteworthy communities." [2] Although many of the explanations of their failure or the causes of their success have little direct relevance to the problems faced by new communities today, in some respects the history of American company towns provides valuable insights into perennial problems in urban development. Their experience demonstrates the need to insure democratic participation by citizens in planning and administration as well as the advisability of joint business-governmental efforts.

Real Estate Communities. The failure of Pullman and other company towns to generate widespread public enthusiasm or to solve major problems of industrialization indicated the failure of paternalism alone as a means to those ends. The large-scale construction and planning involved, however, encouraged other private investors to initiate their own planned communities, albeit for entirely different purposes. The real estate communities were an attempt to create suburbs completely cut off from the industrial process. Through such action, their developers hoped to avoid the problems that had beset company towns.

Riverside, Illinois, established in 1869, was the first of the real estate communities, and attracted a population which stubbornly maintained Frederick Law Olmstead's original plan against the relentless urban growth of the Chicago transportation and recreation systems. Roland Park, a suburban section of Baltimore established in 1891, developed into a self-contained community endowed with unique cultural, religious, and educational facilities, and succeeded in sealing itself off from urban infringements by open space and a high stone wall. The Country Club District of Kansas City emerged in 1906 as a reaction to the industrial belt surrounding the city and attempted to insulate itself from urban growth by comprehensive deed restrictions. Forest Hills Gardens on Long Island, New York (1911), was intended by its developers to be a striking example of a profitable business enterprise and of a comprehensively planned real estate development. It proved to be the most successful of all communities here considered. Finally, Palos Verdes Estates of Los Angeles County (1923) was the most complete expression of community development by business incentive. Owners of securities of the trust indenture were permitted to either retain their securities for speculative purposes or to exchange them for land at cost price. It should be noted that all of these developments except the Country Club District were planned by Frederick Law Olmstead, Sr. or by the firm of Olmstead Brothers. The District was developed by the Sage Foundation.

Unique planning features and comprehensive protection deed restrictions—characterized by stability of land-use, separation of residential and business areas, and a continuous planning function—make these real estate communities significant improvements over the company town idea. In addition, they avoided two of the major short-comings of company towns. First, while the industrial developments had been paternalistic "bordering on the dictatorial," the real estate communities were largely selfgoverning. Second, these communities proved to be fertile ground for the development of a "sense of neighborhood," a "community spirit" so obviously lacking in the later company towns.

Yet, these benefits were purchased at a price which precluded broader application of these developments to the problems of expanding urbanization. The major feature limiting their contemporary relevance was the cost of their construction and subsequent maintenance. Such an investment involved a risk that only financially strong industrial corporations were able to accept. It ultimately precluded any but upper-income housing and thus prohibited a "mix" of citizens differing in social, financial, or ethnic status. Furthermore, in some cases (notably at Palos Verdes Estates) the contradiction between the management's genuine desire to strengthen citizens' participation in policy development and the individual homeowner's personal desire for speculative investment through the sale of land and securities promoted administrative confusion and vacillation. As in the industrial communities—although to a lesser extent—profit rather than long-range public benefit became an inescapable objective. Beyond these drawbacks lay the basic fact that a flight to suburban safety merely ignored, rather than relieved, urban problems of congestion, transportation inefficiency, and inadequate industrial location.

These early suburban developments demonstrated the possibility of large-scale private sponsorship of planned communities. However, neither industry, seeking integration of industrial capacity into planned communities through paternalism, nor private real estate developers, seeking exclusion of industrial capacity through rigorous controls and the profit motive, were able to provide a practical general alternative to unrestricted urban growth.

Garden Cities. The impact of the Progressive political movement at both the national and State levels contributed in the two decades following 1910 to an increased public acceptance of a positive governmental role in the economy and in promoting limited social objectives. Yet, even with the growing awareness of certain urban problems and the increasing popular willingness to sanction a governmental role, efforts to plan new developments or to adopt and publicize innovative theories of community structure were undertaken by individuals having neither enthusiastic public support nor effective communication with their fellow planners. Only the housing shortage of the twenties increased public awareness of community planning and of new towns as a potential channel for expanding urbanization.

Clarence Stein, a planner for the New York Commission for Housing and Regional Planning and for the Regional Planning Association of America synthesized many previous American experiences in planning and gave direction to future planners through his evolution of a program designed to create new towns in America. His theory, which came to be known as the Radburn Idea, was one of the most important milestones in the history of American community planning. It was drawn in part from European experience, yet was wholly native in its proposed solution to problems of urban deterioration and disorderly suburban growth.

The major component in the formulation of the Radburn Idea was the work of Ebenezer Howard. Howard's theories concerning the development of garden cities, presented earlier in the chapter, substantively influenced Stein and through him, all subsequent American community planning.

The other major influence on Stein was the work of Clarence Perry. Perry hypothesized that the total community should be planned as a series of separate neighborhood communities and a common community center linked together by pedestrian thoroughfares separated from those for traffic. Such a settlement of completely integrated neighborhoods, Perry reasoned, could bring to within walking distance a common meeting place for all community inhabitants, with resulting social benefits.

To these two theories, Stein added his own pragmatic justification for the development of new communities. He was convinced that the standard urban growth pattern was overly expensive—due to such invisible costs as lack of accessible recreation facilities and transportation congestion, and that large-scale financial investment over long periods of time, as well as a long-range flexible planning process, could support the building of a town of substantial population, democratically administered, and having a high level and wide range of municipal services. Such community characteristics would eliminate the type of financial arrangements which had supported previous company towns and real estate developments. He suggested that limited dividend corporations or organs of government might serve as sponsors of new communities. Stein, ". . . sharply challenged the traditional assumption that government's role in housing was limited to the enactment of minimum standards legislation. Throughout the

1920's, the [Regional Planning Association of America] pressed for the establishment of financial mechanisms to channel government capital into the housing market. . . . Complaining of a continued scarcity of private capital for housing purposes, Stein's [New York State Commission of Housing and Regional Planning] recommended municipal loans, public housing, and a constitutional amendment authorizing State housing credit." [3]

Such financial backing would make middle- and low-income housing feasible for planned communities. Moreover, Stein's objectives extended the scope of his communities beyond those of the industrial towns. His planning theory assumed that the unusual design of the new town required an unusual form of legal framework to organize and maintain the community. Planning was seen as a social process, rather than as the formulation of a physical objective and the mobilization of existing resources to attain that goal. If a plan was an integral part of social organzation, it would possess vitality; if not, it was lifeless whatever its technical merits.[4] These principles were reflected in four communities which were planned by Stein—Sunnyside Gardens, Radburn, Hillside Homes, and Baldwin Hills Village.

Sunnyside Garden Apartments, a planned neighborhood in New York City, was constructed between 1924 and 1928 and served as the first expression of Stein's planning and social objectives. The preservation of open space through interior parks and gardens, and the use of the "superblock", with its vital community spirit, represented to Stein an important step towards the construction of a complete garden city. What initial and continuing success the community possessed was made possible by the availability of transportation, by rapid, large-scale construction minimizing carrying charges, and by community selfgovernment. Stein had expected that the economics of low-interest capital financing, rapid construction, and centralized purchase and management would offer both a superior residential environment and a substantial reduction in costs. However, in the end Sunnyside houses were more expensive than those provided by speculative developers, because the 6 percent dividend rate was too high to serve the needs of low-income workers (thus preventing the social-financial mix which Stein had sought) and because overhead costs made competition with the speculative builder difficult.

The establishment of Radburn, New Jersey, in 1928, was an attempt by Stein and Henry Wright to build a true garden city. In this respect, it is one of the major experiments in the history of American urban development. The plan was essentially that of Sunnyside but executed in a nonurban and vastly expanded setting. It utilized superblocks, roads for specialzied uses separating pedestrian and motorized travel, and central parks, although it did not include Howard's greenbelt or ties to nearby industrial facilities. Radburn suffered more intensely from financial difficulties than had Sunnyside. Stein himself concluded that unless insurance companies or endowed foundations provided capital assistance in reducing the load of overhead expenses, government cooperation would be essential in taking and holding land, in financing essential utilities, highways, and low-income housing, and in constructing public facilities.

Hillside Homes, New York, continued the tradition of Sunnyside as an apartment complex utilizing indigenous open "green space" within a built-in urban area. It was an example of the governmental financial assistance Stein had earlier recommended, with Federal financing being offered first by the Reconstruction Finance Corporation and subsequently by the Public Works Administration. The full recovery of costs and a vacancy rate of less than one-quarter of one percent in its first 14 years provide an indication of the combination of circumstances necessary to reach a break-even point.

Constructed in 1941, Baldwin Hills Village, located in Los Angeles County, was the last of the communities planned by Stein. It represented the most complete expression of the Radburn Idea. As with Hillside Homes, only government financial assistance, in the form of Federal Housing Administration insurance guarantees, permitted construction of the development. The long-term equilibrium of the community—as demonstrated by the 100 percent occupancy since establishment—illustrates the role that government assistance can play to lessen carrying charges and market pressures during the necessarily extensive planning period. On the other hand, the gradual stabilization of the age and income levels to a mature upper-middle class group indicates that to insure a "mix," a planned community must be large enough (Baldwin Hills has only 1,170 tenants) to accommodate different kinds of living preferences.

The urban design features of the Radburn Idea and the appropriateness of cost analysis as a planning technique are the major legacy of these efforts of the mid-1940's. Experience in other critical areas—notably those dealing with problems of incorporation, unified administrative control versus democratic participation, maintenance of a continuous planning process, the use of a deed restriction process, and the level of community services provided—was much less conclusive. The major problem confronted, that of financing new developments, revealed that many vital aspects of new community development—

such as low-income housing, long-term planning, and large-scale land assembly—may depend upon financial support from the government.

Government Communities—Introduction of the Federal Role

World War I—U.S. Shipping Board Communities. Direct Federal sponsorship of comprehensively designed residential developments began with the October 1917 recommendations of the Advisory Commission of the Council of National Defense in response to severe war industry housing shortages. In March 1918 Congress enacted the necessary housing legislation and appropriated an eventual total of $175 million—$75 million to the Emergency Fleet Corporation (EFC) of the United States Shipping Board and $100 million to the United States Housing Corporation (USHC) through the Labor Administration—for the creation of permanent homes and communities. Absolute control in these projects was maintained by the government, with the USHC building and administering its communities directly, and the EFC maintaining complete control over rental, design, and management policy.

Following Great Britain's precedent in war housing, these communities all relied strongly on the principles of the garden city: curvilinear functional streets favoring natural topography, ample open space, easily accessible community centers, attractive row housing, and the general sense of an overall community plan. The Armistice of 1918 brought curtailment of all work of the Corporation except on projects already begun. In just five months of actual operation, however, the USHC built some 25 developments and made detailed plans for another 55.[5] Certain of the problems involved in this approach were apparent in the disposition of the communities of Yorkship Village, New Jersey; Noreg Village, Pennsylvania; and Cradock and Hilton, Virginia.

Yorkship Village in Camden, New Jersey, was built by a realty company on behalf of the local shipbuilding company, which was ultimately responsible to the United States Shipping Board. In the post-war pressure to dissolve all connections between the Federal Government and housing, the town was sold at auction by the government in December 1922. The sale resulted in the absorption of the Village by the City of Camden, with land ownership divided between the city and the New York Shipbuilding Corporation. This discontinuity of administration very nearly ruined the well-conceived and executed scheme of the village. The conditions of the sale imposed no restrictions on the subsequent development of vacant sites, which were scattered within, as well as along, the periphery of the community. As the 1939 report of the National Resources Committee on Urban Planning and Land Policies reported:

> It may be a platitude to state that the more distinctive and unique the layout and architecture of a community, the less is required to throw the whole composition off balance, thus obtaining not only a less pleasing result by the introduction of incongruous elements but an actual shock and disappointment to the observer when the promise of a culminating feature or a harmonious pattern is suddenly dissipated . . . it brings home with renewed force the great desirability of a continuing agency to function not only actively during the formative stage of a development but extensively and in adaptation during the subsequent periods of its life . . . Yorkship is a good place to observe what a well-designed community might have looked like with proper care.[6]

Another aspect of the unfortunate conditions that resulted from the precipitate and poorly-planned withdrawal of Federal Government influence is illustrated by Noreg Village located near Philadelphia. Following the public auction of the homes in 1923, the town was incorporated under a mayor-council government the following year. Shortly thereafter, the shipyards at Gloucester were abandoned. This destroyed the economic base of the village. The Federal Government continued to hold the mortgages on the homes of the unemployed residents and there were a number of reversions of title. The presence of large portions of such tax exempt property deprived the newly-incorporated town of about one-half of its property tax base. Noreg Village provided living conditions not to be found at comparable prices anywhere else in the Philadelphia area, but its physical plan was inadequate and the financial affairs of the community badly scrambled.

The Corporation's village of Cradock, Virginia, was a depressed area for a short period following the War, due to suspension of construction and provision of utilities, as well as the exodus of the emergency workers from the Portsmouth Navy Yard. No local organization was formed to take over the disposition of the community, and not until 1920 were all the houses sold. In that year, Norfolk County assumed title to roads, parks, underground utilities, and schools. Such authority was soon extended over the town government and administration. The USHC gradually disposed of its holdings with care to prevent undue speculation, thus allowing the county administration to assume control in an orderly fashion.

The United States Shipping Board's first new community was Hilton Village near Newport News, Virginia. The village remained unincorporated after the War and, like Cradock, came under the corporate authority of its county. Unlike Cradock, however, the influence of the Newport News Land Corporation, the company holding the land for the Shipping Board, was reasserted at the close of the War. This influence was maintained through continuously evolving deed restrictions, thus insuring reasonable orderly development.

The most notable achievements of the U. S. Housing Corporation were general town planning, and architectural and design improvements. The Corporation assembled and examined about 5,500 plans. Considering the crisis nature of the period and the assumed objective of standardizing plans and building materials, the Corporation approved and implemented an astonishing variety of imaginative housing and site plans. The Corporation investigated the feasibility of having construction performed by limited-dividend private housing corporations especially created at the local level, but abandoned the plan due to repeated local resistance to the idea. However, the Corporation succeeded in establishing new standards for mass housing and in simplifying heating, plumbing, and millwork.

Four other major accomplishments of the war housing developments are significant for the future establishment of planned communities.[7] First, the program was successful in creating a substantial supply of attractive moderate- and low-income housing, convincing some planners and architects that such a community could be repeated. Second, the potentialities of town planning and the necessity for continuing community administrative authority and local government authority were revealed. Third, there was increased public and professional acceptance of governmental involvement in housing and community development. Fourth, city planning as a profession was encouraged.

Greenbelt Community Development. The exclusively Federal development of the greenbelt communities was made feasible politically by the exigencies of the Depression and economically by the small number and size of the settlements. The 1935 Executive Order creating the Resettlement Administration included a provision for greenbelt towns. Of the 25 cities and possible sites for construction chosen by the Suburban Resettlement Division for intensive study, three project sites eventually were settled upon: Greenbelt (on the outskirts of Washington, D.C.), Greenhills (Cincinnati, Ohio), and Greendale (Milwaukee, Wisconsin).

The planning teams for each of the developments were given complete freedom of design, provided that all communities were to have unified land ownership and use, exclusively low-income housing, coordinated urban-rural attributes and plans, perpetual leasing, and a municipal government suited to the local area.[8]

The planning process and the actual construction of the towns lasted until 1938 and represented the first stage in the settlements' ultimate emergence as independent, incorporated towns. The second stage, from 1938 to approximately 1952, resulted in the gradual reduction of the controls exercised by the Management Division of the Resettlement Administration through tenant selection, organization of local government, maintenance of government facilities, and provision of community managers. The final stage was reached by each of the communities between 1949 and 1953, and involved the liquidation of government holdings and the sale by the Public Housing Administration of all undeveloped land to private nonprofit veterans' associations. With this final step, local governments assumed all powers and services formerly reserved to the Federal Government. An examination of the experience of one of these areas—Greenbelt, Maryland—may provide insights concerning the problems encountered in Federal ownership and administration of communities.

Some attribute the failure of Greenbelt, Maryland, to develop according to its initial plan to the failure of the Federal Government to sufficiently prepare for the transfer of functions to local instrumentalities. Despite strong resident participation in community activities in Greenbelt's early history, by 1952 there was a general lack of public interest in continuing any sort of master planning. Furthermore, the Federal Government's failure to continue a liberal financing policy after the town's chartering in 1937 by the Maryland Legislature destroyed much of the local incentive to continue the original planning process.

Since the Federal Government had assumed full control over all community land, the local government, though endowed with powers similar to those of a standard town administration, was unable to levy property taxes. Hence, Congress in 1936 authorized the Resettlement Administration to support the greenbelt towns via payments in lieu of taxes. During World War II, the Federal Government gradually lost interest in the greenbelt towns and was increasingly reluctant to continue financial support. When Greenbelt was given control over its own finances, all Federal financial aid was terminated. The town had to rely on its own resources, even though it lacked an industrial base.

Greenbelt Homes Inc., the cooperative formed to sell shares in the completed dwelling units and to dispose of much of the vacant land, found the market unprofitable and sold to private subdividers. Failure to impose restrictions on resale standards led to enormous increases in market prices for private homes. The profits available to developers in residential construction and sales discouraged new industrial location in the town. This increased profits for private developers, but provided less revenue for a local government already operating on an inadequate financial basis. When the Baltimore-Washington Expressway and later the Kenilworth Avenue Beltway were cut through the greenbelt, neither the citizens nor the local government objected since the highways would provide better transportation for commuters to urban centers and would bring increased income by attracting business to the town. The result was a dismemberment of the protective greenbelt and the destruction of what little rural character the community had retained. Gradually, the skyrocketing land prices produced a phasing-out of all low-income groups who could not afford to remain in Greenbelt. Greenbelt today is a middle and upper-middle income suburb, lacking a significant social or financial mix.

Since much of the experience of early Greenbelt was conditioned by the extraordinary power wielded by the Federal Government, it provides few relevant guidelines for future planned communities. While some consider the experiments of the Resettlement Administration to have been very much worthwhile, others point to the failure of Greenbelt, Maryland, as a striking illustration of the shortcomings of direct Federal ownership and operation of communities and the lack of financial and political involvement of State and local government. In any case, the Greenbelt experience no doubt contributed to a continuing interest in the potential of the Radburn idea of traffic-free superblocks attained by cluster design and the related characteristic of respect for topography and nature.[9]

Power and Reclamation Projects. The large-scale power and reclamation projects sponsored by the Federal Government in the 1930's also entailed the creation of new communities, but of considerably smaller scale than the Greenbelt towns. Two examples of such communities are Boulder City, Nevada, and Norris, Tennessee.

Boulder City was established in 1930 as a temporary construction site and emerged by 1937 as a permanent town with a master plan. It was administered from the beginning strictly as part of the Hoover (Boulder) Dam project. No machinery was provided for consultation with local residents. The Federal Government's contribution to local services was financed basically out of revenues from the sale of power. All the revenues received from Boulder City were required to be deposited in the Colorado River Dam fund. Until 1948 when project and nonproject costs were segregated, all expenses incurred by the city in its management, operation, and maintenance were paid for out of the fund.

The results of a 1949 survey led to an order of the Secretary of Interior in 1951 appointing a City Manager for Municipal Affairs with an elected Advisory Council of local residents. The Bureau of Reclamation then turned to the Housing and Home Finance Agency requesting them to prepare for the sale of houses and the transfer of service installations to a prospective local government. However, the amount of government land holdings in the municipality substantially cut down the possibilities of revenue from the property tax. The chief source of revenue was to come from the sale of electric power for domestic use. Due to citizen opposition to the transfer, it took the HHFA eight years to dispose of all real property and service installations to the local government. This experience prompted the Comptroller of the Bureau of Reclamation to state: "The time to decide the method of disposition of a town is when the town is started. Later when a community has been nurtured in the atmosphere of Federal subsidy, the selection of a method is tremendously complicated." [10]

Between 1933 and 1935, the Tennessee Valley Authority built Norris, Tennessee, located about 21 miles from Knoxville to house workers employed on the Norris Dam project. The original plans called for construction of permanent, rather than temporary, facilities. Like Boulder City, Norris was under complete Federal supervision and received aid in the form of supplementary police and fire protection and maintenance of utilities. However, the county administered the school program. As early as 1936, a council was elected to serve in an advisory capacity to the city manager. The single management of property and controlled development prevented excessive depreciation and allowed stable town growth. By 1948, the town was put up for sale by the TVA and was bought by Norris Properties, Inc. All local governmental duties were turned over by the TVA to the council of the incorporated municipality. For two years Norris Properties provided police and fire protection, but by 1950 they resold their holdings to the citizenry after having opened many rebuilt lots for development.

As a planned community, Norris achieved a charm and attractiveness that continued during its post-war role as a satellite of Knoxville. Kingsport and Radburn were the chief precedents that the planning staff followed, as revealed by Norris' protective greenbelt, interior parks, pedestrian underpasses, and community centers. The town was developed in isolation from outside urban growth patterns. The rural character and small size of the settlement had special relevance to certain contemporary community builders' efforts. Moreover, the stable, healthy transition to corporate status was a model of positive and long-range planning.

Atomic Energy Towns. The examples provided by Boulder City and Norris, in turn, guided the Atomic Energy Commission in its creation of Oak Ridge, Tennessee; Hanford, Washington; and Los Alamos, New Mexico. None of these communities developed under stable master plans, since requirements were changed several times during their planning and construction. Only since 1947 has permanent construction been substituted for the use of temporary war materials. Because all the communities were affected by the same Congressional legislation, their histories are quite similar. Federal involvement officially ended with the passage of the Atomic Energy Communities Act of 1955. This legislation authorized disposition of the communities and the adoption of local self-government. Oak Ridge achieved independent status in 1960, while Hanford and Los Alamos became autonomous in 1967. Examination of one community will highlight the significance of the AEC experience for future planned communities.

Oak Ridge was constructed by the Turner Construction Company and controlled by the Army through Roane-Anderson Company. Roane-Anderson administered and maintained the transportation system, and provided fire and police protection. A master plan was developed in 1949 by the Oak Ridge Regional Planning Commission to alleviate the overcrowding and inadequate facilities caused by the necessary speed of wartime construction. As early as 1948, plans for incorporation and for transfer of authority were being developed by the Advisory Town Council and the Regional Planning Commission in the form of zoning plans, subdivision by-laws, and drafts of incorporation. Fortunately, the subsequent termination of Federal ownership did not immediately force the community to rely on its own limited financial resources. The Atomic Energy Communities Act required the continuation of annual assistance payments in lieu of taxes for all property remaining under Federal ownership, and also provided special interim payments to sustain the local public bodies until they were providing necessary services and receiving adequate revenues. Municpal Services, Inc., the contractor for the AEC after Roane-Anderson, still operates and maintains a government-owned water system and AEC-owned buildings, equipment, and roads. These Federal procedures allowed maximum flexibility to these local governments in their early years of incorporation.[11]

The AEC communities illustrated the value of adequate transitional financing and local participation in planning for the future. Moreover, policies and procedures for large-scale construction, maintenance, administration, and eventual devolution of authority may serve as an encouragement to the contemporary generation of private community builders.

Developments After 1945

The housing shortage that occurred after World War II had its origins in conditions corresponding to those following the First World War. However, the post-1945 response by the building industry was completely different than the earlier effort. The absence of a post-war recession and the general rise in income created for developers a prosperous market which was stabilized by FHA and veterans' loans. These conditions produced the large-scale merchant builder who merged land purchase, site improvement, house construction, and merchandising in a single firm.[12] This concentration of operational organization permitted greater efficiency and economy for the builder and gave him a unique opportunity. In the years immediately following World War II, Park Forest, Illinois, and the Levittowns in New Jersey, New York, and Pennsylvania, presented alternative approaches to the problems of large-scale community development.

The construction of Park Forest, Illinois, was begun in 1947 by American Community Builders. The development was supported by FHA mortgage insurance totalling $22.5 million and was projected as an eventual satellite city, complete with commercial and recreational facilities, including a greenbelt, adequate public utilities, and a strong industrial base. The first housing units—townhouses—were made available on a rental basis, while later detached units were put up for sale. Four months after the first inhabitants moved into the development, a provisional town government was elected, which soon opted to incorporate the settlement as a village. Resident cooperation and participation in the community at this stage was excellent.

With the advent of local representative government, difficulties arose with public finances, public facilities and the local governmental structure. The village government found that in order to establish and maintain public services, it required a budget equivalent to that of a town many times its size. The property tax was not adequate to cover the costs, and subsidies from the developer were required. Furthermore, the limitation of a developer-oriented local government along with the multiplicity of overlapping local units complicated the resolution of these financial and servicing problems.

Some of these difficulties may be attributed to the inadequacies of the original plan. For example, schools and commercial facilities were not constructed until three years after initial occupancy. The attempt to attract any of the proposed industrial facilities failed. These deficiencies may also be explained in terms of the developer's financial, legal, and political influence on local and county officials and his reluctance to share planning responsibility. The developer's need to remain solvent while assuming the burden of initial construction prompted a downgrading of the village's utilities system. Specifically, four basic reasons for the new community's early financial difficulties may be identified: (1) the tax yield during the initial years of tremendous growth was always one year behind valuation; (2) the owner who bought his home after a tax collection period paid no taxes that year; (3) the provision of facilities for a totally new community at the outset required a budget equivalent to that of a town eight to ten times its size; and (4) the revenues from licenses and fees were severely restricted due to monopolistic control of shopping areas. Such handicaps, especially in a community lacking an industrial capacity, could not be adequately counterbalanced by subsidies from the builder, since he then was forced to cut back in other areas.[13]

Park Forest's development illustrates the need for a sound fiscal plan based on the provision of such basic facilities as utilities and schools. How to carry these basic services until sufficient revenues can be provided remains a critical and so far unanswered question. On the other hand, the enthusiastic citizen participation in the affairs of Park Forest indicates some of the potential inherent in the development of such a community.[14]

Levittown, New Jersey, established in 1958, was the third of the subdivision developments constructed and indirectly administered by its builders, Levitt Brothers and Sons. The community was, in effect, an effort to create a showplace which, through comprehensive planning and provision of good public facilities, would overcome the difficulties of the previous Levittowns constructed on Long Island (1947) and in Pennsylvania (1951). These drawbacks had included piecemeal construction caused by separate negotiations with the several local governments involved, resulting changes in the plan, and the attendant distraction from building and administration, leading to serious omissions and inadequacies in satisfying resident needs.[15]

To avoid these problems, Levitt bought 80 percent of the land required in his master plan and kept options on the remaining sites. Levitt's acreage occupied most of one township. This large rural setting, combined with Levitt's personal philosophy, permitted the company to dominate local politics and administration, as well as the construction of Levittown. The quality and quantity of the township's public services were undoubtedly increased through this approach. It prompted the establishment of a police department and a board of health and the public operation of such Levitt-financed facilities as water, sewage disposal, and garbage removal. The township committee was expanded and a professional city manager appointed. The area's rural past was thrust aside and an active suburban community emerged. However, the expansion process severely tested the Levitt approach. For chiefly financial reasons, Levitt did not experiment with innovative plans, such as use of the Garden City-Radburn principles, or share much of the power he wielded directly or indirectly within the community.

CURRENT NEW COMMUNITY DEVELOPMENT

There has been a significant upsurge in the building of planned new communities in America representing a pace of activity never before approached. Other countries are ahead in the construction of new towns, in the strict sense of self-contained, self-sufficient, independent cities, but in terms of those large-scale planned developments which may be identified more broadly as new communities, none can challenge the United States.

Estimates of the number of new communities vary, and it is difficult to verify or to keep abreast of all developments, since precise definition is difficult and the very nature of large-scale land assembly depends upon secrecy to forestall speculation on tracts to be acquired and to avoid premature development on surrounding property. Estimates range from less than 50 to more than 250 projects which, depending upon definitions and standards, could be designated as new communities. Regardless of the exact number involved, this represents an unprecedented level of activity.

Efforts to develop new communities have produced a wide scope of arrangements in financing, land acquisition, developer organization, and relationships with local governments. They have been undertaken by a variety of developers, including: established developers and merchant builders seeking a wider scope for their activities; financial and investment companies that have entered the construction field in search of new investment opportunities; large holders of land looking for a new marketing approach; banks, insurance companies and related institutions with experience in mortgage banking and investment and with such site location and construction projects as shopping centers, industrial parks, and apartment and commercial buildings. Developers have also included large diversified corporations without previous direct involvement in construction or development, who have moved into the field for additional diversification, an expanded market for some of their products, or a new investment for their funds. In some cases, separate corporate divisions or subsidiaries have been established to handle the direct community development activities.

The majority of new community developments have been undertaken in California, where population growth and the availability of large undeveloped tracts of land have fostered such activity. Other States having several new communities planned and developed include Florida, Illinois, Colorado, Arizona, and Virginia and Maryland in the Washington metropolitan area. These States combined probably account for almost one-half or more of all the new community development under way or planned in the United States today.

The relationship between new community developments and existing governments have taken a variety of forms. Generally speaking, there has been very little legislation enacted specifically to deal with the unique features of new community development. In California, planning, zoning, and land-use control relationships have generally been vested with the county government. Special districts, however, have frequently been established to provide public facilities and amenities. Somewhat similar relationships exist in Florida. In the Washington metropolitan area, where urban counties with very few independent incorporated municipalities surround the District of Columbia, governmental responsibilities have rested with the county, coupled with an emphasis on the use of special assessments and deed covenants by private developers and homeowners and renters associations as a source of finance and control. In Illinois, a tradition of incorporation of municipalities for providing services and planning and land-use control regulation is reflected in the new community developments.

A number of factors have combined to produce the unprecedented interest in the building of new communities. The entry of a number of large corporations into the home building and construction field either as land developers, home builders, diversified contractors, or investors has provided the corporate structure and financing necessary for such undertakings. Sustained population growth and prosperity, coupled with housing replacement needs and the long term effects of the constraints imposed on housing during World War II, have produced the market.

A number of other influences are noteworthy: (1) the increasing shift of industrial expansion to suburban areas outside of the central cities and to locations away from major metropolitan concentrations; (2) the population movement from central cities into suburbs and surrounding undeveloped countryside; (3) the increasing market for second homes, many of which become year around residences; (4) the growth of new urban areas; (5) the continued concern over the type of urban pattern that is emerging in the large metropolitan concentrations and the accompanying tendency to seek the design features, community characteristics, and amenities available in planned new communities.

The Extent of New Community Development

The exact extent of new community development across the country today is extremely difficult to establish. A list could be expanded or contracted depending upon the criteria applied to distinguish new communities from other large-scale developments. Moreover, information about developments is a carefully guarded secret during the initial land acquisition and prelminiary planning stages and then frequently becomes heavily tinged with a promotional tone as soon as the time arrives for public announcement. Using the criteria of at least one thousand acres planned for a minimum three to four thousand residents and sufficient supporting facilities, activities, and uses to constitute a complete community but not necessarily including industry, the number of current new communities has been estimated to be in the vicinity of 200 to 250.[16] Other estimates, applying stricter criteria have ranged as low as 15 or 20. *At the present time, it is doubtful if new communities actually incorporating significant residential, commercial, and industrial features exceed 50 projects in all of the United States.* Preliminary returns from a recently completed survey support this generalization.

A survey conducted by Jeanne M. Davis, an urban planner with the Natural Resources Economics Division of the U.S. Department of Agriculture identified 43 new towns as defined for the study. County extension agents in each of the nation's counties were asked to provide data for all new town planned communities, subdivision or industrial developments of 950 acres or larger within their counties. New towns were defined as developments which include provision for some employment in industrial plants or offices; educational, recreational, and commercial facilities; and a variety of housing types. The new towns identified constituted a little more than 11 percent of the total 376 developments for which construction was reported as having been commenced during 1960–1967 on nearly 1.5 million acres of land.

The acreage incorporated in the new towns constituted 21 percent of the total reported acreage.

An illustrative listing of 52 new community projects which were underway in 18 States by 1968 is presented in Table 1. Although the listing is by no means inclusive, efforts have been made to make it as complete as possible. The projects are clustered in areas of rapid urban growth and in the warm weather States—the Washington metropolitan area, Florida and along the Gulf Coast, Colorado, Arizona, and New Mexico, and most notably, California. In numerical terms new community development is uniquely a California phenomenon even though two of the most widely publicized examples are Columbia, Maryland, and Reston, Virginia, in the Washington metropolitan area.

Design and Location Characteristics of New Communities

There is a wide variety of styles and types in the new communities being built across the nation today. Some have little except their size and the presence of shopping centers to distinguish them from any large subdivision consisting of single family houses on individual lots with separate driveways and garages lining curving streets and cul de sacs. But most combine single family, individual lot houses with townhouses and garden and high-rise apartments. Extensive use is generally made of open spaces, both as common urban space around which houses or apartments are grouped, and community open space separating types of housing from other land uses. Clustering provisions are also common, allowing smaller lots or higher densities in townhouses and apartments in exchange for common open space. Greater flexibility in the relationship of different types of land uses—based on special planned unit development, floating zones, and other special zoning provisions—is another fairly usual feature.

The net result of these special characteristics of new communities is a distinct departure from the typical street layout and sharply separated single family, multi-family, and retail-commercial development patterns. What emerges is a more dynamic and harmonious relationship among the elements of the urban scene, as exemplified by: a general pattern of curving streets; superblocks with houses, townhouses, and apartments clustered around common open space; and varying land densities frequently separated by open space and parks. Shopping centers often are designed around a core of buildings, malls, and walkways surrounded by parking space with circumferential drives. Industrial parks may have a similar design, with encircling through-traffic patterns.

Table I / New Community Developments, March 1968

New communities	Location	Acres	Projected housing units	Projected population	Housing units rented or sold
Arizona:					
Litchfield Park.............	Maricopa County......	13,000	22,000	75,000	150
Lake Havasu City..........	Mohave County.......	13,000	—	50,000	600
Tucson Green Valley........	Pima County..........	10,000	—	25,000	500
Sun City [1]................	Maricopa County......	14,000	—	75,000	—
Arkansas: Maumelle..........	Pulaski County........	5,300	—	60,000	—
California:					
El Dorado Hills.............	Sacramento County....	9,800	20,000	75,000	400
Foster City................	San Mateo County.....	2,700	11,000	35,000	9,000
Rosmoor Leisure World [1][2]...	Contra Costa County...	2,100	10,000	20,000	—
Valencia...................	Los Angeles County....	4,300	—	30,000	360
Diamond Bar................	do...............	8,000	20,000	75,000	2,500
Porter Ranch...............	do...............	4,100	12,000	43,000	—
Mountain Park..............	do...............	7,150	—	60,000	—
Crummer Ranch............	Los Angelas and Ventura Counties....	6,300	—	50,000	—
Westlake Village............	do...............	11,500	—	100,000	—
Conejo Village.............	Ventura County.......	11,000	—	87,000	—
Irvine Ranch...............	Orange County........	33,000 [3]88,000	—	300,000	1,000
Rossmoor Leisure World [1].......	do...............	2,465	18,000	30,000	6,000
Laguna Niguel..............	do...............	7,100	—	90,000	—
Mission Viejo..............	do...............	11,000 [3]53,000	—	50,000	—
San Carlos [2]..............	San Diego County.....	5,000	9,000	35,000	2,000
Rancho Bernardo............	do...............	5,400	11,000	33,000	—
University City [2].............	do...............	13,000	—	—	3,000
California City.............	Kern County..........	101,120	—	600,000	—
Rancho California..........	Riverside County......	87,000	—	400,000	—
Colorado:					
Montbello [2]..............	Denver...............	7,000	—	—	—

— Information not available.

[1] Primarily a retirement community.

[2] Partially or wholly annexed to an adjacent municipality.

[3] Total.

Source: "House and Home," February 1964, p. 125, as modified by information from: Edwaı P. Eichler and Marshall Kaplan, "The Community Builders" (Berkeley and Los Angeles: Unı versity of California Press, 1967). Appendix I, p. 185; unpublished survey conducted by Jeanı M. Davis, Economic Research Service, U.S. Department of Agriculture; and unpublished infoı mation from the Land and Facilities Development Administration, U.S. Department of Housiı and Urban Development.

ble I / *New Community Developments, March 1968—continued*

New communities	Location	Acres	Projected housing units	Projected population	Housing units rented or sold
Colorado City..............Pueblo County........		5,000	—	30,000	—
Pikes Peak Park [2]...........El Paso County........		4,300	—	30,000	—
North Glen................ Adams County........		2,528	—	20,000	6,100
Daware: Mill Creek......... North of Wilmington..		1,300	5,000	13,000	—
rida:					
Miami Lakes...............Dade County..........		3,000	6,000	25,000	—
Canaveral Princeton........ Brevard County.......		2,500	—	43,000	—
Port Charlotte [1]............ Charlotte County......		92,700	—	100,000	6,000
Palm Beach Lakes.......... Palm Beach County....		7,000	25,000	70,000	—
Lehigh Acres...............Lee County...........		60,000	—	80,000	6,000
Deltona [1]..................Volusia County.......		15,000	41,000	75,000	100
Coral Springs..............Broward County.......		10,400	—	60,000	—
Spring Hill................Hernando County.....		17,000	—	50,000	100
orgia: Chapell Hill......... Atlanta..............		1,100	2,900	12,000	—
nois:					
Elk Grove................. Cook County.........		3,000	10,000	35,000	—
Oak Brook.................Du Page County.......		3,600	—	25,000	—
ntucky: Oxmoor........... West of Louisville.....		1,000	—	15,000	—
uisiana: New Orleans East...East of New Orleans...		32,000	—	100,000	930
aryland:					
Columbia.................Howard County.......		14,100	29,000	110,000	300
Toppatowne...............Harford County		1,300	3,000	10,000	1,600
Northampton..............Prince George's County		2,200	8,000	25,000	—
nnesota: Jonathan..........Hennepin County......		2,200	—	50,000	—
ssachusetts: New Seabury [1]. Barnstable County.....		3,000	3,750	16,000	100
w Mexico: Paradise Hills....West of Albuquerque..		8,500	—	60,000	—
w York: Sterling Forest..... Orange County........		20,500	—	—	—
egon: Somerset West.......West of Portland......		6,600	12,000	40,000	—
xas:					
Clear Lake City........... South of Houston......		15,000	40,000	150,000	—
Horizon City...............El Paso County........		65,000	—	100,000	—
rginia: Reston.............Fairfax County........		6,750	24,885	75,000	1,000

Information not available.

Primarily a retirement community.

Partially or wholly annexed to an adjacent municipality.

Total.

Source: "House and Home," February 1964, p. 125, as modified by information from: Edward Eichler and Marshall Kaplan, "The Community Builders" (Berkeley and Los Angeles: University of California Press, 1967). Appendix I, p. 185; unpublished survey conducted by Jeanne . Davis, Economic Research Service, U.S. Department of Agriculture; and unpublished information from the Land and Facilities Development Administration, U.S. Department of Housing d Urban Development.

Both as an urban design feature and as a method of incorporating efficient and economic staged development, the larger new communities generally favor the neighborhood and village approach, with residences, schools, and churches grouped around a small commercial and activity center. The villages, in turn, are oriented around a larger town center, which is the major commercial and retail focus for the new community.

Park Forest, Illinois, is an early example of a central core shopping center supplemented by smaller neighborhood centers. A separate industrial park with streets and utilities have also been provided in Litchfield Park, Arizona; Columbia, Maryland; and Reston, Virginia. The Irvine Ranch Properties are being developed on the neighborhood village and town center pattern. Litchfield Park is planned to go one step further by combining villages into communities, each having a high school and a community commercial center.

Some of the new communities are specifically identified by their developers as providing an opportunity for experimentation. Westinghouse Electric Corporation, for example, has indicated that its new town—Coral Springs, near Fort Lauderdale, Florida—will serve as an "urban laboratory" where the company will develop and test products for the construction market. Walt Disney Productions', Inc. new project EPCOT (Experimental Prototype Community of Tomorrow), to be located near Orlando, Florida, will be used to introduce, test, and demonstrate new ideas and technologies.

A number of the new communities are located beside lakes or other bodies of water. Both Columbia and Reston incorporate manmade lakes. Lake Havasu City is located on Havasu Lake, a reservoir on the Colorado River formed by Parker Dam. El Dorado Hills, California, north of Sacramento, includes a portion fronting on Lake Folsom. Clear Lake City, Texas, just south of Houston, includes a portion fronting on a lake. New communities of the future will probably stress water sites.

Another major geographic characteristic of the new communities is the proximity of an expressway interchange. The interstate system and State and local expressway decisions are particularly significant influences in the location of new communities. Columbia, Maryland, is strategically located on highways running between Baltimore and Washington. Valencia, Janss/Conejo, Irvine, and Mission Viejo—the four large new communities in the Los Angeles area—are all traversed by, bordered by, or closely adjacent to a major freeway. However, very few of the new communities have an internal mass transportation facility or are located on a major regular mass transit line. Park Forest,

Illinois, is unique in having a regularly scheduled bus line with several different routes running through the community, and in being located on the Illinois Central Railroad suburban service. Columbia, Maryland, has an internal mini-bus service operating on special roadways and connecting with highway buses on the Baltimore to Washington Expressway. In general, however, the new communities are automobile and expressway oriented.

GOVERNMENT AND NEW COMMUNITIES

Because of their scale and objectives, new communities present special governmental problems. First, adequate public authority for planning, guiding, and regulating urban growth must be provided. Second, a level of public services adequate to meet the needs of a concentrated urban community must be developed and maintained. Third, a governmental framework must be established within which the new community's pattern and objectives as formulated by the developer will not be thwarted. Finally, an opportunity must be afforded for participation in public decision-making both by its residents and by larger affected jurisdictions. Normally, meeting these needs will call for a changing set of relationships and a shift in official status as the community is planned, developed, occupied, and expanded.

Governmental Framework

In the great majority of cases, new community development has started under county jurisdiction, usually in predominantly rural counties. Single-purpose special districts frequently have been used to provide such urban services as water supply and sewage disposal, and in a few instances, multi-purpose special districts having broad governing powers over the area encompassing a projected new community have been established. Special homeowners' or developers' organizations, in other instances, have sometimes been used to provide services on a special fee or assessment basis. There also are a limited number of examples of a large new community area being annexed to an existing municipality prior to or at an early stage in its development. Conversely, in a number of cases, new communities have absorbed existing small incorporated or unincorporated municipalities.

While the normal course taken by an unincorporated community is to seek incorporation after reaching a certain population size, this course of action is not necessarily followed by new communities. Due to varying circumstances, including State practices and customs and an evaluation of services available and costs involved, new communities have frequently remained unincorporated within a county. In Virginia and Maryland, where a number of new communities are being developed, incorporations are limited, with urban counties providing the government for a number of unincorporated communities. In California, the decision to incorporate appears to hinge on whether satisfactory service arrangements, including the formation of special districts, can be accomplished under the county government. On the other hand, if the area of the new community lies in several competing incorporated places, detachments and a new incorporation may be the preferred approach.

The development of most of the large new communities in the unincorporated territory of rural counties presents perhaps the greatest governmental difficulties because basic decisions concerning planning, financing, and providing services and facilities must be made immediately upon the initiation of the project. Yet, the county involved is usually ill-prepared to assist in or to assume these functions. Such problems usually will not be as acute in the unincorporated outlying areas of larger urban counties, since necessary governmental structure, powers, and financing are more likely to be present. Relatively fewer problems are posed by the rarely used approach of annexing the area encompassed in a new community to an existing municipality.

Planning

In perhaps a majority of the counties where the current new communities were started, county planning was either nonexistent or of such a limited scope as to prove of little assistance. Even in those counties having a planning staff, their capability to cope with the impact of a development covering 5,000 to 30,000 acres, with a projected population of 40,000 to 1,000,000, was severely tested. Furthermore, as indicated in the ACIR/AIP questionnaire, areawide planning agencies have given little thought to the location of new communities and their relationship to existing and projected urban growth patterns. Thus the major planning initiative has usually fallen to the developers and their planning and design consultants.

In a few cases, the county planning staff has participated and given guidance and direction from the initiation of a new community proposal. For example, the Alameda County, California, planning agency, in conjunction with Contra Costa County and the developer and property owners, prepared a preliminary plan for a new community named San Ramon Village. A system of streets related to the general county land use plan, an integrated network of community facilities, and a full range of land uses were provided for. Increasingly, counties with prior experience in new community development are acquiring this type of capability. Ventura County, California, for example, after its initial role of responding to proposals for the new community of Conejo has now strengthened its planning function so that it can do advanced planning for newly urbanized areas rather than merely responding to a completed developer's plan. The Orange County, California, supervision of the Irvine Company planning for its new community has been identified as superior to what would have been available within an incorporated city.

The experience with Columbia and rural Howard County, Maryland, and with Conejo in Ventura County, California, was more typical. The Howard County Commissioners had been elected on a platform promising to encourage large-lot zoning and thus to discourage growth. The county general plan made no provision for a development such as Columbia and the Columbia development plan was drawn up by the developer. Steps subsequently were taken to incorporate and integrate the Columbia development plan into the county general plan. Ventura County at the time of the initial proposal for Conejo was a largely rural county having little experience with large-scale community development. The county was in the position of reacting to the plans and proposals of the developer's highly qualified and technically competent staff and consultants.

A cooperative relationship between developers and public planning jurisdictions facilitates the evolution of an effective planning process when the capabilities of the public agencies are adequate to assure independent initiative and evaluation. Fortunately, the necessity of coping with such new development has served in a number of counties as the impetus for establishing a strong effective planning staff capable of dealing with developers on equal terms.

Land-Use and Development Regulation

Similar problems have been faced in providing adequate land-use and development regulation provisions and suitable administrative organization. Large-scale new communities have need of the positive guidance for sound urban growth and the traditional emphasis on protection against abuses and unsound development that public agencies can provide. Yet, many of the counties involved initially lacked planning, zoning, and subdivision control authority. Rural counties frequently have depended on part-time boards and regulatory agencies to administer land-use development controls. Furthermore, those counties that did have such authority frequently were limited to the more conventional zoning approaches which are designed primarily to cope with small subdivision development.

To fill the void left by ineffective public agencies, private associations and privately adopted but publicly enforceable regulatory measures have been employed in a number of communities. Several developments, particularly those making wide use of cluster site design with common open space, have relied heavily on homeowners' and residents' associations and on covenants. The homeowners associations are both areawide—for the supervision and management of common open space in a particular cluster, and communitywide—for the provision of recreational services. They are a method of enforcing certain regulatory measures which were either adopted by the association and incorporated into its articles and by-laws, or incorporated in deed covenants for the property. A more detailed discussion of present practices and new approaches to large-scale development guidance and control is provided in Chapter V.

Public Facilities and Services

Particular difficulties are faced in providing public facilities and services for new communities in areas which are usually equipped to furnish only rural services. In these instances, public jurisdictions face relatively the same problems as the developer. Such facilities must be provided for anticipated demand at a time when property values and economic activity do not produce sufficient revenue to support such expenditures. A variety of approaches has been used both by developers and by government to cope with this problem.

Perhaps the most extensively used technique is the establishment of new special districts or the annexation of the new community to existing special districts. The formation of special districts facilitates the provision of public facilities and improvements which would otherwise have to be provided by the county, another general unit of government, or by the developer. Because of its legal provisions for the formation of special districts and local government custom and practice, California has had considerable experience in using them to provide facilities for new communities. Developer-formed special districts have been able to issue revenue bonds, and in some cases, when given taxing powers, to issue general obligation bonds. Funds were then available for construction of water supply and sewerage disposal systems, streets and roads, and parks and recreational facilities. The powers and structure of these districts varied considerably. Some were limited to single purposes and could issue only revenue bonds, while others had broad powers and constituted almost a limited-purpose local government with authority both to charge fees and to levy taxes.

The best known use of the special district approach to providing public services and facilities is the Estero municipal improvement district, a multi-purpose special district authorized by special act of the Calfornia legislature in September 1960. It provides a number of services for the Foster City new community. It can perform a wide range of functions and its governmental organization is in many respects typical of the California developer-formed districts of the late 50's. The developer is in control, since two of the three district directors are elected by property owners on the basis of the assessed value of their holdings. Expensive land fill operations to reclaim low swamplands were the major initial activity of the Estero district. Plans call for a 2,600 acre development worth $650 million when developed to accommodate 35,000 residents.

Although special districts can facilitate the financing of a higher level of facilities and services for a new community, they can create a number of problems. They form a special level of government, in effect, and may not adequately relate representation of the interests of the developer and those of the residents as the area grows. They may not sufficiently relate their financing, planning, facilities, and functions to the efforts of general and areawide governments. Moreover, in a time of readily available investment funds, they can become overextended by borrowing beyond their capacity.

A number of measures have been inaugurated in California to avoid the abuses that developed in some of the special districts. Stricter special district incorporation requirements were adopted; the powers of the District Securities Commission to review the economic feasibility of proposed special districts were expanded; and, perhaps most significantly, local agency boundary commissions were established to supervise the formation, consolidation, and dissolution of local governments. The local agency formation commissions, functioning on a county-wide basis, represent the county, cities within the county, and the public. They exercise review and approval powers in connection with changes in status and in the area of all types of local governments, including special districts. Recently, increased emphasis has been placed upon their positive role in guiding the development of appropriate governmental organization for urban areas. As stated in the law: "Among the purposes of a local agency formation commission are the discouragement of urban sprawl and the encouragement of the orderly formation and development of local governmental agencies based upon local conditions and circumstances."

Intergovernmental contracts and agreements provide a method for a special district or a municipality to furnish services and facilities which might otherwise be beyond the capacity of their own staff, administrative organization, and financial capacity. They serve as a means of realizing economies of scale by participating in cooperative undertakings. They clearly have particular relevance for new communities which are just developing their own governmental structure. The advantages of more specialized programs and a higher level of services that might otherwise be available can be realized through this device. Moreover, expertise can be provided through contracts with established municipalities or with a county.

One of the difficulties in using this method in a new community may be the lack of an adequate tax base to provide necessary revenue. Furthermore, the availability of services through contract or agreement may encourage governmental fragmentation by facilitating small incorporations of municipalities and of special districts.

Another approach to providing the necessary level of facilities and services for new communities is the creation of a county subordinate service or taxing area. With this device, the levying of special taxes or charges is authorized in specific areas for the provision of a higher level of facilities or services. The distinguishing feature of the approach is that the area does not attain an independent status but remains completely under the county government. This method makes it possible to relate more directly the public services and facilities provided to the revenue necessary to pay for them. The major difficulty in its application to new communities is the necessity to provide financing for facilities in advance of the economic base necessary to produce revenues.

An adaptaton of this approach to municipal government was developed to facilitate the annexation of Redwood Shores, a new community development, to the neighboring incorporated community of Redwood City, California. To gain the advantages of an existing municipal government for the new community without burdening the taxpayers of an established community with the costs of major capital projects, such as marshland reclamation and necessary public works, a special fiscal mechanism was created under Redwood City's basic grant of power over "municipal affairs." The Redwood City General Improvement District was established as an arm of city government with the city council serving as the governing board. The District can levy property taxes and issue bonds to obtain capital financing for projects within its borders. The existing developed city is thereby insulated from the liability of financing such projects and the responsibility of repayment falls on the property directly benefitted.

New community developers have used two other approaches which do not depend upon the formation of public agencies or special districts to provide services and facilities. Some developers have themselves undertaken the construction of facilities. In some instances this has been done with the understanding that the facilities subsequently would be purchased by an appropriate public entity when development provided an adequate tax base. In the early development of Park Forest, Illinois, the developer made sites available and built the first school buildings for subsequent purchase by the school district over a period of time. The company also drilled the original wells and built the water plant for later purchase by the community.

Some developers have viewed the establishment of a private water supply or sewage disposal company as a sound investment. Rather than seeking the extension of public facilities or the formation of a special district, they have incorporated a subsidiary or independent company and have constructed their own facilities. After a community services district plan was defeated at the polls, the Janss Corporation, developer of Conejo in Ventura County, California, joined with five smaller developers and a nearby college to establish the Conejo Valley Sanitary Company to provide trunk line and disposal facilities. The company operates as a privately owned public utility and the developer may actually realize a net profit on the enterprise. However, this approach does create some problems, particularly if there is not adequate public regulation similar to the public controls over regular privately owned public utilities. Furthermore, it may not prove financially feasible for development companies already undertaking expensive borrowing. Also, urban counties increasingly are seeking control of existing private utilities and are discouraging the formation of new ones.

Through the formation of nonprofit communitywide corporations and cluster area homeowners' associations, additional services and amenities can be provided on a fee or share basis. Membership and participation may be voluntary, but frequently the so-called automatic homeowners' association is used, especially for cluster developments. A person buying property or renting apartments or townhouses automatically becomes a member of the association and is subject to annual dues or assessments. Some of the communitywide, nonprofit organizations combine automatic membership features with voluntary participation by corporations, businesses, and interested individuals.

When it did not prove possible to use a special district approach for the provision of a number of the facilities and amenities that were desired by the Columbia, Maryland developers, a nonprofit corporation, the Columbia Park and Recreation Association was formed for this purpose. All residents of Columbia normally become members upon moving into a house or apartment. Membership is also available for businesses and industry. The Association is responsible for financing, constructing, and maintaining various types of community buildings and service facilities, swimming pools, parks and Association open space, lakes, pathways, and some roads. It supervises the operation of the bus system, the child and day care programs, tennis and golf courses, arts and crafts classes, and boating on the lakes. Its properties and maintenance activities are supported by an assessment not to exceed 75 cents per $100 of evaluation on real estate. Apartment assessments are included in the rent. At the outset, the Association has nine board members, seven representing the developer and two ex-officio. As development proceeds, additional members will be elected to represent the growing number of residents and in time residents will gain control.

NOTES

[1] *Urban Planning and Land Policies,* Vol. II of the Supplementary Report of the Urbanism Committee to the National Resources Committee (Washington, D.C., 1939), pp. 3–161.

[2] John W. Reps, *The Making of Urban America* (Princeton, N.J.: Princeton University Press, 1965), p. 438.

[3] Roy Lubove, *Community Planning in the 1920's: The Contribution of the Regional Planning Association of America* (Pittsburgh: University of Pittsburgh Press, 1963), pp. 71 and 74.

[4] T. S. Simey, "Dynamic Cities," *Town Planning Review,* Vol. XXII, No. 4 (January, 1952), p. 208.

[5] Report of the U. S. Housing Corporation, Vol. 1 (1920), p. 40.

[6] *Urban Planning and Land Policies,* Vol. II of the Supplementary Report of the Urbanism Committee to the National Resources Committee (Washington, D.C., 1937).

[7] Roy Lubove, "Homes and 'A Few Well-Placed Fruit Trees': An Objective Lesson in Federal Housing," *Social Research,* Vol. 28, No. 4 (Winter, 1965), p. 476.

[8] Paul K. Conkin, *Tomorrow A New World: The New Deal Community Program* (Ithaca, N.Y.: Cornell University Press, 1959), pp. 307–309.

[9] See Albert Mayer, "Greenbelt Towns Revisited," a series of three articles

in *The Journal of Housing*, Vol. 24, No. 1 (Jan. 1967), pp. 12–26; No. 2 (Feb.-March 1967), pp. 80–85; and No. 3 (Apr. 1967), pp. 151–160.

[10] D. Denit, "Boulder City—Government Town Problem," *Public Administration Review*, Vol. XII (1952), pp. 97–105.

[11] At Los Alamos, the Federal Housing Administration developed the master plan, drafted zoning ordinances and building codes, and surveyed and platted the entire area.

[12] Edward P. Eichler and Marshall Kaplan, *The Community Builders* (Berkeley, California: University of California Press, 1967), p. 21.

[13] Jack Meltzer, "Administrative Problems of New Towns," *Planning 1952* (Chicago: American Society of Planning Officials, 1953), pp. 77–78.

[14] William H. Whyte, Jr., *The Organization Man* (New York: Simon and Schuster, Inc., 1956).

[15] Herbert Gans, *The Levittowners: How People Live and Politic in Suburbia* (New York: Random House, 1967), pp. 4–5.

[16] Craig S. Noren, "New Towns in the United States" (Washington, D.C.: National Association of Home Builders Land Use and Development Department, 1967), p. 5.

19. A Fresh Scene in the Clean Dream

WOLF VON ECKARDT

Columbia, Maryland, the most advanced of our new communities, is advertised as "the Next America." At first it does not look much different from today's suburbia, only somewhat more sanitized. There is none of the excitement of Cumbernault, the new town near Glasgow, or of the modern charm of Finland's Tapiola or even of Lake Anne Plaza in Reston, Virginia, America's other well-known new town. It is far from the utopian megastructures Paolo Soleri and other architectural visionaries are dreaming of. Columbia only hints at the promise of the growing new-town movement. But at least it points the way.

New towns supposedly will help people leave the slums and ghettos, allowing us to rebuild the rotting inner city and to put workers and jobs together again in real communities that give citizens a sense of belonging. But how do the inhabitants feel about living in these laboratories? Clearly, most of the roughly 13,000 people living in Columbia, located in Howard County between Baltimore and Washington, D.C., or of the 12,000 who live in Reston, seem to be aware that they are participating in an experiment. They also seem anxious for it to succeed. A majority of Columbia residents (51 per cent in 1969, according to a University of Michigan study, but there must be more, now that the town is better known) were attracted by the idea of a fresh start—"the Clean Dream," as an Antioch College professor has called it. They are eager to pioneer. But some people (21 per cent, say the Michigan pollsters) moved to Columbia because it was close to their work. It is not surprising, therefore, to encounter Columbians who are not quite sure what a new town is or stands for. Like many suburbanites everywhere, they complain about the new buildings

Wolf Von Eckardt, "A Fresh Scene in the Clean Dream," *Saturday Review*, May 15, 1971, pp. 21–23. Copyright 1971 Saturday Review, Inc. (Wolf Von Eckardt is architecture critic of *The Washington Post*).

going up around them, particularly the low-rent housing (9 per cent, say the pollsters, expressed disappointment with the plans and programs of the developer).

It is risky to try to assess life in this four-year-old town. Columbia is only one example of one kind of new community. Like Reston, Jonathan in Minnesota, and other American new towns, it is essentially a "garden city" of the sort invented in England at the start of this century. It's also an essentially private development whose backers are out to prove that if you plan comprehensively and put everything together—housing, industry, recreation, and shopping— you can create a good living environment as profitably as a dull, one-class, one-color, dormitory subdivision. Columbia is being developed by James R. Rouse, and to judge from the price of Rouse Company stock, the theory seems valid. Planned for 110,000 people, the town is to be completed ten years from now.

The first thing one sees when arriving there via U.S. 29, which bisects the town's 14,000 acres, or twenty-one square miles, is one of the city's man-made lakes with small sailboats, ducks, and boys with fishing tackle. Beyond the lake are the first large business buildings that herald Columbia's "downtown." A huge shopping center with a covered mall, which is to serve not just the city but the region around it, is under construction and is scheduled to open this fall. There is also to be an amusement park—Ferris wheels and all. Columbia, says one of its advertisements, is to be the kind of place "where you can get a pastrami on rye at 4 o'clock in the morning."

That doesn't seem very convincing as one drives along the new city's wide and winding blacktop roads lined with a variety of subdivision homes, clusters of townhouses, and occasional, bulky apartment buildings. Like most other new towns, however, this leisurely, neat, and verdant sprawl has been organized into neighborhoods, each with its elementary school, neighborhood center, swimming pool, other outdoor recreation facilities, and a "convenience store," as it is called, where you can get essential groceries, though not at 4 o'clock in the morning.

Three or four neighborhoods form a "village." The village center includes a middle school, a meeting hall, a variety of shops and stores clustered around a very sociable little plaza with benches, statuary, and a fountain. All this is connected by walkways that never come in contact with the highways, so kids can walk or bicycle to school and people can shop without using their cars. Nevertheless, Columbia's first completed village center, Lake Wilde, has a drive-in bank, and its parking lot is usually full.

The Cove, stucco and brick garden apartments and town houses, overlooking the 25-acre man-made *Wilde Lake,* occupy their own park in Columbia, Maryland. Residents enjoy free boating privileges via a private dock and gazebo on the apartment premises.

Photo credit: The Rouse Company

Lake Wilde is Columbia's showcase. It has a covered, year-round swimming pool, a good bookstore where a lot of teen-agers hang out and listen to records, one of the best butcher stores in Maryland, and an "Interfaith Center," where Catholics, Jews, and Protestants hold religious services and seminars and which operates a "cooperative ministry." There is also a community center, called Slayton House, which hosts such activities as informal coffee discussions with local politicians, "slimnastic" courses, movies, and amateur theater productions.

Slayton House is also the scene of heated "confrontations" between the Columbia Association and residents who demand to know what they are getting for their dues. The association, with its sizable staff, takes care of the landscaping and other amenities and initiates and runs Columbia's social and recreational programs, while the schools and police and fire protection remain the responsibility of Howard County. The Columbia Association's board of directors is dominated by the developer to make sure the residents do not suddenly change his plans. This precaution is taken—and often much resented by the citizens—in all new towns, even the government-sponsored British communities that eventually become true municipalities with an elected mayor and council. "If citizens were totally involved," said city planner David Godschalk in a recent conference on new-town management, "Columbia, for instance, would probably end up all low-density."

In Columbia, nevertheless, Rouse has promised to relinquish his parental control as the city grows up—and it is growing fast. Two of the seven planned villages have been completed, and a third is nearing completion. Columbia already has a community college and a branch of Antioch. It has a health clinic that is part of an innovative, prepaid family health plan, worked out and operated by Johns Hopkins University. Ground has been broken for a 180-bed hospital. There are a golf course and riding stables.

The regular run of Columbia's mini-buses, which was part of the plan, has been abolished, however. There was not enough demand. Since early this year, the mini-buses provide only rush-hour service from the villages' centers to "downtown," where they link up with commuter buses to Washington and Baltimore, or to Columbia's industrial park.

So far only 15 per cent of Columbia's residents also work in Columbia. In Tapiola, Finland, the figure is about 40 per cent. In most British new towns, industrial jobs now outnumber workers available, though the goal had been to match employment capacity to local

Residential section of Bryant Woods Neighborhood in Columbia, Maryland. Streets are laid out in cul-de-sac formation. Custom houses and apartments face on Wilde Lake with docks for sailboats. *Photo credit: The Rouse Company*

population. Therefore, many workers now commute to the new towns. This will happen in Columbia, too, if Rouse reaches his goal of providing 50,000 jobs for a town of 110,000 residents. He probably will. Columbia's two industrial parks are growing even faster than the town itself.

Critics charge that new towns cater to the middle-class dream. They forget that the black and the poor share this ideal. Ghetto dwellers also prefer to see ducks rather than rats when they look out the window. If "Soul City," the new town by and for blacks, ever gets built, it will not look much different from Columbia.

An estimated 15 to 18 per cent of Columbia's population is black. In Reston, the percentage is probably a little lower because some blacks do not relish the thought of moving to Virginia. There are also a few people with below-average incomes in both towns, and there would be a greater number if the federal government had acted more expeditiously on applications for housing subsidies. So far it has given little more than lip service to the idea of socially and economically balanced new communities.

Columbia has just completed the last of 300 subsidized housing units for people of moderate income. Rents range from $99 for a one-bedroom apartment to $151.50 for a four-bedroom townhouse. To avoid being tagged low-income ghettos, these units have been built on five different sites. The houses are as handsomely designed as any in Columbia, and I, for one, could not tell them from the rest. They are sponsored by the Columbia Interfaith Housing Corporation, which grew out of the cooperative ministry.

Reston has put its 198 moderate-income families together into one apartment house complex called Cedar Ridge, which teems with some 700 children. Ten of the Cedar Ridge apartments are rented to families on welfare, but their identities are not known to the others. None of these people have come from the Washington or Baltimore ghettos. Nor are all of them black. They are young teachers, factory workers, and store clerks, many of whom work in the new town and all of whom had lived in the surrounding rural country.

Neither Rouse nor the Gulf Oil Corporation, Reston's owner, claims that their privately built new towns could or would attempt to house substantial numbers of inner-city poor. Columbia and Reston aim only to make sure that everyone who works in these towns will be able to live there, and they realize, as an Interfaith Housing official put it, that "industry usually has more janitors than presidents." Furthermore, there is a sincere will to build economically and socially inclusive rather than exclusive communities. "If Columbia is to be an experiment in building for the Next America," the Interfaith official said, "then it must be workable for all Americans."

So far the new towns seem to be more workable than suburbia for a good many Americans. The people who moved into these communities because they saw in them a new urban frontier are proud of their racial and economic mix. In Reston, a vocal group of early settlers has banded together in a group called Black Focus and keeps urging the developer to make greater efforts to open the town to black people, to show black faces in their promotion pictures, and to hire black salesmen. And these urgings have had some effect. In Columbia, liberals keep saying residents who probably voted for George Wallace (he got a considerable vote in all of Maryland) live contentedly on the same street with blacks and members of various ethnic groups who were attracted by Columbia's promise of racial and ethnic harmony. This pioneering spirit seems to be contagious. The Michigan University poll found that 56 per cent of the respondents wanted people of different racial backgrounds in the neighborhoods.

But how meaningful is this? The majority of these black neighbors are highly educated members of the middle class, and some of them have complaints. For instance, June Caldwell, a black psychologist who moved to Columbia from Baltimore, told Washington Post reporter Michael Kernan: "I don't know. Columbia seemed like a good idea, but I don't know. I think it all still has that concept of property values. All the American prejudices about low-rent housing are being preserved intact here. If something is stolen, everyone looks at the Interfaith (low-income housing) kids."

The new towns, in short, are by no means free of the stress and distress of our society. In the new towns, too, most people fear change and the depreciation of their property and surroundings. But despite Mrs. Caldwell's doubts, I would say there is somewhat less fear of change in a new town because the change is planned. One knows what will happen. There is order. Columbia and Reston tend to substantiate the contention frequently made by sociologists that most whites of all income groups do not object to racial integration as long as they are sure that the white group remains in the majority. That is surely "racist" of them. But there is hope that planned communities can help overcome this racism by—homeopathically, as it were—taking this prejudice into account.

A new town, better than an impersonal city or suburb, is able to work things out in a spirit of community. Unruly youngsters are a current problem in both Columbia and Reston, as they are almost

Aerial view of 15-story Heron House, 30-acre Lake Anne, and sections of Lake Anne Village. Land planning at Reston, Virginia concentrates on leaving abundant open spaces, pleasant walkways and bridges for pedestrians and convenient shopping only ten minutes away from the farthest point by foot.

Photo credit: Blue Ridge Aerial Surveys

everywhere else. In Reston last summer, the lovely Lake Anne Plaza was badly vandalized one night. Some blamed "a bunch of Georgetown freaks," though there is little doubt that young Restonians were among them. Meetings and soul-searching among concerned citizens still continue. In Columbia, the teen centers—one called the Orange Propeller; the other, the cooperative ministry's coffee house, named It's Open—have been invaded by youngsters from outside the new city who have no place else to go. There also has been trouble with drugs, and that, too, has sparked not so much acrimony as earnest discussion, a spirit of care.

In one of these meetings a while ago, a woman spoke up and told Rouse rather emotionally that he must consider the reputation of his town and throw the freaks out. Applause. Rouse said he sympathized. But he also said he hoped the lady did not mean to suggest that the problem be swept under the rug. There must be a more creative answer. The hippies, he added, "may be saying something that we should hear." He got far more applause than the woman.

According to the Columbia Association, Columbia residents are from forty-three states and fourteen countries, all kinds of people with all kinds of views. Most residents found what they expected to find, according to the Michigan study. About 25 per cent said things were better than they had anticipated; 9 per cent said they were worse. So it would appear that America's most advanced new town has gotten off to a good start—though it still does not attract the poor and the rich, it is creating a new kind of living environment. There are no statistical data yet that would satisfy the sociologists as to how "effective" this environment is in terms of reduced crime or improved educational achievement or whatever. We do know that it gives people another choice of a way to live.

The few new towns in America, however, are just a beginning. In Great Britain, where the movement originated, the new-community builders have gone on from garden cities, like Columbia, to a second and third generation of new towns that are to the first as a jet plane and superjet are to a propeller aircraft. An example of the second generation is Cumbernault, begun in the late 1950's. It is compact and hard with granite cobblestones, is dedicated to keeping care entirely out of the way of people, and all but does away with neighborhoods and neighborhood centers. Instead, Cumbernault's communal life is focused on one big, bustling town center—a weird, complex megastructure with shops, apartments, meeting halls, neon lights, and fish 'n' chips smell—that straddles a super-highway. No bourgeois coziness here.

The third generation of British new towns is still in the planning stage. The towns are to be larger—a quarter-million inhabitants or more—but they also return to lower densities, separate neighborhoods, and green and pleasant openness. This is to be brought about by a rapid-transit system that is built into the town much as elevators are built into a high-rise building.

The hope is that they will be cities, as Lewis Mumford once put it, that "forget about the damn motorcars" and that are planned, "or the human scale for lovers and for friends."

VII

SOLID WASTE DISPOSAL

A combination of growing affluence and technological developments has produced a flood of waste materials in the United States which is becoming increasingly difficult to handle. The increase in population in urban areas and the accompanying rise in certain types of waste materials has created a disposal problem which present methods are incapable of handling. Solid wastes from the nation's urban areas is estimated to amount to one billion pounds a day or 185 million tons a year. Although moneys on the order of $3 billion a year are spent to remove this material, the sum is inadequate. Not only is more money required but new and better methods of disposing of waste materials are needed.

Throughout its history, the United States has assumed the attitude of using and disposing of—not reusing—its products with the result that the amount of solid waste matter produced each year is rapidly increasing. In 1920, refuse collected amounted to 2.75 pounds per person per day. This figure has nearly doubled to 5 pounds in 1970 and by 1980 is expected to reach 8 pounds. Moreover, much of the increase is in the form of non-biodegradable plastics which not only do not decay but which create dangerous products when burned. By the early 1970's, it had become clear that the technology of solid waste collection and disposal had not kept pace with this growing burden.

Collection methods (with one exception) have changed only insignificantly since the era of the horse drawn cart. This accounts for the fact that up to 80 percent of the funds spent on solid waste management goes into collection. The compactor truck is the only innovation which can make any claim to improving this situation, but the compression approach does not lend itself to the recycling of reusable waste materials.

Disposal methods are numerous, but similarly inadequate. At present, 77 percent of all collected solid waste is disposed of in open *dumps and another 13 percent is deposited in sanitary landfills. The remaining 10 percent is almost all disposed of through incineration. Recycling has not been adopted on a large scale because it requires major alterations in public attitudes, pricing, and industrial methods.*

With time, people are becoming more and more aware of the fact that much of what is routinely thrown away is salvageable—abandoned automobiles, waste paper and other products can be reclaimed and reused. But America has only begun to move in this direction. Today a majority of these waste materials are left to rot, creating eyesores on our landscapes as well as hazards to our water systems. This is due in large part to the problem of making reclamation profitable.

It is ironic that the great wealth of the United States enables the nation to produce such tremendous amounts of waste, yet it has failed to spend equally its financial and technical resources to solve the problems of waste disposal. Little attempt has been made to relate the production of goods with the collection and disposal of these same goods. There is no attempt to establish criteria for manufacturing processes aimed at simple, low cost reclamation of finished products. It is still a revolutionary idea to consider, as the state of Wisconsin is already doing, charging a fee with the purchase of every automobile to cover the cost of the eventual disposal of that vehicle. In this case, as it could be in other areas of the disposal problem, the cost of disposal has been incorporated into the cost of the product and passed along to the consumer who has benefitted from the ownership of the automobile. Nevertheless, manufacturers do not often accept responsibility for the costs of getting rid of the products they produce.

A problem of major proportions in the area of solid waste disposal concerns politics rather than technology. Disposal programs, like other environmental programs, are best dealt with on a regional basis; but present practice gives responsibility for these programs to local governments. Many small municipalities having responsibility for waste disposal do not have adequate resources to cope with the problem, nor have they shown any inclination to pool resources with neighboring communities. The same local governments are also increasingly faced with problems of sanitation employee dissatisfaction and demands for higher salaries.

Since 1965, the federal government has been able to provide assistance to states and municipalities in dealing with this problem. The Solid Waste Disposal Act authorizes the federal government to provide grants for several purposes, including demonstration projects of new waste disposal technology, development of new solid waste management systems and state surveys of solid waste handling needs and plans to meet these needs. The act also supports research into new methodology, training programs to provide much needed new personnel and technical assistance. The primary focus of projects carried out to date under this act has been on developing constructive uses for waste materials.

Robert R. Grinstead in "The New Resource" describes the methods available to deal with the solid waste problem. Grinstead concentrates on the reuseability of trash since he views wastes as a resource which we can ill afford to lose. There are several problems involved in establishing recycling methods on a large scale; probably the most significant first step must be to alter the public's attitude that materials are to be used once only and then discarded. The pile of wastes can grow too high.

In "Whisking the Garbage," Bertram B. Johansson describes a system for waste collection and disposal currently in use in several large suburbs of Stockholm and already planned for several new developments in the United States. The method uses pipes, built into apartment buildings. Refuse is dropped into disposal chutes which open into a vacuum tube speeding the refuse to a centralized collection center. There one man at a control panel can operate the completely mechanized incineration process. Although the initial installation cost of such a system is high, the investment is repaid within a few years.

The magnitude of the solid waste problem demands that careful evaluation of disposal methods be considered for their possible environmental impact. In this respect, it seems reasonable to conclude that because the refuse we produce is so vast, and because our resources are limited, we must concentrate much of our effort on developing recycling methods for as much of our refuse as possible. In addition, emphasis should be focused on the production side to develop products that can be recycled more easily or, if not, can be disposed of in a manner not harmful to the environment. This approach would stress greater use of returnables as well as reclaimed materials.

20. The New Resource

ROBERT R. GRINSTEAD

"Trash Is Our Only Growing Resource,"

U. S. Undersecretary of the Interior Hollis Dole told participants at a conference on solid wastes in Houston last March. This point of view is becoming increasingly prevalent among public officials, scientists, and businessmen concerned with the problem of what to do with the growing mountains of solid waste accumulating in and around cities in the U. S.

Getting rid of trash has been a problem since the first caveman threw a broken bone into the nearest bush. The solutions developed by the earliest men—burning, burying, or carting the material somewhere out of the way—are still the major methods in use today, albeit with some new twists. While these practices presented few problems for cavemen, the modern trinity of escalating population, intensifying concentration in urban centers, and skyrocketing consumption of material goods, has fashioned a triple threat to the age-old practice of dumping wastes onto the nearest unoccupied space.

Gradually, as the awareness of air pollution and public health problems has dawned, the plumes of smoke which used to identify local dumps have been disappearing; these eyesores have largely been replaced by landfills, where raw waste is quickly covered with a layer of earth. Currently, about 90 percent[1] of the trash collected in the U. S. is disposed of either by open dumping and burning or by landfilling. The latter has proven a fairly satisfactory means of solid waste disposal, since the land used has been of low economic value, and since the filled areas remain available for numerous uses, particularly recreational ones.

Robert R. Grinstead, "The New Resource," ENVIRONMENT, Vol. XII, No. 10 (December, 1970), pp. 3–17. Copyright 1970 Committee for Environmental Information.

The landfill process, however, is a ravenous devourer of land. New York City has been consuming land for this purpose at the rate of about 200 acres a year. Some cities, including San Francisco, have already run out of space and are shipping their trash to other areas. Others have switched to incinerators, by which the volume of trash can be reduced substantially to a mineral residue, extending the life and improving the quality of the landfill site by severalfold.

The incinerator is not without its problems, however. Faced with increasingly rigid air pollution restrictions on one side, increasing corrosiveness of flue gases produced by certain plastics on another, and increasing capital and operating costs as a result of these two problems, the incinerator may well find itself becoming obsolete before it becomes fashionable.

Presented with this dilemma, authorities are thinking a good deal about longer-range solutions, and support is beginning to crystallize around the concept of reclamation—or recycling, as it is more popularly known. Rather than viewing trash as a useless waste to be stored away somewhere, the recycling concept views it as a resource to be exploited, as Undersecretary Dole suggested.

Stated in these terms, three powerful reasons support the recycling approach: first, the waste material is diminished or eliminated; second, credit may be obtained toward the cost of managing the waste material; and third, pressure on the corresponding virgin material source is reduced.

Recycling, which literally means returning to the beginning of the cycle, suggests separating the trash into its components, which may then be returned to the place of manufacture; for example, paper waste may be remade into paper products, tin cans returned to the steel mill, and bottles to the glass furnace.

However, it is not necessary to return the components of trash to their original form in order to obtain some further usefulness from them, and the aim of current recycling efforts is simply to return the wastes to the economy in a way that will provide some utility in *any* form.

With this definition, even landfilling can be termed a recycling use. Los Angeles, for example, has filled pits and gullies on which have been built golf courses and a botanical garden. Virginia Beach, Virginia is building a 60-foot hill of trash on which will be constructed an amphitheatre, a soapbox derby run, and a winter sledding course. Yet the value of fill—around one dollar per ton—is rather nominal considering the relatively expensive materials which went into the trash. The question really is: can we utilize trash in a more valuable way, and if so, how much more?

What's in Trash?

Some 200 million tons of trash (about one ton per person) are currently collected each year by towns and cities in the U. S. About 80 percent of the cost of managing this river of waste lies in the *collection* system,[2] the *disposal* currently accounting for only a minor share, due to the prevalence of relatively inexpensive landfills. Landfill costs amount to only one to three dollars per ton, compared for example to incineration, where costs run from about three to ten dollars[3] per ton, depending on the size of the installation and whether some use is made of the heat generated. Increasingly sophisticated stack gas cleaning equipment, dictated by stricter air pollution standards, can be expected to raise these costs still further. Large-scale composting, in the few places where it is done in the U. S., has a comparable price tag, about five to ten dollars per ton,[4] minus whatever credit can be obtained from the sale of compost and other reclaimed materials.

Against this background, let us examine the trash itself and see what is actually in it, both physically and economically. The first column in Table 1 gives a very rough breakdown of the components of typical trash. The numbers vary, depending upon the economic level of the city, the season, and other factors, but quite clearly paper products constitute the major portion.[5] Next let us look at the potential value of this interesting ore. We shall assume, as a first step, that wastes will be recycled to those industries from which they originally

Table I / Potential Values in Trash

	Percent by Weight	Potential Value of Component $/Ton of Component	$/Ton Trash
Paper, Paperboard	50	100	50
Ferrous metal	9	20	2
Aluminum	1	200	2
Glass, Ceramics	10	10	1
Garbage, Yard Waste	20	5*	1
Misc.: Plastics, Textiles, etc.	10	5**	0.50

* Value as compost
** Value as fuel

came. The second column, therefore, lists the values of the bulk material (scrap iron, aluminum, scrap glass, and clean wastepaper). For the food/yard waste fraction, the value of compost is used, since although this material cannot be directly recycled to produce food and flowers, it can be *indirectly* recycled as compost to the soil.

The remainder, consisting of miscellaneous materials including plastics, rubber, fabrics, wood and leather, shall be assigned only fuel value, since the fraction contains little of any one material, and its fuel value is high. While reclamation of some of these miscellaneous materials can be envisioned, no simple means is on the horizon.

The final column, the product of the numbers in the first two columns, gives the potential value of the components of trash if these materials could all be recycled as the forms shown.

The interesting picture that emerges from this exercise is that the potential value of paper literally dwarfs the other values in ordinary trash. The reason, of course, is twofold: the predominance of paper products in trash, and the considerably higher unit value of cellulose fiber.

It must be emphasized that a number of hurdles lie between the city dump and the industrial stockpile of recycled materials, and that the potential values listed above represent only the upper—and probably unrealizable—limits to the value of those materials. Nevertheless, the concept of potential value provides one convenient yardstick with which we may be able to compare the merits of various proposals for recycling trash.

Three other yardsticks are useful for evaluating proposals for recycling trash: one, the cost of separating the material from trash and converting it to a form which can be used by the appropriate industry (processing losses and degradation of the material are part of this cost); two, the existence of markets which are large enough to absorb the volumes of recycled materials, and which are close enough to provide acceptable shipping costs; and three, the amount and difficulty of disposal of final residue remaining after all materials which can be recycled have been removed.

Current Recycling Methods

Equipped with these yardsticks, we shall now venture into the realm of trash reclamation technology.

Incineration. Incineration qualifies as a recycling process on two counts: heat recovery during burning and material recovery from the residue. Incinerators with steam generation equipment for power production have been in use in Europe for many years, and new installations in the U. S. are beginning to adopt this improvement. In this instance, of course, paper serves as fuel, which is of relatively low value compared to the potential value of paper listed in Table 1.

The incinerator is still an evolving species, and some newer designs involve such variations as gas turbines to generate power, or very high temperatures to melt and further shrink the volume of residue.

The major source of reclaimed values from incineration might, however, lie in the residue which, in a well-operated installation, would have a composition given in Table 2.

Table II / Composition of Typical Municipal Incinerator Residue
(Average of five Washington, D.C. incinerators)

Material	Percent by Weight
Tin cans	17
Other iron and steel	11
Other metals	2
Glass	44
Ceramics, stones, bricks	2
Partially burned or unburned organic matter	9
Ash	15

Source: *U.S. Bureau of Mines Report 7204*, 1968.

U. S. Bureau of Mines scientists have developed a process utilizing relatively simple equipment (mainly screens and magnetic devices) which separates the major portions of this residue. In addition, a very high-intensity magnet separates the colored (iron-containing) glass from the clear glass. Costs of operating this process are estimated to be only about four dollars per ton of residue.[6] Although the value of the products has not yet been established, it will probably exceed the four-dollar-per-ton processing costs, and it seems very likely that in concert with the generation of power, incineration might be brought close to the break-even point.

The attractiveness of incineration at the present time is that it can reduce trash to somewhere between 10 and 20 percent of the original volume. For more advanced "slagging" incinerators, which operate at high enough temperatures to produce molten residue, the volume is shrunk to only 2 to 3 percent of the original.[7] Even with no reclamation of the residue, the life of an existing landfill site can thus be increased severalfold.

While the burning of trash has thus come a long way from the smoldering city dump of a generation ago, the major problem with incinerators is still air pollution. Equipped with a variety of scrubbers, filters, and precipitators, existing technology can probably cope with the increasingly strict air pollution standards in urban areas, but the question is whether it can be done economically in the face of other alternatives.

Pyrolysis: New Name, Old Process. A close cousin of incineration, pyrolysis differs only in the fact that air is excluded and heat is applied externally. Known in earlier days as "destructive distillation," the process was used to convert wood and coal into charcoal and various chemical products. Recent studies using trash as a feed[8] have shown that a variety of gaseous and liquid organic materials, including methyl alcohol, acetic acid, and some heavier oils, are driven off, and charcoal and some ash are left as residues. The ash is similar to that from incinerators, but the other products are combustible and are currently viewed mainly as fuels, although some limited credit for chemical products may be obtainable. Unfortunately, none of the chemical products reported to date enjoy markets which could absorb more than a small percentage of the huge quantities of these chemicals potentially available in the U. S. trash output.

A related process developed by the U. S. Bureau of Mines involves reacting trash with carbon monoxide under high temperatures and pressures to produce an oil,[9] similar in characteristics to crude petroleum. Although this is a dramatic technical accomplishment, oil, used mainly as fuel, actually has a relatively low economic value. To be sure, the fuel value of oil is two to three times that of raw trash, but only about half of the trash weight is obtained as oil, and little, if any, increase in the overall fuel value is likely.

Construction of the first major trash pyrolysis plant[10] has been announced by the state of Delaware, where it will be located, and by the Hercules Corporation, which will operate it. The operation of the ten million dollar plant, which will handle 500 tons of wastes a day, is based on a composting step which will handle the bulk of the material, followed by removal of the metal and glass for recycling and by pyrolysis of the residual material.

One knotty problem which may prove the value of pyrolysis techniques is the recycling of old rubber vehicle tires. The problem of what to do with the 100 million tires discarded annually in the U. S. seems well on the way to a solution with the announcement by the Firestone Rubber Company of a process wherein tires are pyrolyzed[11] to yield about 45 percent solid carbonized residue as in other pyrolysis operations. The remaining 55 percent is a mixture of gases and liquids similar to petroleum compounds.

The important feature of the pyrolysis process is its ability to convert most organic materials to charcoal (which may be recovered for sale or for fuel) and volatile organic compounds. Conversion of trash to more manageable fuels in this way may, some experts think, simplify the problems of extracting the heat values and meeting air pollution standards.

Composting. Although widely used in Europe, large-scale composting has never been an attractive proposition in the U. S.,[12] because it has not been economically competitive with landfilling. The compost has generally been viewed as a product to be sold, and major markets for this material have not developed here. A number of composting operations have existed in the U. S., but only three were still in operation last year,[13] and these have depended upon obtaining a disposal fee from the city.

Composting is essentially biological oxidation of the organic constituents of trash to relatively stable compounds. Trash is usually ground or shredded and allowed to cure, either in windrows which are turned occasionally over a several-week period, or for three to five days in a large, slowly rotating, horizontal cylinder. Sewage sludge is often added to provide moisture and nutrients which aid in the composting process. The product is usually screened to remove plastic, metal, and larger pieces of glass. Paper and other cellulosic materials undergo composting readily, so the process has the advantage of being able to assimilate the bulk of trash components. Costs of composting are in the range of five to ten dollars per ton of trash, from which perhaps one-half or two-thirds of a ton of compost can be obtained. The finished product sells for about six dollars per ton, but is low in fertilizer nutrients, and finds its main value as an additive [14] which helps to maintain good soil condition in high-value specialty crops.

In some situations compost may be in demand for reclamation of barren or dry land and strip-mined coal fields; it could also be useful for stabilization of steep slopes (as in Europe), road embankments, and mine-tailing piles.

Because of compost's relatively low value, the trend in thinking seems to be away from producing it as a salable product, and viewing it rather as simply a means of converting the unwanted organic components of trash into a material which can be returned to the environment without damage. The emphasis is accordingly shifting toward salvaging as much material as possible prior to the composting step.

Typical of existing composting plants [15] is the one run by the Metropolitan Waste Conversion Corporation in Houston, Texas. Here paper and other easily identifiable materials are sorted, partly by hand and partly by mechanical methods. Iron is removed magnetically, and the residue is composted.

Viewed as simply a disposal method for the organic wastes, however, composting will have to compete with incineration or pyrolysis, which are more versatile means for accomplishing the same end. The residues from incineration and pyrolysis are smaller, and the by-product power available from both finds a ready market in the urban complex. Also, in urban areas at least, composting suffers in comparison with incineration and pyrolysis because of the distance between the urban area which produces the compost and the rural area which must absorb it.

If, as appears likely, demand for compost at any price does not materialize, it becomes simply a disposal problem instead of a resource, and the relatively large volumes and transportation requirements are distinct disadvantages. Thus, at least in more densely populated areas, composting may be heading toward the same fate as the fading landfill, which is being literally crowded into oblivion by the strangling growth of urban centers.

Cellulose Fiber Recovery. Of the roughly 55 million tons of paper and paperboard made in the U. S. each year, about 20 percent is already made from waste paper. The waste, however, comes not from trash, but mainly from commercial sources. Over 70 percent consists of either corrugated board, newsprint, or what is known as No. 1 mixed.[16] The latter is low-grade paper waste collected from office buildings and other similar commercial establishments. Much newsprint comes through collections from volunteer organizations, but the remainder is collected by dealers, who sort, bale and ship it to paper mills. Most of this waste goes into cardboard or construction paper, where bulk, rather than high strength or whiteness, is the major consideration.

Within the past few years, two approaches to the problem of separating waste paper from trash have developed in the U. S. Some composting plants, such as Metropolitan Waste, have begun removing some paper from raw trash by various mechanical methods, and selling it.

A second approach, announced only last year by the Black Clawson Company,[17] a manufacturer of papermaking equipment, involves pulping raw trash directly in water in something resembling a giant kitchen blender. A series of mechanical separations including screens and centrifugal devices remove large nondisintegrating objects such as cans, shoes, bones, and broken glass, after which a fine screen catches the cellulose fibers. About half of the cellulose fiber can be recovered as a crude product valued, according to company officials, at about $25 a ton. Metal and glass, which are recovered separately, can be sold also.

With the aid of a grant from the U. S. Bureau of Solid Wastes Management, the city of Franklin, Ohio is constructing a 50-ton-per-day trash reclamation plant which will use this process. Company spokesmen estimate that a plant treating about 1,000 tons of trash a day (an amount equivalent to that produced by a city of about 500,000 people) would break even, while larger plants would presumably produce a profit for the operating agency.

A similar project is under way at the U. S. Forest Products Lab (FPL) at Madison, Wisconsin.[18] The project combines the "dry sort" methods of the composting plants with Black Clawson's wet-pulping method. FPL scientists envision ultimately upgrading the crude pulp to material of still higher value by appropriate chemical processing; the scientists note that this is a necessary development if recycled fiber is to compete for uses currently filled by virgin fiber. The bottle-neck limiting preparation of high-grade pulp, they point out, may not be the "casual" contaminants, such as the garbage put into a paper product during use and disposal by the user, but rather the "intentional" contaminants (such as waxes, pigments, and plastics) put into the paper by manufacturers.

The second major problem in recycling paper is a marketing problem and stems from the fact that most paper products—as much as 70 to 80 percent according to one estimate—are discarded in trash. If substantial quantities of high-grade recycled fiber should become available from trash, this fiber would compete with virgin material for paper products uses. To be sure, the market is large enough to absorb this recycled fiber, but only if the quality is competitive, and only at the expense of a corresponding reduction in the demand for virgin fiber. Reduction of demand on virgin raw materials is, of course, one of the aims of the recycling approach, and would be welcomed by conservationists as a step forward, though it might be greeted with something less than wild enthusiasm by the producers of virgin materials—in this case, the pulp manufacturers.

The Indestructible Pair. The above survey of current trash disposal ideas has centered on the uses to which paper wastes are put in each process. What about the metal and glass in trash?

The answer to this question is based on two factors. First of all, we saw in Table 1 that the maximum credit obtainable for either fraction was only a few dollars per ton of trash. While this could be a significant credit in some cases, paper wastes are potentially more valuable and certainly more abundant; they would consequently have greater leverage in determining the economics of any given disposal scheme.

The other major factor is that, with a few exceptions, both metal and glass would be unaffected by any of the processing schemes listed. Therefore, recovery of either metal or glass could probably be accomplished either from the residues of any of these processes, with only minor differences in equipment and economics. The exceptions to this generalization are those processes involving heating, in which alloying of the metallic constituents with each other complicates subsequent separation of the metals.

At the present time the most effective means for sorting out these materials are, for iron, various magnetic devices, and for glass, some form of air classification in which an upward air stream carries lighter materials away. No simple means has been reported for removing the aluminum, but the problem is under study.

It probably will come as a surprise to no one that the ubiquitous "tin" can is the major metal item in trash, constituting about two-thirds of the metal found there. Estimates generally place the total amount of iron and steel items in trash in the vicinity of ten to fifteen million tons per year,[19] or about 10 percent of the U. S. steel production. Another million tons or so of other metals, mainly aluminum, are also discarded in trash. Sizable quantities of cans are already salvaged in the western U. S. for use in recovering copper from low-grade-ore processing. This is a limited market, and it appears that significant expansion of steel-can reclamation will require recycling to steel furnaces, where the cans are now generally unacceptable because of their tin coating. Since the technology of detinning steel is well known, there seems to be no technological problem with recycling cans. However, steel scrap is valued at only about twenty dollars per ton, most of which would likely be eaten up by the combination of detinning and transportation from trash collection to steel mill.

A big boost to can recycling may be on the way in the form of the trend toward what is known as TFS, or tin-free steel cans, in which the tin coating is replaced by a chromium and resin film, which would presumably be directly acceptable into the steel furnace.

All of the scrap iron, however, is not in the trash can. A large source of steel scrap is the junked automobile,[20] of which some seven or eight million appear each year in the U. S. Most of these find their way to junkyards, but probably several hundred thousand are abandoned in the countryside and in cities where they become part of the urban trash problem. New York City, for example, hauled away 50,000 such cars in 1969 alone!

The major technical problems of recycling automobiles are the same as those of recycling cans, namely, the elimination of undesirable metals and the transportation of the steel to a buyer, in this case a scrap yard. In the U. S. the principal development for separating these metals for recycling is a shearing machine which produces fist-size chunks that are sorted by magnetic equipment to yield iron and steel.

Although the glass content of trash is mainly bottles and jars, most bulk-separation methods would probably pick out stones, ceramics, and concrete, in addition to glass of nearly every shade of the visible spectrum. While scrap glass is recycled to glassmaking furnaces, it must be sorted by color, and extraneous materials such as rocks and metal must be eliminated.

The nub of the problem—sorting the glass by color—is being approached from two directions. The U. S. Bureau of Mines uses a very high-intensity magnetic field to separate colored glass according to its iron content, which is related to color. Other devices divert glass fragments passing a sensor to appropriate bins, depending upon the color of light transmitted by the fragment.[21]

Since scrap glass, or cullet as it is known, is valued at about fifteen dollars per ton,[22] it is questionable whether large quantities of glass can economically be reclaimed from trash, sorted, and transported to a glass factory. In many locations the problem may be mainly a matter of how to dispose of the glass in an environmentally acceptable way. Ideas on this subject are numerous and generally involve incorporating the ground glass, which is nearly indistinguishable from sand, into building blocks, tile, or "blacktop" aggregate. The latter, dubbed "glasphalt," has been used by the Owens Illinois Company to pave a street.[23] While the value of this type of scrap glass is only that of sand or crushed rock, three to four dollars per ton, construction and paving uses represent large outlets in populated areas, eliminating the need for transportation to distant glass furnaces.

Shape of the Future

It should be clear that there has been no dearth of ideas for transmuting trash into something nobler and more valuable. Besides those

Table III / Comparison of Major Trash Recycling Processes

Process (Use)	Quantity, Tons per Ton of Wastepaper	Value, $ per Ton of Material	Value of Recycled Paper, $ per Ton of Original Paper	Processing Complexity and Cost	Marketing Fit	Probable Net Credit (+) or Cost (−) of Process, $ per Ton of Trash
Landfill	1	1	1	low	becoming poorer in urban areas	−1 to 2
Incinerator* (fuel)	1	3	3	low to moderate	good	−1 to 5
Compost	0.7	6	4	moderate	poor	−5 to 10
Pyrolysis (fuel)	0.5	5–10	2–5	moderate	good	similar to incineration
Carbon Monoxide (oil)	0.3	20	6	high	good	probably (−) and large
Fiber Recovery**	0.5	25	12	moderate to high	good	about zero

* For incinerator utilizing heat
** Based on Black Clawson process

described above, many others have been put forth, ranging from some interesting and potentially valuable biological processes for production of alcohol, sugar and protein,[24] to the farfetched suggestion that trash be put through a hydrogen fusion torch which would break it down for reclamation into its constituent elements. To attempt to predict the ultimate winners in this technological contest would be as imprudent as attempting to pick the winner of a horse race before the pack rounds the first turn. Nevertheless, some conclusions are emerging, in general form if not in fine detail.

Table 3 lists the major processing schemes described above, together with some information about product yields and potential values. Estimates of final nonrecyclable residue have not been included, since most proposals envision burning or pyrolyzing any such residue to an ash. The final residues may, therefore, be roughly comparable. Based on the above discussion, an attempt has been made to provide a rough assessment of the difficulties to be expected in processing and marketing the products.

The foremost conclusion which can be drawn, and perhaps the firmest, is that the classical methods—landfilling, incinerating, and composting—are characterized mainly by the fact that the paper products are recycled into an end use of fairly low value. For the moment this may be sufficient, since the one to ten dollars-per-ton cost of the disposal process is a secondary factor alongside the twenty to fifty dollars-per-ton cost of the collection system which precedes it.

Given the range of possibilities, however, it appears that the action will inevitably shift to the reclamation of cellulose fiber, where the value of the product offers ultimately a greater chance for a net positive return. As exemplified by the Black Clawson and Forest Products Lab efforts, this goal has already become discernible on the technological horizon, although production of high quality, contaminant-free fiber is some years away.

This is not to predict the disappearance of other processes from the waste-processing field. Due to the spectrum of situations where domestic trash is generated, conditions may in some cases favor a process which is not applicable in others; for example, a smaller city considerably removed from markets for either pyrolysis chemicals or fiber, but surrounded by an agricultural area, might find composting an attractive process, although it might not be profitable in a major urban area.

Bypassing the Trash Collector

Up to now we have been discussing the prospects for recycling trash after it has been collected in a central location. Two other recycling routes exist, however, both of which bypass trash collection. One of these is the voluntary sorting of trash at home and delivery to collection centers, where it can be turned over directly to industries. This movement, organized by numerous ecology-oriented volunteer groups around the U. S., and assisted by the industries involved, has been the stimulus for much of the new awareness of the recycling problem in this country.

A second and similar route is utilized by the commercial scrap dealers, who collect or buy scrap metal, paper, glass, fabrics, plastics and other materials, usually from commercial and industrial sources, sort it if necessary, and sell it to manufacturing industries. This eight billion dollar secondary (waste) materials industry is responsible for most of the recycling done currently,[25] including 30 percent of all the aluminum currently produced, 45 percent of the copper and brass, 52 percent of the lead, and 20 percent of the paper.

Both the volunteers and the dealers are eager to increase the amount of recycling of materials. The question is, can an expansion of the existing channels for collection of secondary materials—home sorting, scrap dealers, and the volunteer movement—provide an alternate channel for recycling the bulk of the components of trash? At this writing the answer seems to be no, for a number of reasons.

The secondary materials industries now work mainly with commercial scrap and obtain very little of their material from trash sources. If they tried to expand by sorting material from trash, it would be a very costly operation since, at the current state of technological development, it would probably require expensive hand labor, plus some additional processing to clean up the material for sale.

With some form of subsidy, either in the form of volunteer effort, or from the public treasury, no doubt an extra increment of value could be skimmed from trash. However, neither the volunteer movement nor the commercial scrap dealers seem likely to be able to manage the entire trash problem, including disposal of those final residues remaining after sorting out the materials of value.

Finally, to the extent that recycled materials are diverted from trash through either of these channels, additional collection systems, be it trucks or individual autos, are required. Since in conventional trash management practice the collection process usurps some 80 percent of the cost, further fragmentation of the collection system seems likely to be a step in the wrong direction. Rather, as the technology of recycling develops, it seems probable that there will be an increasing reliance on a single trash collection system, combined with large-scale sorting and processing methods at a central location.

This is not to deny the value of the volunteer recycling drives or the commercial scrap industry. Central sorting plants and sophisticated recycling processes are not yet in sight, and for the time being there is no alternative to everyone saving his own aluminum, washing labels off his own bottles, and tying up his own newspapers. Perhaps even more important, however, is the educational impact resulting from involvement in recycling drives. Through the efforts of recycling centers, and through the publicity given their activities by the press, millions of Americans are aware that newspapers can be recycled and that aluminum is a relatively valuable material, and they are developing some long overdue appreciation for the unbridled extravagance of the U.S. materials economy.

New Attitudes and Technologies Needed

In very general terms, the roadblock to recycling our trash has been the attitude that materials are to be used once and discarded, and that the management of the waste piles thus created can somehow be taken care of.

Thanks to the new awareness of and concern about the environment, this attitude is changing. But we are finding that more than attitudes may need changing if many of our environmental problems are to be solved.

Looking at the trash problem, one of the major deficiencies seems to be that our materials technology needs to be extended to include the production of materials not only from virgin sources, but also from wastes. A tree contains about 50 percent cellulose fiber, just about the same as a truckload of urban trash. Yet we get most of our paper from trees, because, at our present state of knowledge, it is simply less expensive to do so. A large part of the reason for this is that the technology of papermaking arose at a time when wastes were almost nonexistent and virgin sources unchallenged. The technologies of papermaking, steelmaking, glassmaking, and numerous other industries, have all been laboriously constructed over many decades to their present highly refined state on a foundation of virgin material. Yet to a hypothetical scientist from outer space, unfamiliar with our history, there would seem to be no *a priori* reason why we could not, with adequate research effort, utilize the 50 percent of cellulose fiber, or, for that matter, the glass, iron, aluminum, and other materials in the trash.

Thus we need, among other things, new attitudes about producing materials which will be reused, rather than discarded after a single pass through the economy. But we need just as badly some new technology for salvaging these materials from wastes. This will cost money, and it will take time. It is at this point that the need for federal government activity becomes visible.

The Solid Waste Act of 1965 placed the primary responsibility for dealing with the solid waste problem in the Bureau of Solid Wastes Management (BSWM) in the Department of Health, Education and Welfare, some additional duties for mineral and fuel wastes being given to the Bureau of Mines in the Department of the Interior. The interest at that time was nominal by current standards of funding, and the total budgets of these two agencies have since then amounted to only about fifteen million dollars per year. Much of the effort of the BSWM during this initial period was devoted simply to assessing the problem and the existing means for dealing with it.

The mood is now shifting. A bill introduced in Congress in 1969 by Senator Muskie to extend the Solid Waste Act of 1965 was buffeted about for over a year and emerged as the Resource Recovery Act of 1969. Development of technology for recycling of materials is a major emphasis in this bill, for which $461 million was authorized,[26] several times the 1968 budget for solid wastes. While expenditures are thus *authorized*, funds have yet to be *appropriated*, and the sincerity of Congress will be more adequately measured by the extent to which their appropriations match their rhetoric.

Two changes in our official attitudes seem called for, if we are serious about increasing our utilization of waste materials. First, we need to treat waste material industries on at least an equal basis with virgin material industries. In fact, until the technology of recycling matures, we may have to go a step further and favor it for a time, using such devices as subsidies for waste material industries, and a reduction or elimination of existing depletion allowances, favored tax positions, and lower freight rates for virgin materials.

The second change would be the establishment of some sort of feedback between the disposal process and the material manufacturing process. Thus, while it may be perfectly possible to come up with ways to recycle currently available materials, in the absence of restraints, the rapid appearance of new items in our trash cans may outstrip the ability of the waste processor to separate and reclaim them.

If the material producer can somehow be given at least part of the responsibility for the disposal problem, a powerful brake on extravagance would exist. At this time, however, no consensus has been reached on how to do this.

The role of the federal government in this field so far has thus been neither carrot nor stick—neither taxes nor incentives—for the management of trash and solid wastes. It is, to pursue the analogy, rather more like the shovel, which through the support of research and development, is smoothing the path along which the proverbial animal must tread. Plenty of carrot-and-stick legislation has been discussed and even introduced in Congress and state legislatures to accomplish a variety of ends. Few bills have actually been passed into law, because in this rapidly developing field it is not clear how the government should play its regulatory and incentive cards.

NOTES

[1] Office of Science and Technology, "Solid Waste Management: A Comprehensive Assessment of Solid Waste Problems, Practices, and Needs," 1969.

[2] Ibid.

[3] Engdahl, R. B., "Solid Waste Processing," Report SW-4C, U.S. Bureau of Solid Waste Management, p. 16, 1969.

[4] Snell, J. R., "How Much Does Composting Cost Per Ton?" Compost Science, p. 17, Spring-Summer 1967. Univ. of Calif. Sanitary Engineering Lab, "Comprehensive Studies of Solid Waste Management," Second Annual Report, Report SW 3-rg, U.S. Bureau of Solid Waste Management, p. 63.

[5] "Cleaning Our Environment," report by the American Chemical Society, 1969, p. 165.

[6] Stanczyck, M. H., "Beneficiation of Metals and Minerals in Incinerator Residues," Proceedings of the Second Mineral Waste Utilization Symposium, Illinois Institute of Technology Research Institute, Chicago, Illinois, p. 255, 1970.

[7] Zinn, R., C. LaMantia, W. Niessen, "Total Incineration," Industrial Water Engineering, p. 29, July 1970.

[8] "Refuse Can Yield Profits, Waste Technologists Say," Chemical and Engineering News, p. 38, April 6, 1970.

[9] "Novel Process Could Aid in Waste Disposal," Chemical and Engineering News, p. 43, Nov. 17, 1969.

[10] "Reclaiming Solid Wastes for Profit," Environmental Science and Technology, p. 729, Sept. 1969.

[11] "Disposal Problem Solved," Chemical and Engineering News, p. 12, June 8, 1970.

[12] Hart, S. A., "Composting: European Activity and American Potential," Report SW-2c, U.S. Bureau of Solid Waste Management, 1968.

[13] "Cleaning Our Environment," op. cit., p. 177.

[14] Hart, *loc. cit.*

[15] Prescott, J. M., "Composting Plant Converts Refuse into Organic Soil Conditioner," *Chemical Engineering*, p. 232, Nov. 6, 1967.

[16] Bergstrom, D. W., "Economics of Secondary Fiber Usage," *Technical Association of the Pulp and Paper Industries Journal*, p. 76A, April 1968.

[17] Williams, Ward C., "Use It—Reuse It!" *Pulp and Paper*, p. 61, Sept. 1970.

[18] "FPL Recycles Municipal Trash for Fiber Products," *Forest Products Journal*, p. 11, August 1970.

[19] National Academy of Engineering, National Academy of Sciences, "Policies for Solid Waste Management," Report SW-11c, U.S. Bureau of Solid Waste Management, 1970.

[20] Salpukas, A., "Abandoned Cars Blight the Nation," *San Francisco Chronicle*, Oct. 25, 1970. "Can Engineering Cope with the Debris of Affluence?" *Product Engineering*, p. 37, Oct. 9, 1967.

[21] Abrahams, J. H., Jr., "Glass Containers as a Factor in Municipal Solid Waste Disposal," *The Glass Industry*, p. 216, May 1970.

[22] "Waste Recovery: Big Business in the 70's," *Chemical and Engineering News*, p. 14, March 2, 1970.

[23] Abrahams, J. H., Jr., "Utilization of Waste Container Glass," *Waste Age*, p. 9, July-Aug. 1970.

[24] Meller, F. H., "Conversion of Organic Solid Wastes into Yeast," Public Health Service Publ. 1909, 1969.

[25] Abrahams, J. H., Jr., "Packaging Industry Looks at Waste Utilization," *Compost Science*, Vol. 10, No. 1-2, 1969.

[26] "Solid Waste Bill Signed," *Air & Water News*, p. 1, Nov. 2, 1970.

USING SANITARY LANDFILL TO BUILD OUTDOOR RECREATION AREAS:
Mt. Trashmore and Others

By the beginning of 1960 more than 1,400 cities were reportedly using the sanitary landfill method. The advantages of this method of waste disposal are primarily twofold: It is a convenient way of disposing of waste materials especially on sites which can be improved by filling; and once a sanitary landfill has been completed the land is free to be used for a variety of purposes. Thus, it improves the land rather than destroying it. The method is useful only where potential fill areas are available. Many large cities, including New York and Baltimore, are turning to other methods because sites are not available at reasonable distances. Smaller cities, however, continue to use this method.

One of the most spectacular recreation areas constructed largely of waste materials is Mt. Trashmore, a small hill in Evanston, Illinois which is now extensively used for a variety of recreation activities. Surprisingly, the Trashmore example has so far attracted few imitators, although a similar operation may be on its way in Virginia. In view of the dearth of landfill sites in many densely settled urban areas the possibility of creating new trash hills—or even mountain ranges—seems to warrant close attention.

ROBERT E. JAMES PARK, EVANSTON, ILLINOIS

(Mt. Trashmore)
48.2 acres, 65 feet at highest point

Background: The area was a claypit with a depth of 80 feet when it was purchased by the city in 1943. Until 1965 it was used for the dumping of incinerated residue. In the 1940s, plans were drawn by a landscape architect for the eventual development of the site as a city park.

RECREATION FACILITIES:

1 shelter house with concessions, wash rooms, large rest area, office and equipment storage space
4 lighted softball fields (converted to 2 football fields in season)
5 unlighted softball fields
2 unlighted baseball fields
2 unlighted soccer fields
6 tennis courts
1 coasting and toboggan hill with:
  2 toboggan runs
  1 long sled hill for adults and older children
  1 shorter sled hill for younger children

USAGE:	No. days open	Total admissions	Aver. daily use
1965–1966*	30	14,857	495
1966–1967	27	7,645	283
1967–1968	16	4,253	266

* No fee was charged that year.

21. Whisking the Garbage

BERTRAM B. JOHANSSON

The Swedish zeal for preserving the environment reflects a recognition that the individual human is as responsible for pollution as is industry. This national characteristic expresses itself in many ways —from the housewife's sloshing of water over the front steps of her home every morning to the government's willingness to pay up to half the cost of the modern sewage disposal facilities all municipalities and towns in Sweden are required to put into operation by 1972. Among the multitude of efforts to deal with pollution at the points where it originates is one that is only now becoming widely known. It is directed at garbage and refuse disposal and follows a logic of revolutionary simplicity couched in a single question: If pipes can be used to bring water to houses and apartments and industrial plants, and if pipes can be used to take away sewage, why can't pipes also be used to get rid of the rubbish of life in the home, office, and factory? Anyone can discover the answer for himself by visiting Sundbyberg, a town on the northwestern edge of Stockholm.

Sundbyberg is spreading a population of 30,000 persons westward from a nucleus that is half a century old. Within its growing perimeter are three new and spacious neighborhoods of three- and four-story apartment buildings punctuated here and there with higher rising towers. These places are notable for landscaped courtyards, full of flower gardens and playgrounds. Children romp in these light, airy spaces, free of automobiles, trucks, and carbon monoxide fumes. There are no threatening roads or driveways, not even narrow paths to facilitate the household amenities common to all towns. Pickups of garbage are as unnecessary here as is the clanking of ashcans.

Bertram B. Johansson, "Whisking the Garbage," *Saturday Review*, July 3, 1971, pp. 40–43.

Sundbyberg housewives bag their garbage in their kitchens, as city residents almost universally do. The bags are then dropped into chutes recessed in the walls of apartment houses.

Up to that point, the Sundbyberg refuse collection system is identical with all other urban waste collection systems. At that point, however, the resemblance ends.

The Sundbyberg garbage bags, instead of dropping into an incinerating pit at the bottom of the disposal chute, fall only a few feet before being stopped by a steel disc about three feet across. The disc is a valve that opens into a spiral-welded steel pipe hidden within the walls of the apartment complex. Periodically, the valve turns momentarily. Whatever is resting on it at that moment empties into the pipe, the inner diameter of which ranges from sixteen to twenty-four inches while the thickness of its walls is between two-tenths and three-tenths of an inch in order to withstand the pressure of the vacuum it contains.

When the valve opens, the vacuum's pull sucks it clean, whisking its burden away at very high speed. En route to that point, the pipe may slope as much as twenty degrees off the horizontal and follow curves of five to seven feet radius over stretches up to a mile and a half in length without diminishing efficiency. Beneath and between the apartment buildings the pipe occupies the same trench as the water and sewer mains. At the central collection point flexible joints (to minimize noise) connect the pipes to pumps that maintain the vacuum and heap all the rubbish together.

The central refuse pile may contain such disparate items as Christmas trees, heavy steam irons, coat hangers, umbrellas, paint cans, bottles, paper, and cardboard—in fact, anything that can be pushed through the chute openings in the apartment house hallway walls. An automatic process sifts glass and metals out of the heap. Putrid odors are removed from the air before it is expelled. The refuse remaining in the pile is whisked on into an incinerator to provide heat for the 1,100 apartments that now use the vacuum disposal system.

Since 65 per cent of the refuse at Sundbyberg is paper, the heat obtained from the incinerator averages about 2,200 to 2,500 calories per kilo (2.2 pounds) of rubbish, or approximately one-fourth of the heat that would be produced by the burning of fuel oil. In summer, the vacuum system of garbage disposal thus provides hot water for all apartments served by the system. In winter, the burning of the refuse alone obviously cannot heat Sundbyberg, but it does reduce the burden on the oil burners and hence saves money. Efficiency is attested by the fact that the original 1,100-apartment system in the

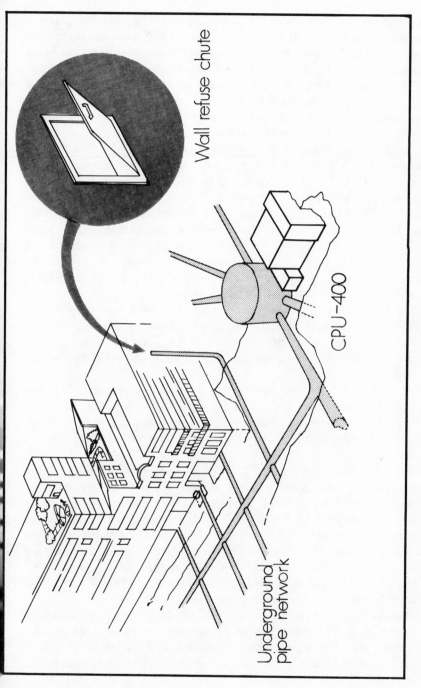

Wall refuse chute

CPU-400

Underground pipe network

—*Doug Anderson, after Combustion Power Company Sketch.*

Sketch above shows how new Swedish vacuum system of garbage and trash disposal can be hooked up to an experimental American garbage and trash burner (CPU-400) designed to convert heat into electric power and so reduce energy requirements of the system.

Sundbyberg subdivision of Or, after five years of operation, is now being matched by another system serving 1,800 more apartments in the subdivision of Hallonbergen. And still more apartments are being hooked up in a third subdivision of Sundbyberg—Storskorgen.

The trash gathered by the vacuum collectors in Sundbyberg is incinerated about half a mile from the apartment complexes; thus the fumes, which are scrubbed relatively clean in the chimney stacks, rarely reach the apartments. But the Swedes think they can do better than that, and they have installed a variant of the Sundbyberg vacuum system—one without an incinerator—at another Stockholm suburb, Sollentuna. This innovation is designed to serve 1,250 apartments initially. At its underground receiving station, the trash, instead of being burned, is compressed into containers twenty to thirty feet long. Trucks transport these portable bins to one of four large incinerators that are being erected by the city on the outskirts of Stockholm, far from residential centers. In addition to chimney scrubbers similar to those at Sundbyberg, the Sollentuna incinerator is eqipped with special air filtering devices.

Housewives living in the Sundbyberg apartments told me they are hardly aware that the vacuum disposal system is operating in their buildings. They take the convenience for granted. They are, of course, grateful for the absence of odors, dust, and whining garbage trucks.

The Swedes have been perfecting vacuum conveyance of refuse for at least a decade. Calor-Celcius, Sweden's largest manufacturer of piping, has done the pioneering through a subsidiary, Centralsug. Seven examples of the Centralsug system are operating in Sweden today.

The first was designed in 1960 for a hospital at Solleftea in northern Sweden. By then it was commonplace for hospitals to dispose of soiled linen through a vacuum system with inlets set in the walls of each floor of the institution. The architect responsible for planning the Solleftea hospital asked if the Centralsug engineers couldn't augment this ordinary disposal system with an extraordinary one that would carry off all hospital garbage and refuse as well. Centralsug came up with two separate systems—one for the linens, the other for the refuse—which were duly built.

Installation occurred in 1961. The system worked so well that Centralsug determined to further explore the potential of the vacuum disposal idea. The Sundbyberg project was undertaken. It was completed in 1966. Three years later, the experiment was repeated twice:

in a hospital at Lowenstromska and in the Hallonbergen apartment block in Sundbyberg. The Sollentuna complex northeast of Stockholm came next, in 1970, accompanied in the same year by a 3,900-apartment installation at Osterhaninge, south of Stockholm. In April 1971, vacuum collection service was made available to 1,200 apartments in Bagarmossen, also on Stockholm's southern rim.

One of the more novel applications of the vacuum disposal principle to industry has been ventured in the Pripps brewery, the largest in Sweden. There a million bottles of beer are filled very day. Thousands of broken bottles are shunted away, and tons of beer mash are whooshed off to containers for sale as animal feed.

Centralsug does not claim its vacuum waste disposal system is foolproof. Operating problems do arise. Valves sometimes stick. Electrical systems occasionally fail. But repairs seldom take longer than a few hours. Fires can break out as readily as in other chute systems if someone drops a match or a lighted cigarette into it. Usually the rushing winds in the pipes extinguish the flames, but, if not, automatic sprinklers go into action.

Housewives I have interviewed here are unanimous in their favorable opinion of the vacuum system. But they have not been the decisive element in spreading word of the effectiveness of vacuum disposal of solid waste. The benefits of the system are most appreciated by municipal or communal agencies that normally pay for garbage collection. Although capital investment costs seem high when considered in isolation, operating expense, when cost-accounted over a twenty-year period, begins to break even with manual collection expense within six years. The big savings come in wages, which account for 80 per cent of manual collection costs but only 5 per cent of the total cost of the vacuum system.

The average Swede produces about 2.2 pounds of refuse per day. The volume the nation must dispose of is increasing at the rate of 3 to 4 per cent per year (7 per cent in Stockholm, according to one recent study). This amounts to a doubling of the volume of refuse every eighteen years. In most Swedish apartment houses served by manual collection systems, refuse collection rooms are already becoming too small and the collectors must call more frequently to keep the problem within manageable proportions.

Consequently, vacuum collection systems are especially appealing because of their great reserve capacity. They currently operate three times a day, running for only one hour altogether. Wind velocities in the pipes are so high that collections from 1,000 apartments are completed in twenty minutes. A single man with the help of an automatic electronic panel can collect waste from 1,100 to 2,200 apartments.

The savings in labor costs are not due alone to wage savings. Rates of absenteeism among garbage collectors are high. These men are out sick for 20 per cent of any given work week. Generally, the reasons given are back ailments due to lifting heavy objects and cuts and wounds inflicted by glass or sharp metal surfaces.

The Swedish experience with vacuum collection of solid waste has encouraged some Swedes to look forward to the day when refuse collection systems are installed in their downtown shopping centers. All that anyone then would have to do to get rid of garbage, office papers, or other trash would be to open a receptacle standing on the sidewalk and drop in the refuse, which would be whisked miles away to a collection center.

What Centralsug engineers expect to be the prototype for such a system is now being installed at Walt Disney World outside Orlando, Florida, through a licensing arrangement with Environgenics Company, a division of General Tire & Rubber's subsidiary, Aerojet-General Corporation. Fifteen trash collection stations scattered over the Disney grounds will feed into an automatically controlled underground network of more than a mile of twenty-inch pipe running from the Contemporary Resort Hotel into and around the "magic kingdom" park and emptying into a well-hidden collection receptacle, where the trash will be baled preparatory to haulage in closed vehicles to an incinerator several miles away. The incinerator, one of the world's most efficient, will wash out all smoke and particulates before venting air from the system. Fifty tons of solid waste a day— popcorn boxes, hot dog wrappers, and the like—will thus be reduced to an insignificant heap of sterile ash.

Other vacuum system installations planned for the United States under the Aerojet-General license include one for a huge housing project on Welfare Island in the East River between the boroughs of Manhattan and Queens in New York City. Another installation is being considered for Mount Sinai Hospital, and a third is set for the Mutual Redevelopment Housing complex, otherwise known as Penn Station South, or the Chelsea Development, between Eighth and Ninth avenues and 23rd and 27th streets in Manhattan. In announcing the award of a half-million-dollar grant in federal funds to help pay for the Penn Station South work, Richard D. Vaughan, director of solid-waste management administration in what is now the Environmental Protection Agency, said, "The introduction of a pneumatic transport system in this country could revolutionize refuse collection for high-rise multi-building complexes."

There is a special engineering challenge in this last-mentioned project, for the houses have been standing for fifteen years. Installation of the underground piping will be much more complicated than it would be in buildings presently under construction. Officials of the United Housing Foundation, which owns and rents the houses, have decided against incineration on location, on the premise that no matter how sophisticated chimney-scrubbing devices may have become, some smoke poisons could be discharged into the city's already heavily polluted air. So the collected refuse will be compacted and carted off to a distant incinerator.

Still another American application of the vacuum collection principle is under contract between Aerojet-General and the Martin Luther King, Jr. Memorial Hospital in the Watts section of Los Angeles.

Per Hallstrom, managing director of Centralsug in Stockholm, told me that if only presently standing orders are counted, 330 vacuum systems for disposal of solid waste will be operating in various parts of the world by mid-1973. Outside London, England, for example, more than 200 acres of idle railroad yards are being occupied by a Westminster housing project containing 1,600 apartments with vacuum disposal facilities; the construction job is due to be completed next November. In Grenoble, France, a block of 4,000 apartments will be similarly equipped by 1972. Caracas, Venezuela, has scheduled a vacuum serviced settlement of 7,500 apartments. Two vacuum contracts are under way in Denmark. Important Japanese firms are bidding for licensing rights in their country. A Centralsug subsidiary in West Germany has contracted to install vacuum disposal equipment at four places, one being the 1972 Olympic Village at Munich, which includes 5,500 units of athletes' quarters. After the Olympics, this part of the village will become a residential suburb of Munich.

VIII

AESTHETICS

The visual appearance of the world in which we live is one feature of the environmental crisis often neglected since it is considered to be a matter of cosmetics instead of survival. One reason for this relatively low priority is that even those most sensitive to the appearance and quality of the environment are unable to quantify such values. (See Melvin R. Levin's article on environmental costs, Chapter 24.) Nonetheless, today's citizens are seeking better environments, not only to escape pollution and the general deterioration of many urban areas but to find a home in what they consider pleasanter surroundings. People object to noise, overcrowding, offensive odors and unsightly views, and they are increasingly expressing their displeasure by avoiding areas that assault their senses.

Many planners and architects, to mention only two concerned professions, would like to be able to prove that bad environments produce bad people, but the evidence to support such a thesis does not exist. Nevertheless, there are grounds for believing that unhealthy surroundings may produce unhealthy effects in humans; however, this conclusion has been based primarily on research with rats and mice under severe conditions of overcrowding.

More extensive research in the human environment has been conducted in Europe, especially in Yugoslavia, Austria and France. In all, the conclusion seems inevitable that there is a relationship between mental health and housing, or what Dr. Maximilian Piperek, president of the Austrian Society of Psychology, calls "housing psychology." His research in Vienna shows that modern housing projects increased the pathology of their residents, some of whom reacted with increased hostility or aggression and others with increased depression.

In the first of the readings which follow, Ada Louise Huxtable, architecture critic of the New York Times, describes several successful architectural undertakings. From her book, Will They Ever

Finish Bruckner Boulevard?, *the four projects presented here are among the few for which Huxtable finds words of praise. The vast majority of cases which she describes can only be called disasters. However, these occasional triumphs offer proof that American designers and builders, be they private business (office buildings on Broadway), public housing (Riverbend) or government buildings (Boston City Hall), can, after all, create visually satisfying architecture. London's Civic Amenities Act, described in the final section, demonstrates how a city with a tradition to preserve has been able to protect its historic treasures while at the same time providing new buildings. America has a number of accomplishments in this area as well, of which Savannah, Georgia, might be cited as an outstanding example. In spite of these few bright spots, Huxtable concludes:*

> What is being designed privately and publicly with alarming consistency is instant blight. We are building blight for the next hundred years. The environment is being sealed systematically into sterility and its social problems are being compounded and immortalized by substandard design. The failure of the environment is our theme.

The second article in this section consists of three selections from Bernard Rudofsky's Streets for People. *This work provides an unusual statement of the environments built to human scale that man is capable of producing, usually without the help of professional planners. (For an expanded consideration of this latter point, see Rudofsky's* Architecture Without Architects.) *The selections included here are:* The Canopied Street, The Maze, *and* The Care and Feeding of The Pedestrian.

Although the canopied street has a long history, the example described here—Galleria Vittorio Emanuele in Milan—is only one hundred years old. Mark Twain, who visited the Galleria the year it opened, remarked that he would like to spend the rest of his life in it.

Examples of the Maze can be seen in the street patterns of many Italian towns, of which Apulia's Martina Franca is an excellent example. Many similar examples can be found in cities throughout Italy. Greece also has many illustrations of this form of street pattern as do other Mediterranean countries. Modern cities were rarely allowed to develop in this manner, however, although some might claim that the streets of a city such as Boston were laid out according to the meanderings of the inhabitants' cows. Nevertheless, the more formal geometric patterns of American streets do not reflect the influence of the human element as readily as the labyrinthine patterns which seem so human in scale and style.

The café is also a stranger to the American scene. In some areas of the United States the weather conditions may not lend themselves to this style of living, while in many of our urban areas, the proximity of automobile noise and exhaust fumes, plus construction noise, join to create an environment which has none of the peacefulness associated with the café way of life. This problem may be overcome in a number of areas of the country as more and more climate-controlled shopping centers are built. Examples of these developments are increasingly evident throughout the United States in climates which otherwise would not permit the establishment of cafés. And the impetus for this style of architecture and planning may grow with the return from abroad of Americans who have been impressed by street planning focused around cafés and sidewalk terraces.

22. Will They Ever Finish Bruckner Boulevard?

ADA LOUISE HUXTABLE

Sometimes We Do It Right

When it is good, New York is very, very good, Which is why New Yorkers put up with so much that is bad.

When it is good, this is a city of fantastic strength, sophistication and beauty. It is like no other city in time or place. Visitors and even natives rarely use the words "urban character" or "environmental style," but that is what they are reacting to with awe in the presence of massed, concentrated steel, stone, power and life. It is a quality of urban greatness that may not solve racial or social tension or the human or economic crises to which a city is prone, but it survives them.

In this sense, one small piece of downtown Manhattan is very, very good. For a demonstration of New York at its physical best, go to Broadway between Cedar and Liberty streets and face east. You will be standing in front of the new building at 140 Broadway, one of the handsomest in the city, and you will not be able to miss the twenty-eight-foot high vermilion steel cube by Isamu Noguchi that balances on one point in front of it, at the north end of a travertine plaza.

Look to your left (Liberty Street) and you will see the small turn-of-the-century French pastry in creamy, classically detailed stone that houses the neighboring Chamber of Commerce. To your right (Cedar Street) is a stone-faced building of the first great skyscraper period (pre-World War I through the 1930's).

Move on toward the East River, following the travertine plaza that flows elegantly on either side of the slender new shaft, noting how well the block size of the marble under foot scales the space.

Surprisingly, the site and the fifty-two-story tower are trapezoidal in shape.

At Broad Street, the 140 Broadway plaza stops and Chase Manhattan Plaza begins. There is an unfortunate wall between them, due to abrupt changes in ground level and the fact that the architects of both buildings, Skidmore, Owings and Merrill, had no idea when they did Chase in the early 1960's that they would be doing the adjoining building less than a decade later.

But the open space continues, even with this barrier. Closing it and facing Chase's gleaming sixty-story tower across Liberty Street is the stony vastness of the 1924 Federal Reserve Building by York and Sawyer, its superscaled, cut limestone, Strozzi-type Florentine facade making a powerful play against Chase's bright aluminum and glass. A more conventional masonry-faced structure walls the plaza to the south.

There will be still more open space west of 140 Broadway, following the same axis. Just opposite the new building is the U.S. Steel site, where the Singer Building stood. That landmark loss to New York's skyline will be replaced by a skyscraper by the same architects who have done Chase Manhattan and 140 Broadway, Skidmore, Owings and Merrill.

The architects and owners have received approval from the City Planning Commission to adjust the zoning of the two-block site to extend the present pedestrian channel farther toward the Hudson River. The Liberty-Cedar block west of Broadway will be another open plaza, paralleling the existing one. The new skyscraper will be constructed on the block to the north.

Still farther west, slightly off this axis, will be the giant World Trade Center twin towers and plaza. For much of this, underground connections are being planned.

The result, a striking slice through one of the densest, most dramatic cityscapes in the world, is a stunning success in terms of urban design. For once, the losses, such as the Singer Building, are at least being balanced by rational gains. For once, there has been intelligent, sensitive capitalization on one of this century's most fantastic urban phenomena. Instead of thoughtless destruction through new construction, there is a calculated relationship between past and present and between buildings and spaces.

This small segment of New York compares in effect and elegance with any celebrated Renaissance plaza or Baroque vista. The scale of the buildings, the use of open space, the views revealed or suggested, the contrasts of architectural style and material, of sculptured stone against satin-smooth metal and glass, the visible change and continuity of New York's remarkable skyscraper history, the brilliant accent of the poised Noguchi cube—color, size, style, mass, space, light, dark, solids, voids, highs and lows—all are just right. These few blocks provide (why equivocate?) one of the most magnificent examples of twentieth-century urbanism anywhere in the world.

Not the least contribution is the new building, for which Gordon Bunshaft was partner-in-charge at S.O.M. One forty Broadway is a "skin" building—the kind of flat, sheer, curtain wall that it has become chic to reject. Younger architects, off on a wild, Arthurian search for the *nouveau* picturesque, and an uninformed public that never understood or accepted what was happening have turned their backs on one of the miracles of modern building: the skyscraper wall reduced to gossamer minimums of shining, thin material hung on a frame of extraordinary strength through superb contemporary technology.

The significance and beauty of this achievement are not dimmed by the instances of its commercial prostitution as the unjustly denigrated "glass box." It is still one of the great developments and most remarkable expressions in all of architectural history from Stonehenge to the present. It has produced some masterpieces and made a lot of commercial building palatable. One forty Broadway is a commercial building, not a monument. Here the skin is handled with suave expertise.

It is New York's ultimate skin building. The wall is held unrelentingly flat; there are no tricks with projecting or extended mullions; thin and flush, they are used only to divide the window glass. The metal spandrel facing, in one smooth piece, echoes the placing of structural steel and seeks no "artful" plasticity. The taut, shiny-dark sleekness of matte black aluminum and gleaming bronze glass is an architectural statement of positive excellence as well as a foil for the ornate masonry around it. The quiet assurance of this building makes even Chase look a little gaudy.

What next? Probably destruction. One ill-conceived neighboring plaza will kill this carefully calculated channel of related space and buildings. Seagram was semi-sabotaged by the recent construction on its south; it can happen here. It only takes one opening in the wrong place, one "bonus" space placed according to current zoning (read "business") practice, to ruin it all.

Space is meaningless without scale, containment, boundaries and direction. The fabled massing of the Wall Street skyscrapers has been given masterful urban definition by the architects' ordering of these few blocks of new construction. It has been done by concerned, coordinated effort. This is planning, whether it is merely fortuitous or foresighted. It is the opposite of non-planning, or the normal pattern of New York development. See and savor it now, before it is carelessly disposed of.

Riverbend Houses: It Can Happen Here

Imagine, if you can in New York, duplex apartments designed like town houses, each with its own front door reached through a small, walled terrace from an outside gallery that runs the length of the building or from a "sky street" for duplexes stacked above. Each duplex is floor-through, with windows on both sides. There are spectacular river views or an outlook on a landscaped plaza connecting the buildings like a private park for tenant use. Picture eight of these structures attached to two towers with simplex apartments; each of these has sliding doors to its own terrace and city views.

We are not putting you on. That would be cruel in a city where housing is as critical as it is in New York. Nor are we indulging in Utopian housing dreams, an easy thing to do when rentals in "good" neighborhoods are an unabashed $125 a room and a modest co-op is an unblushing $50,000.

This housing exists. But it is not for the Rolls-Royce trade. It is in Harlem. This is Riverbend, built under the Mitchell-Lama limited profit housing program and through the city's Housing and Development Administration. It is a $14 million, 624-family moderate-income cooperative on a triangular 3.7-acre site bounded by Fifth Avenue, the Harlem River Drive and 138th Street. Apartment purchase costs are less than $500 a room, with an average $32 a room carrying charge.

What Riverbend proves is that well-designed housing at a rational price can be built in New York. But it cannot be done without subsidy. This is a fact of New York real estate known by all but faced by few.

Design, however, is independent of subsidy. The point here is that Riverbend, with or without subsidy, would be handsome, imaginative and desirable and offer alternative options for living to the stereotyped minimum formulas provided by New York's apartment house builders, who may well give the least for the money in any major American city, even taking into account New York's extraordinary land and construction costs. The exterior design and materials of one of the city's most expensive and visible new cooperatives are so crudely detailed that one wonders if the affluent are blind. Amenities deal in gilded faucets.

The HRH Construction Corporation, which sponsored and built Riverbend, says that commercial developers can reproduce Riverbend's standards of housing design at competitive private sector prices. But they don't. The same old brick boxes are flung in the public's face whether the money market is tight or loose and regardless of rate or cost of construction. And when costs are too high, nothing is built. When New York builders do build, you know what you are going to get for that ever-increasing slice of that ever-diminishing take-home dollar. It is a sure, standardized profit-formula thing.

What makes the difference at Riverbend? The builder, the architects and the sponsoring city agency. They were a determined triumvirate, slogging through a six-year obstacle course, since everything in American society and municipal bureaucracy seems stacked against doing something different. Richard Ravitch of HRH, Davis, Brody and Associates, the architects, and Samuel Ratensky of the Housing and Development Administration all share a knowledge of what good housing design is. It was a matter of principle and standards to them to produce it.

It can probably be fairly said that a lot of New York builders have absolutely no idea of what good housing design is. What they don't know certainly hasn't hurt them financially. Nor has good housing design ever been understood or encouraged by some of the city's largest non-profit housing sponsors, who keep both rents and standards low. You don't quarrel in New York with what you can afford. Even the best-intentioned housing "experts" fail to grasp the idea that design is the concept, not a bit of trim.

The firm of Davis, Brody is one of the more talented in the city. You will not find any speculative apartment houses by this office, and, except for a rarity or two, by any other firm of comparable creative stature. New York apartment houses are not designed; they are punched out to meet the standard formula.

There is no standard formula at Riverbend. The results are not even recognizable as Mitchell-Lama housing, which carries its rigidly specified trademarks and economies from project to project. From hardware to graphics, from special brick to sprayed wall and ceiling finishes, better answers have been sought. These buildings are a notable demonstration of how creativity and taste can lead to improvements and economies, as well as to distinguished architectural results.

Examples: that handsome, rugged, oversize brick that gives character to the brick and concrete structures was much cheaper to lay
than the conventional kind that carries an institutional stamp. With
careful site planning and building relationships, the higher floors of
the duplex blocks are served by elevators in the two towers through
connecting corridors, eliminating the expense of elevators in a large
number of the ten buildings.

The particularly attractive lighting fixtures designed by the architects to illuminate the duplex front doors serve two at once and ultimately proved cheaper than available standard fixtures. Those raised
community plazas between the buildings in place of bleak, open space
conceal required parking underneath at the same time that they turn
the space into a social amenity.

The architects lost money at Riverbend, in the time spent on special
design, specification and supervision, but it was a calculated risk that
has paid off in experience and other jobs. They are also the architects for city-sponsored houses in construction in the Bellevue South
renewal area, and for Waterside, another breakthrough in design
and urban land use. City fees are higher now, but city contract
problems remain.

Waterside, the city's pioneering attempt at mixed-income housing
that is yet to be built, has drawn blood from proponents of low-
income housing as offering too many apartments to those who are
not poor and whose lives are not infested with rats. The argument
is strong. Riverbend will probably provoke the same criticism, although its beneficiaries are not white. They are middle income,
middle class and black. Most of the people buying the apartments
want it just this way. Black or white, this is a group essential to the
city's support.

The idea that the city might purchase some units for subsidized
low-income housing was outspokenly opposed. Even a liquor store
was vetoed as a commercial rental because it might attract trouble.
The black middle class making it now is too close to misery to want
any part of it. The polemics of integration and housing priorities
interest these people less than questions of security, from the alarms
installed on doors during construction that many will keep, to the
inviolability of their new neighborhood. Riverbend is part of a growing black middle-class enclave. Anyone interested in the other side
of the coin of Harlem sociology would do well to study it.

The significance of Riverbend, however, is beyond controversy.
It is simply that the same thoughtful standards of design can be
brought to bear on every kind of housing, from low to high income,

in ghettos and out. The dignity of the environment has a lot to do with the dignity of man.

London: Putting the Breaks on "Progress"

What is popularly called progress in American cities is being stopped dead in its tracks, or at least slowed to a stumbling halt in London. A strong government brake is being put on the private development of large parts of this city's older, historic areas, the kind of places and names that form a litany of London history, character and beauty for both residents and visitors.

Under the Civic Amenities Act of 1967, a law just getting into high gear, these districts can be protected as officially designated conservation areas. Town-planning authorities, who select such conservation areas, have the right either to prohibit any demolition or new construction or to control development through necessary permissions to owners and builders.

At least eight sizable London districts have been designated as conservation areas this year. They are the major parts of Mayfair, Belgravia, Bloomsbury and St. John's Wood and sections of Paddington, Pimlico, Baywater and Kensington. A considerable part of Soho is in the process of designation now, and areas around St. James's Place, Whitehall, Parliament and Westminster Abbey are being studied for future action.

There is no lack of desire among private developers in London to rip down whole blocks for profitable new commercial construction. The urge is international and the need of such construction is real. It is not so easy to do in London as in New York, because permission is needed from the planning authorities here for the erection of office buildings.

But as blankly depressing expanses of new office blocks have gone up in older neighborhoods, bringing with them a singular absence of style, Londoners have become angrily aware of the erosion of the past. Even with planning control, damage to the traditional fabric of the city is obvious.

The building that blew the fuse was the London Hilton's twenty-eight-story tower, which disrupted the traditional, five-story serenity of Mayfair in 1963. In the subsequent five years there has been strong public agitation for preservation of the traditional character of special neighborhoods. Popular sentiment against change is backed by the more sophisticated preservation objectives of the Georgian and Victorian societies, which enjoy a remarkable status in Britain.

Under the leadership of Duncan Sandys, a Minister of Housing from 1954 to 1957, the Civic Amenities Act was passed last year, adding powers of architecture and urban preservation to the functions of the earlier town-planning acts.

The process of creating conservation areas is not so high-handed as it sounds. There are inquiries and hearings, and appeal of decision is possible. Under the town and country planning acts enacted since 1947, British cities have immense planning powers and responsibilities. Land is bought and sold privately and freely. But permission for commercial development of the land, which has been generally programed under London's master plan now being revised, must be gotten from the planning authorities. The process is frequently a compromise between the desires of the developers willing to invest hard cash and the objectives of the city.

According to Frank West, director of architecture and planning for the City of Westminster, which has been designating many of London's conservation areas, the individual whose property rights are involved cannot bring suit as he does in the United States. The matter is dealt with in London administratively, not judicially, by public inquiry, with decision made by the local planning authorities. These decisions can be appealed to the Minister of Housing, whose action is final. The matter does not go through the courts at all.

There are some forms of "permitted" development that do not require government approval, such as the extension of an existing building by 10 per cent of its floor space.

Under the town and country planning acts, compensation must be paid to the owner who is refused his development rights. These sums come from grants made to planning bodies by the government.

The key word to the whole preservation program is the word "amenities" in the Civic Amenities Act. As understood in England, amenities in this sense covers a civilized concept of total environmental excellence. The term refers to the complete effect of an attractive or pleasurable neighborhood, or of an architecturally or historically important district, whether its quality is due to planning or design excellence, the stamp of the past or simply to a style of life.

What is involved in these criteria is what is sacrificed constantly in New York while preservationists look for "landmarks"; as they look, a street or neighborhood of less than landmark importance, but of genuine urban value, is demolished. These losses are irreparable in any city. The British concept of preservation as an act that is involved with, not isolated from, the living fabric of the city leaves United States policy on the subject in the dark ages.

London's examples of conservation areas range from a striking series of uniform, cool, clean, white streetscapes built at the same time and offering a single style, such as Belgravia's nineteenth-century classical facades, to the frequently architecturally undistinguished but lively streets of Soho that house equally irreplaceable small shops and services. The amenity standard can include just the grouping of compatible buildings around one of London's lush, green squares.

Under the Civic Amenities Act a builder can no longer get approval for such development as the kind of undistinguished, unrelated apartment houses with a luxury label at the south end of Montagu Square in the Portman Estates, which have shattered the square's period style and scale.

Under the act a new Soho hotel is being designed with the collaboration of the developer and his architect and the architects and planners of the City of Westminster, not only to avoid disruption of existing character, but also to reinforce the area's intimate, diversified humanity.

The big hurdle ahead will be financial compensation to those whose development plans are refused. It will take Solomon-like decisions to determine where the funds are to be given in the light of the massive designation of conservation areas, and on those decisions historic London will stand or fall.

Boston City Hall: A Winner

"Whatever it is, it's not beautiful," said the Boston cab driver taking the visitor to the new City Hall. "What would you call it, Gothic?" asked another. Which about sums up the architectural gap, or abyss, as it exists between those who design and those who use the twentieth-century's buildings.

The new $26.3 million Boston City Hall has been an object of international attention and debate since the architects Kallmann, McKinnell and Knowles won the competition for its design in 1962. A week of festivities marked its opening seven years later.

Boston can celebrate with the knowledge that it has produced a superior public building in an age that values cheapness over quality as a form of public virtue. It also has one of the handsomest buildings around, and thus far, one of the least understood. It is not Gothic. ("No kiddin'," said the cab driver.) It is a product of this moment and these times—something that can be said of successful art of any period. And it is a winner in more ways than one.

Not only cab drivers are puzzled by the unconventional structure. Cultural and community leaders who are also society's decision

Boston's successful City Hall.

Center Photo Service.

makers and a public with more and higher education than at any time in history also draw a blank. Too bad about that architecture gap. It has a lot to do with the meanness of our cities.

Boston's new City Hall is a solid, impressive demonstration of creativity and quality—uncommon currencies in today's environment. A powerful focus for the new Government Center that has replaced the sordid charms of the old Scollay Square, it makes a motley collection of very large, very average new buildings around it look good. It confers, in a kind of architectural status transferral, an instant image of progressive excellence on a city government traditionally known for something less than creativity and quality. That is an old trick of architecture called symbolism.

They call it the new Boston, but inside the new structure Councilors Saltonstall and Timilty work side by side at old desks moved from the old City Hall that suggest the old politics. The City Council gave itself a raise but voted down the $24,000, room-size horseshoe installation that would have completed the Council Chamber and accommodated all its members in the new style. Tradition dies hard in Boston.

The building will survive the councilors' objections and the Mayor's ideas of decoration. Its rugged cast-in-place and precast concrete and brick construction inside and out (the New Brutalism, for those who like stylistic labels) is meant to be impervious to the vicissitudes of changing tastes and administrations.

The monumentality of this public building—and it is magnificently monumental without a single one of those pompous pratfalls to the classical past that building committees clutch like Linus's blanket—is neither forbidding nor austere.

It is an "open" City Hall. At ground level it is meant to serve as a concourse to other parts of the city, and there are views of the city from every part of the structure. The visitor is made aware of the city in a very special way—of its history in the architects' sensitively glass-framed vistas through deep concrete modular window reveals of adjoining Federal brick buildings and Faneuil Hall and the granite Quincy Market and waterfront to the east, and of its burgeoning growth in new construction to west, north and south.

This appropriate and finely calculated sense of historic continuity is no small architectural achievement.

Today's buildings rupture historic scale and this one was placed in the heart of historic Boston. But there is no "style-dropping" here. The architects have neatly disposed of Preservation Fallacy Number

Boston's new downtown governmental buildings surrounded by Faneuil Hall and the Haymarket in the foreground and Beacon Hill and Back Bay in the background, a photograph of Boston City Hall and Government Center.

Photo credit: Aerial Photos of New England

One. There are none of the overblown vestigial traditional details or "recalls" considered "appropriate" in such situations, milked of architectural meaning and offered as pious ligaments between old and new to create caricatures of both. This is subtle, dramatic, respectful homage to the past by an uncompromising present. It is a lesson in proper preservation philosophy and esthetics.

There is also a lesson in that basic element of building, the use of space. The entire structure is conceived as a progression of functional and hierarchical spaces. Its striking exterior reflects this arrangement.

This is not space as a container. See any office building for that. It is space molded to function, form and expressive purpose. The striking irregular shapes and surfaces that show the functions and mechanical services, all of which are more commonly hidden behind flat walls and ceiling slabs, are part of the visual and sensuous impact.

The building is a hollow rectangle around a court. Its focus is the lobby, which rises a dramatic six of the building's nine stories on two sides to skylights, and centers on a platform of ascending brick steps. This is a space equally satisfactory to connoisseurs of the art of architecture and the art of sit-ins, and that is exactly what the designers had in mind as public architecture.

Above the lobby are the Council Chamber and offices and the Mayor's quarters. These large, ceremonial rooms are visible outside as rugged projections on the building's east and west facades and as strong, broken wall planes inside, within the soaring skylight shafts. The upper levels are office space. This also shows clearly on the outside as a massive, stepped "cornice" at the top.

The building stands, not in isolation, but on a still unfinished fan-shaped brick plaza of stepped levels that will embrace the neighboring structures.

It is as certain as politics and taxes that without the national competition that was held for this building nothing like it would have been designed or constructed. Mr. Kallmann and Mr. McKinnell were young and unknown as architects when they won. The usual route of public building commissions is through political patronage or to familiar, established names.

The architects have worked with the Boston firm of Campbell, Aldrich and Nulty, and Le Messurier Associates, structural engineers. Virtually no changes were made in the prize-winning design. The result is a tough and complex building for a tough and complex age, a structure of dignity, humanism and power. It mixes strengths with subtleties. It will outlast the last hurrah.

23. Streets for People

BERNARD RUDOFSKY

The Canopied Street

The only modern covered street comparable in scale to the ancient ones is perhaps Milan's *Galleria Vittorio Emanuele*. Less of a tourist attraction than a landmark, it received recognition, ironically, only as late as 1967, at the ripe old age of one hundred years. This is not to say that it did not find admirers in earlier days; on the contrary. One of them, Mark Twain, who visited it the year it opened to the public, was so taken by its grandeur and the goings-on it sheltered that he would have liked, he said, to spend the rest of his life in it. "In Milan," he wrote in his affectionately mocking chronicle *A Tramp Abroad*, "we spent most of our time in the vast and beautiful Arcade or Gallery, or whatever it is called. Blocks of new buildings of the most sumptuous sort, rich with decoration and graced with statues, the streets between these blocks roofed over with glass at a great height, the pavements all of smooth and variegated marble, arranged in tasteful patterns—little tables all over these marble streets, people sitting at them, eating, drinking, or smoking—crowds of other people strolling by—such is the Arcade. I should like to live in it all my life. The windows of the sumptuous restaurants stand open, and one breakfasts and enjoys the passing show."[1]

Milan, Italy's most populous and least antiquated city, has always been a lively place. Already in the eleventh century, it was one of Europe's richest towns, politically important, and on the way to becoming what it is today, the peninsula's moral capital. Long a bone of contention between the great powers, variously under French, Spanish, and Austrian rule, Milan saw the last occupation army leave in 1859. The occasion called for celebrating, and the Milanese chose

To Saul Steinberg, who spent ten years of his youth in Milan, the Galleria was agora, seminar and world theater, with Biffi at its nub. This 1949 drawing attests as much to his training as an architect as to his insight into the Italians' natural bent. His graphic record of a people's rhetorical genius explains their need for a grandiose environment better than volumes of architectural history could.

to build a sort of *via triumphalis* as a memorial to Italy's unification. Unlike the triumphal avenues of the Caesars, however, they intended it as a monument to their own happy temperament.

The idea of a covered street leading to the centrally located cathedral had been in the air for centuries. Milan's gigantic *Duomo*, built on the site of an ancient Christian basilica, was only slowly taking shape. It stood in a poor quarter and was not enhanced by its cathedral square where for five hundred years chickens and wine were sold. The town had barely escaped Napoleon's disastrous urban renewal scheme that called for demolishing half of Milan and creating a net of avenues to converge on the Dome. Fortunately nothing came of it, but the clamor for a dignified town center persisted, and in 1860 the mayor of Milan took the unprecedented step of consulting the citizens rather than a planning committee in this matter. Perhaps mindful of architects' occupational limitations, he invited people regardless of their vocation to offer ideas, and although this was not a proper competition, it had every aspect of it. The public, long familiar with and sympathetic to the idea of a town center, answered the call enthusiastically. Artists and writers, even architects, sent two hundred and twenty projects, no mean feat for a town of 240,000. A lottery to finance the enterprise was less successful, and the project had to be shelved.

A covered street was nothing new to Milan. The year 1832 had witnessed the opening of the Galleria De Cristoforis, built by two millionaire brothers. A marvel of architecture, "all glass and mirrors," it even had a mirrored ceiling and, when illuminated at night, resembled a ballroom. Although it had attracted some of the town's smartest shops, it slowly declined, being somewhat out of the way. The need for a large and centrally located galleria brought on a second competition, which produced a solution acceptable to all. Nobody seemed to mind that the winner, Giuseppe Mengoni, had never studied architecture. Mengoni freely admitted that he had only taken lessons in perspective drawing at the studio of an artist friend. "Architecture," he wrote, "I studied by traveling and visiting monuments, by staying all over Europe wherever there were things to be admired."[2] At any rate, his architectural pilgrimages had helped him to develop a flawless sense for the grandiose. Not the least of his talents was his ability to find foreign capital to finance his project. A British syndicate bought the land for the buildings, although the area covered by the Galleria remained city property and was declared a public street.

Modern Milan's great enterprise was watched by all of Europe.

Crowned heads came to visit the building site, where work went on day and night, and in 1867 the King of Italy inaugurated the architectural complex that was to carry his name to the applause of the civilized world. Thus Milan acquired an institution that was, and still is, unique in modern times, despite a subsequent crop of similar but lesser galleries. Its very dimensions are on a scale not matched since antiquity. Two covered streets intersect in the form of a Latin cross, 643 feet and 344 feet long respectively. The top of the glass roof is 88 feet high and reaches 160 feet in the central cupola. In summertime it is the city's coolest place. Predictions that drafts might make the Galleria inhospitable did not materialize, but in 1874, on a hot summer day, a hailstorm demolished the glorious roof within minutes. The hailstones, as big as apples—three to a pound—did not leave a single pane intact. Three years later, Mengoni added a macabre footnote to his masterpiece; one day, while inspecting work in progress high above ground, he slipped and fell to his death.

For a century, through booming years and wartime austerity, the Galleria has been forum and foyer to the Milanese. To call it a shopping center is no more accurate than referring to Tiffany's as a stationery store. Both have more to offer. To house close to one hundred elegant shops under one roof as a permanent exhibition of Italy's industrial products was doubtless a clever move. Yet what made history were the new restaurants, cafés, and bars. The restaurant Biffi in the Octagon under the fresco of Africa became famous overnight. Savini, its competitor, is still on Michelin's list of Italy's top eating places, and the bars of Campari the distiller and Motta the baker—names as hallowed to the Italians as Ford and Edison to the Americans—became sanctuaries within the general refuge. Here met statesmen and captains of industry, writers, opera singers, and conductors. The heroes of the musical world—La Scala is only a few hundred feet from the Galleria's North Portal—mingled with Milan's lesser citizens and the inevitable crowd of peddlers and pickpockets, tourists and prostitutes. Evenings, when the place was bathed, as the newspapers put it, in an ocean of gaslight; when row upon row of marble tables appeared on the tessellated pavement, and the sound of orchestra music merged with the drone of people's voices, the Galleria achieved a near-apotheosis of the Italian street: a theater where actors and spectators merged and became indistinguishable from each other.

The Milanese's love affair with their Galleria has been recorded in word and deed over and again. Artists paid tribute to its spaces: cubists and romanticists painted it with equal relish; the panegyrics and poems written in its honor fill volumes. Even foreigners fell under its spell. Mark Twain was quoted earlier. Hemingway evoked a scene dimmed by years of war. "We had a lovely time that summer," he wrote in *A Farewell to Arms*, "we went to dinner at Biffi's or the Gran Italia and sat at tables outside on the floor of the galleria. The waiters came in and out and there were people going by and candles with shades on the table-cloths and after we decided that we liked the Gran Italia best, George, the head-waiter, saved us a table. He was a fine waiter and we let him order the meal while we looked at the people, and the great galleria in the dusk, and each other . . . After dinner we walked through the galleria, past the other restaurants and the shops with their steel shutters down, and stopped at the little place where they sold sandwiches; ham and lettuce sandwiches and anchovy sandwiches made of very tiny brown glazed rolls and only about as long as your finger. They were to eat in the night when we were hungry. Then we got into an open carriage outside the galleria in front of the cathedral and rode to the hospital." [3]

The first world war spared Milan but the second did not. An aerial bombardment in 1943 left the Galleria in ruins, to be resurrected only twelve years later. Its architecture was faithfully rebuilt from the wreckage, but life under the glass roof has never been the same. Although the tables are again set out on the highly polished floor, no latter-day Verdis and Puccinis lend distinction to the scene. Biffi has been turned into a snack bar with self-service on the upper floor. Campari left without a trace. Motta's bar, once among Europe's most elegant and intimate rendez-vous, has been enlarged to several times its former size. Instead of *rustici*, the superlative appetizers of yesteryear, ice cream and solid foods are sold in a new setting as alluring as a laundromat.

The clientele is equally up to date. In summertime, the Galleria is nearly deserted by Italians. In their place, those most pathetic of outcasts, modern tourists, wend their way in as shock troops or as stragglers through an incomprehensible streetscape. They are as leery of things foreign as they are ignorant of their purpose. Some, emboldened by the pervasive sensuality of the environment, have been seen to visit the Galleria in beach attire, probably unaware that the sea is fully a hundred miles away.

Mazes

Where the heel joins the Italian boot, in the region of Apulia, lies Martina Franca, a quiet town of about forty thousand. Neither Baedeker nor Michelin hint at its pleasures. For generations standard

English guidebooks have stopped at Naples, and a most up-to-date American *Guide* for the illiterate tourist proclaims that "there is nothing between Salerno and Reggio—just a waste." And a barren wasteland is what Edmund Stillman, a contemporary writer, calls Italy south of Naples. Organized banditry, he says, still endures; "not many travelers even in our day penetrate there."[4] Although such reporting amounts to sheer slander, it helps to deflect the annual tourist migration with its pernicious influence on the country.

To put the record straight, the Apulian wasteland has an enviable climate and splendid scenery: vineyards and olive groves, almond orchards and vegetable gardens, forests, and a spectacular coastline with grottoes and sandy beaches. From the point of view of architecture it is an incomparable sampler: Neolithic villages, dolmen, menhirs, and trulli, some of the most exquisite Romanesque cathedrals, super-Baroque palaces, Swabian and Norman castles, and the latest version of motels, superbly situated and imaginatively planned. Withal, Apulia's greatest appeal lies in its vernacular architecture, a variety as unself-conscious as it is pure and, seemingly, everlasting. "I have seen the most beautiful cities in the world," wrote the philosopher George Berkeley in 1717 on returning from an exploratory visit to Apulia—a rather sweeping statement, considering that two and a half centuries ago *most* cities on the European continent were beautiful. At that time, too, Apulia was thought to be inaccessible; only a foolhardy Irishman would venture into the Italian South with its bloodthirsty anopheles and tarantulas—Berkeley dismissed the fear of bandits as a "mere bugbear"—depending for guidance as he did on such superannuated writers as Horace, Pliny, and Strabo. Yet for years nobody tried to repeat his performance.

The entries in his diary for May and June tell of his journey in a horse-drawn chaise past "painted meadows" and "delicious vineyards, gardens, powdered with little white houses." But the principal attraction was Apulia's white towns. So greedy was he for their beauty that he once managed to see "five fair cities in one day [Barletta, Trani, Bisceglie, Molfetta, and Bari], the most part in white marble, whereof the names are not known to Englishmen."[5] They still aren't. The distance he covered that day was only thirty-three miles yet, as he noted, the country is "thick planted with towns."

His surprise and delight at their streets are reflected in his ceaseless reiteration of their good points. On the way to Apulia he had admired Beneventum's streets, "paved with marble."[6] Barletta impressed him with its "wide fair well built streets, all hewn stone, diamondcut." At Trani he noted that "this city, as Barletta, [is] paved and built almost entirely of white marble."[7] (There will be more on Englishmen's praise of Italian street pavements in the next chapter.) Again, Molfetta, "a small walled city, walls, towers, buildings of white marble." This infatuation with crystalline whiteness marked his deliverance, albeit short-lived, from the memory of his own country's lurid towns. Two hundred years later, Sir Osbert Sitwell was still extolling the "extraordinary whiteness that envelops the houses of Southern Puglie and makes them assume a thousand subtle and almost indefinable tones."[8]

Whatever Berkeley's authority, whatever the attractions of the towns he saw, there can be no doubt that Apulia did then, as it does now, harbor some matchless architecture. Having had many a good look at it myself, I am inclined to side with Berkeley.

To be sure, the objects of our admiration are not identical. Although some of the sights one sees today were probably much the same a couple of centuries ago, the passage of time accounts for changes. Devastations by earthquakes, wars, and progress, while only slightly affecting a solidly built church or castle, are bound to disfigure the humble parts of a town. Besides, whereas a cathedral or castle is recognized as a work of art, a whole town is seldom thought of as a monument or, indeed, as architecture. (The great exception is Venice.) At best, some part of a town—a particular square or street, or the skyline that confers uniqueness upon an otherwise unexceptional townscape—etches itself on people's minds and is respected and treasured for its own sake. Occasionally, such a characteristic feature becomes a sort of trademark. In the past, painters often chose to immortalize it as background for a Biblical scene, and today it figures prominently in travel posters and on picture postcards. The point is that a familiar vista causes sentimental attachment and a desire for its preservation, whereas anonymity condemns it to oblivion. An architectural setting without the all-important quality of déjà-vu leaves no lasting impression. So far Apulia is still terra incognita, at least for Americans; the "most beautiful cities in the world" are for all practical purposes nonexistent.

Martina Franca is but one of them. Its beginnings go back to A.D. 927, when the Greek population of the nearby Tarentum fled before the advancing Saracens and settled on Mount Martino. In his *Description of All Italy*, Leon Battista Alberti refers to it as a "castle" surrounded by rich pastures and shady woods. During the four intervening centuries the woods have disappeared, and so have the town walls and two dozen towers which might have suggested a castle. Martina—as the inhabitants call it for short—has grown to

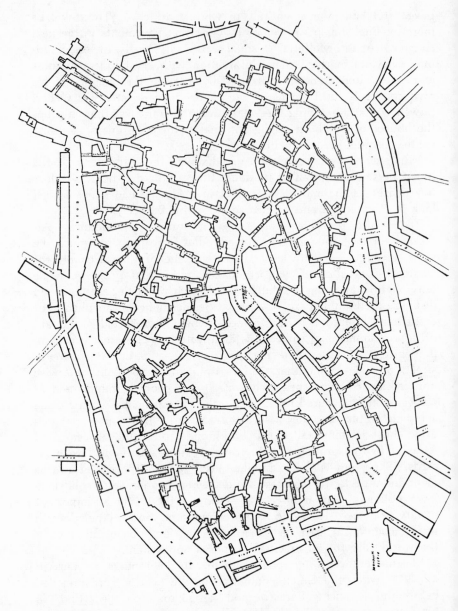

Labyrinthine towns hold a singular fascination for people whose flow of imagination has not dried up by living on streets that run for miles in a straight line. One of the best-preserved mazes is Apulia's Martina Franca. Its narrow twisted streets, branching off into a hundred and sixty blind alleys, resemble corridors of a single monolithic building.

three times its former size. The new quarters' architectural style might be classified as Contemporary Banalism, indistinguishable from that of modern Karachi or Casablanca—houses aligned in military ranks, uniform as soldiers but without physiognomy or bearing. Martina is unremarkable except for its old, oviform part, ringed by relatively recent buildings, if the town hall, a palace built to Bernini's plans, can be called recent. Even a short walk discloses a labyrinth that would baffle a Theseus—a tangle of streets impervious to the passage of vehicles, and some hundred and sixty blind alleys that spell haven for the citizen. Although Alberti may never have entered Martina, his description of the ideal urban street suits the old town to perfection. "Within the heart of the town," he wrote in the *Ten Works of Architecture*, "it will be handsomer not to have the streets straight, but winding about." Narrow streets, he maintained, are welcome in hot weather by keeping the sun out while allowing for good ventilation. Winding streets will catch gentle breezes but break icy blasts. And out of this arise esthetic advantages; the winding street, Alberti adds, "will make the passenger at every step discover a new structure, and the front and door of every house will directly face the middle of the street . . . it will be both healthy and pleasant to have such an open view from every house by means of the turn of the street." [9]

Martina, that white elephant of a town, fulfills every one of these requirements. Its plan bespeaks its structure better than words ever could. It is an "unplanned" town, if there ever was one. Its streets seem to have been traced by lightning. To call them forked, twisted, or zigzagging does not do them justice. They are all that and more. Their width varies constantly. The building lines are rarely parallel; houses jut out into the street like the wings of an old-fashioned stage. Indeed, at every step, comparisons with a stage come to mind—not Broadway, but those "real streets, artfully and pleasingly contrived" of the early Renaissance theater. What makes them look archaic and quaint is the absence of the sort of junk that confers legitimacy upon traffic streets: lampposts, traffic lights, no-parking signs and parking meters, trash cans, and trash at large.

The town is all of one fabric. There are no slums, no poor streets. Baroque palazzi and palazetti, churches and convents, are evenly spread among the lesser houses which are plain but of noble cast. Elaborate stone portals, stone window frames, and ironwork balconies stand out against the blinding white background like so many exhibits hung on museum walls. Some of the houses are six centuries old, and yet they are as good or better than those built today. Not one is in disrepair. They are all of about the same height—no more than three stories—favoring conversation from rooftop to street. For intimate, sustained talk, chairs are brought into the street. There is no need for sidewalks; the old, indestructible flagstone pavement insinuates itself into house entrances and inner corridors. It is kept immaculately clean but no one can tell for how much longer. Any day, the millenarian tradition of urban cleanliness may give way to the exigenices of modern life.

On a hill, three and a half miles north of Martina Franca, stands Locorotondo, another one of Apulia's white labyrinths. The name means "round place," and in part the town has preserved its rotundity; from a distance it looks like a petrified merry-go-round. At its peripheral street—a belvedere in the grand tradition—the houses end abruptly. Beyond the parapet, terraced fields step down to the plain, which in springtime is clouded with the white blossoms of almond trees. In the middle distance stretches the Adriatic Sea. Locorotondo's inner streets, none more than a few minutes' walk from the fields, are of the same order as Martina's: a children's haven, a playground without racks and gallows.

Halfway up the Italian shin, not far from Rome, lies the maze of Sperlonga. Although it is commonly referred to as a fishing village, it is no more a village than the Apulian towns. It rather suggests a sort of Neuschwanstein by the Sea, a salty version of Ludwig's folly, built on a Mediterranean promontory. If anything, it carries the tang of a pirates' nest—despite its inception as a middle-class bathing resort. Here, people whose health has been sapped by the ravages of sedentary habits get a new lease on life; the city's rejects learn to walk again. If walking leads to meditation, climbing Sperlonga's staired streets engenders sprightliness. Those in command of their legs who like to temper exercise with reverie find the community and its environs bristling with classical associations. The noblest wine of antiquity, *vinum caecubum*, was produced in the vicinity. Tiberius, the most illustrious vacationer at *Speluncae*—as the place was called in his time—occupied a beach grotto with his imperial retinue, and was nearly buried alive in it during an earthquake.

A reminder of ever-present seismic hazards, flying buttresses hover over Sperlonga's streets like so many haloes. A "motif" much sought out by Sunday painters, they serve an important function. By cushioning the houses against the nervous tremors of a rebellious soil, they keep them in good shape for a terminal catastrophe. To banish the specter of fear from visitors' minds, and also to offer relief from the exertions of climbing, the natives have strategically placed a number of first-aid stations along the streets—wine cellars, underground restaurants, and assorted *Spelunken*.

The true epicure should at least once in his lifetime assay the luxury of a stroll in the streets of Greek island towns that have held out against wheeled vehicles. There are still a good many of them. Although the ancient Greeks were among the first nations to develop a passenger conveyance, the chariot, at the time of the country's liberation from Turkish dominion, carriages were known from pictures only. A full century later, this was still true for some of the islands. In the nineteen-twenties, Thera, with a population of fifteen thousand distributed over seven towns, had no need for vehicles; the only wheels in existence were those used in windmills. To cover long distances, people traveled on muleback or by sailboat. Even so, Thera was not a pauper's island. Among its permanent residents were rich landowners and tired men of business, the sort one expects to prefer San Sebastian or Cannes to an active volcano. And of course any number of retired captains, still sailing the seven seas in their thoughts. Since then, the island has seen changes; earthquakes, tourists, and motor vehicles have altered its physiognomy. But the complexities of the terrain have not disappeared, and neither have its rugged streets.

Earthquakes being more violent in Greece and Italy than in the rest of Europe, flying buttresses are a familiar sight in the streets. These arches are often used as substructures for additional floors of a building. The result is the *floating flat* (a term I just made up), by which I mean the part of a house that straddles a street; an apartment suspended in mid-air, anchored in houses on both sides of a street. An old method of construction, known throughout the world, it is never mentioned in textbooks and encyclopedias for it belongs to vernacular architecture, a branch ignored by architects and historians alike.

Although common enough in Mediterranean countries, the floating flat comes truly into its own in hot zones. In the towns at the northern border of the African desert, the streets are overcast by the houses' upper stories. In fact, the streets would be pitch dark were it not for the light wells that are placed at intervals to feed them some of the brilliance of the sky, and also to keep them cool and ventilated. An aerial view discloses no streets at all; seen from above, the towns present a solid mass of buildings, punctured by inner courtyards, resembling for all the world a giant Swiss cheese with square holes. The practical advantages of this building type are self-evident: it acts as a solid canopy for the street and utilizes space that otherwise goes to waste.

Less obvious are its esthetic and psychological rewards. A street with its view curtained off at every step by overhead structures makes for a succession of well-defined spaces, forming, as it were, a suite of outdoor chambers. This compartmentalized streetspace enfolds the pedestrian, imparting a singular sense of privacy. Italians are partial to this floating architecture and, not surprisingly, have a word for it. They call it *case pensili*, hanging houses, formed on the analogy of hanging gardens. Examples, ranging from rustic to aristocratic, are scattered throughout the peninsula, and nowhere are they more conspicuous than in the ancient towns of Umbria and Tuscany.

Thanks to case pensili, Perugia contains some of the starkest streetscapes in the Western world, a succession of majestic corridors, vaulted over, and topped by aeries in stone. They fit Alberti's description of the ideal street, winding up and down as they do, turning abruptly, resulting in space constellations that never entered the modern architect's vocabulary. Nobody has troubled to record this robust architecture, nor does it catch the casual visitor's fancy. Still, a few impressionable souls whose wells of imagination have not dried up in America's urban deserts, who managed to escape the clutches of official guides, live or printed, have been known to fall under its spell. Even such an obdurate man as Hawthorne relented. Probing Perugia's labyrinth, he wrote with his heart in his throat—and for once he sounds more like Alice going down the rabbit hole than the eternally frustrated pilgrim—"We plunged from the upper city down through the strangest passages that ever were called streets; some of them, indeed, being arched over, and, going down into the unknown darkness, looked like caverns; and we followed one of them doubtfully, till it opened out upon the light. The houses on each side were divided only by a pace or two, and communicated with one another, here and there, by arched passages. They looked very ancient, and may have been inhabited by Etruscan princes, judging from the massiveness of some of the foundation stones." [10] Etruscan princes indeed! Hawthorne's estimate was off by a couple of thousand years; the Etruscans decamped when the ancient Perusia, one of the twelve confederate cities of Etruria, fell into the hands of the Romans in 310 B.C. To be sure, the streets *are* old and they look it, yet Hawthorne's intelligence that "thousands of generations" had trod them before is poetic license or poor arithmetics.

The Care and Feeding of the Pedestrian

The original, out-of-print, three-volume, two-thousand-page Baedeker of Italy—still a marvel of information—states that Italians, as well as foreigners who stay at a hotel, have their breakfast at a café. And so they do. It is a pleasure few would be willing to forgo. Baedeker's equally bulky English-language edition characteristically omits this kind of intelligence, doubtless in recognition of the Englishman's and American's resolve never to notice, still less to partake of, alien customs. *Their* idea of how to begin a day when vacationing abroad is to have breakfast in bed, or at least in their room, which satisfies their ego as much as their idea of comfort. What this really comes to is a refusal to face another day, an unavowed desire to prolong yesterday into the morrow. (A laudable exception was Mark Twain, whom we observed earlier, on page   ? , breakfasting in Milan's Galleria.)

People with a sunny disposition who crave the light of a new day can't wait to get out into the street. Their first deliberate action of the morning is to walk to the neighborhood coffee bar, not for a meal washed down with quantities of coffee-flavored hot water but to sip what deserves to be called an elixir. (For the hungry there are always brioches, fresh from the baker, around the clock.) The Italian depends on a street shop rather than his own kitchen for a cup of the only acceptable brew because the machine necessary to produce it, far from being a household appliance, is gigantic and costs a fortune. He is not alone in his devotion to the aromatic drink. In Brazil, it is not unusual for a man daily to consume several dozen cups of coffee out of doors, while talking business in the middle of the street where waiters are continuously passing full trays. To be sure, the cups are doll-size, holding only a few drops of the precious liquid, and the street happens to be in the business district from which vehicles are banned during the day. The street functions as a cross between exchange and corso; there is a gaiety about it not found in an office—rather like that of a garden party.

The authentic café is almost always part of the street, sidewalk or no sidewalk. (The term "sidewalk café" is an Anglicism with more than a pleonastic touch.) It represents a stationary version of the promenade—a pedestrians' depot, so to speak. In countries where the café is redolent of the soil—if only of asphalt or cobblestones—it serves as extension of that mother lode of sociability, the indoor café. Spreading out over street or square, particularly at late hours, a café's seating capacity, aided by inexhaustible reserves of chairs, is prodigious. In Europe, facilities for sitting in the open air are mostly taken for granted; a restaurant or café will not succeed if it cannot offer its patrons outdoor space for the better part of the year. Whether open to the winds, or walled in by glass panels, shaded by trees or awnings, the outdoor café affords the habitué an unobstructed view of street life. Bad weather will seldom dislodge it; during the cold season, every heating system short of a bonfire is used to make it inhabitable. Balmy nights bring out a city's entire café population and merge it into one big wide-awake family. Rome's night air, so fatal to Daisy Miller, acts as a tonic for Italians, young and old. They savor the scene of which they are part, and find in it sustenance for their minds. The charm of the spectacle never palls on them, since machine entertainment—movies and television—has only limited appeal to people who daily produce their own quota of theater in the round.

A strictly urban institution, the café is rarely found in villages. To the city-dweller it is chiefly a second home. *Not* a substitute home or a club, or an asylum for waifs and strays, but a complement to his domicile. Like a mistress, it fills a role that a wife will not play. Laborer and scholar depend equally on the café. The French sociologist Chombart de Lauwe considers it indispensable to city life. Loath to hear it called "salon of the poor," he vindicated its honor and status in an ecological study, sorting out neighborhood cafés according to their types of customers. He lists cafés for sports enthusiasts and for professionals, cafés for the old, cafés for the young, quiet cafés, noisy cafés, cafés with a history, dance cafés, hotel cafés, cafés for amorous rendez-vous, gambling cafés, and so forth.[11] None of them has much in common with the cafés where tourists congregate, the chic and expensive hangouts for fashionable artists and their coteries.

England, too, had its kind of philosophical café, now defunct, which was run, the English maintain, on the plan of the continental café, and became a political, social, and literary center. "It was in the early coffeehouses," argues Aytoun Ellis in his monograph *The Penny Universities*, "that the great struggle for political liberty was really fought and won. They were open to anyone and everyone, irrespective of rank, creed, station or political leaning, who paid a penny at the bar [no liquor was sold] and agreed to observe certain rules of conduct and behavior . . . A man entering was free to take a vacant seat and to engage his neighbor in conversation. If unable to read, he might hear the news read out aloud from the Government's *Gazette* by one of the company; or he would listen to the poets as they read and discussed their work, or hear the informed opinions on the latest play."[12] Odd as it may sound, even Rome once had an English coffeehouse, complete with English newspapers.

Poetry readings and discussions have been held in American cafés by the social dropouts of the 1960s without, however, affecting the nation's ways. Besides, the American coffeehouse is an eatery, not a café. Since clients and would-be waiters are usually in a hurry, the pleasures of dining are accordingly abbreviated. Staples consist mostly of instant food, like sandwiches and, for a beverage—of all things—coffee, to go with everything. The custom of serving food is also followed by cafés in foreign countries. Paris's Coupole, the former Mecca of American literati, has on its menu casserole of goose toulousain and poularde à la mode des Andelys, while Lyon's Café Neuf is famous for its gratin of crayfish and duck with goose liver. French coffeehouse owners may not be uncontrollably altruistic but, to all appearances, welcome the slow coffee sipper as much as the good trencherman. They know how to balance hospitality against profit.

In this country, the one place where one can go for a cup of coffee without being obliged to consume food is the drugstore, and even there it might be refused during meal hours. Only a hardened nation with its senses inured to the drugstore will eat and drink in its atmosphere. Granted, one can always close one's eyes to the array of merchandise that calls attention like no other to the human body's imperfections, but, lacking nose lids, one cannot shut one's nostrils to the exhalations of perfumes and soaps.

The genuine café—with the acute accent—never took root in America. Not for lack of coffee beans (although the preparation of the beverage has remained a mystery hereabouts) but because Americans distrust the potion's physiological action. They are by temperament and upbringing indifferent, if not hostile, to everything the café stands for; they scorn the state of mind it induces—the mixture of contemplativeness and introspection. What Frances Trollope said about Americans still holds true—they have no inclination for those moments of délassement that all other people indulge in. They prefer to take "coffee breaks" at a vending machine.

Lately though, even the least observant of ambulatory sidewalk superintendents could not have failed to notice an outbreak of outdoor cafés in New York, an unprecedented occurrence among a population most of whose habits were set hundreds of years ago. It would be difficult to show that a desire for sidewalk cafés has been dormant ever since Captain John Smith, the founder of Virginia, brought coffee to America in 1607. Nothing could have been further from the Americans' mind. As recently as 1956, New York City had no more than three sidewalk cafés, or roughly one for every three million inhabitants, and no pressing need seemed to exist for adding a fourth. Twelve years later, their number had increased to one hundred. In 1968 alone, twenty sprang up, not only in Manhattan's mildly cosmopolitan quarters but in rustic Brooklyn and Queens. Surely, it could not have been the stimulus of the rapidly deteriorating physical environment with its sooty, malodorous air that brought chairs and tables into the street. Nor could the new trend be caused by a few travel-addicted New Yorkers' moral disintegration with its attendant desire to imitate foreign customs. Sitting in open-air cafés has never been regarded as wholesome or decent in this country. What did bring about the marriage of café and street, at least in New York, was not a sudden reversal of people's tastes but a nudge to business. License requirements that formerly prohibited the encroachment on sidewalks were relaxed, and coffeehouse owners are actually encouraged to abstract floor space from the sidewalk.

Unfortunately, an uncongenial soil prevents a new sidewalk café society from unfolding. The cities simply lack the wide marginal spaces to allow for a deployment of coffeehouse tables in depth. Whatever the other factors, a high density of café clientele is imperative. It is directly related to the café's success, and not just to its solvency. Rubbing elbows and ankles generates a physical esprit de corps, while debate builds up mental solidarity. The chief attraction of this sidewalk institution is the trompe-l'oreille perpetrated within its charmed circle—not the babble of the crowd but the tidy conversation of cultivated spontaneity. Careful enunciation carries address and rejoinder with varying degrees of intimacy to adjoining tables for the benefit of acoustical voyeurs. Abroad, one is always aware of a collective effervescence, a quality that is absent hereabouts. As far as togetherness is concerned, the American sidewalk café is a failure.

The deeper reason for trying to get people into the street with coffeehouses as a lure is therefore anything but self-evident. As it turns out, the importance of the American street café is not cultural or commercial but strategic. In 1967 the New York City's Sidewalk Study Committee (which sounds like an anthropological society's subsidiary) reported to the mayor that "more sidewalk cafés and later closing hours would bring the people back into the streets, thereby reducing the likelihood of crime in the streets."[13] This is of course a pathetic conceit, and an insult to the café. People are not going to sit on sidewalks, patiently waiting for their chance to witness a minor street fight, when at home they have at their finger-tips the whole gamut of violence—a murder every thirty-one minutes, a violent incident every sixteen. Only a street-alienated nation could think of the café as a crime deterrent; a couple of customers and a few waiters are unlikely to distract a thug from the pursuit of his calling. The unfolding of the American sidewalk café is hampered by the lack of a suitable milieu as well as by its unattractive appear-ance. Its newest edition is but a lean-to for accommodating an extra row of tables. With its picket fence or fly screen it looks no more inviting than a chicken coop.

More daring than the café's invasion of the sidewalk is the appro-priation of the street itself by those outdoor restaurants that spring up in southern countries at the beginning of the warm season. In Spain no respectable restaurant opens its doors for dinner before 11 P.M., the time when street traffic has come to a trickle, and the day's heat has vanished. Then, tables and chairs are set up in front of the premises under a canopy of plane trees or palms, or in a minia-ture park across the street, or sometimes on a traffic island. The distance from kitchen stove to dining table may be half a city block or more, but thanks to long experience, the excellence of the dishes does not suffer.

Of course, eating in the street is not to everybody's taste. Some people have strong reservations about it; they might find it shocking, and not without reason. Psychologists have likened the act of eating in public to the indecent exposure of the body. Just as sensations of corporeal modesty are determined by such extraneous factors as climate, season, place—not to mention law—eating in full view of non-eaters is often felt to be improper, if not altogether offensive. Even simulated intake of food, such as the habit of chewing gum, is considered unspeakably vulgar when publicly indulged. "The great fundamental function of eating," asserted Havelock Ellis, "is almost as conspicuous as that of loving."

Such thinking does not necessarily denote decadence. Some primi-tive tribes who are unashamed of their nakedness will not allow themselves to be seen eating or drinking. The modest man retires to eat, and so do many animals. Emily Post fails to give advice on how to dine correctly of a hot dog bought from an ambulant vendor. The safest way would seem to stay close to his cart and avert one's eyes from passers-by. Certainly, eating is table-bound; much as bed is the best place for copulation, a dining table makes the sight of masticating bearable.

Convivial company mitigates the unesthetic aspect of food inges-tion. To let their clients dine al fresco, Italian restaurateurs might occupy a substantial part of a street or square and defend it against the wash of human waves. These places are not sidewalk establish-ments in the strict sense of the word. They are true street restaurants that expand at their owners' discretion and with the authorities' con-nivance. Occasionally an entire street is closed off, even to pedes-trians, to harbor an eating place whose owner is eager to double or triple his premises. This happens not just in sleepy provincial towns but in the capital. On festival days the city holds open house. A Saturnalian fever grips the populace, and the distinction between public and private property is blithely ignored. Public dinners, whether catered or self-served, turn an entire ward into a banquet hall. The amenities range from rustic boards and benches compactly arranged against the enobling background of churches and palaces, to immaculately set tables, screened from intruding eyes by shrub-bery and boxed trees.

The American block party—the nearest approximation to the culinary foregatherings in Latin countries—is stand-offish by com-parison. Admittance is upon invitation only. Participants are tagged. The street has no room for tables and chairs; the only furniture in sight is sawhorse barricades. No attempts are made to overcome the street's drabness with light or color. There is no gamboling Brueghel style; the party is choreographed by the police.

To find a gayer crowd, one must leave the Puritan neighborhoods and repair to those districts where Italians, Germans, or Chinese congregate. The setting for their festivals is the ubiquitous leprous architecture, with fire escapes shamelessly draped over walls and windows alike. Only when night falls do rows of rickety arches, studded with naked light bulbs, help to ward off the evil eye of the city. Food is consumed by the ton, and money splurged on fireworks. Outdoor orchestras and singers, however, with their hoary repertories of Rossini overtures and Verdi arias, are a thing of the past. The last street concert in honor of Saint Anthony was held on New York's Sullivan Street in 1966.

NOTES

[1] Samuel Langhorne Clemens, *A Tramp Abroad*, 1880, p. 119.

[2] Giuseppe Barigazzi, *Cento Anni in Galleria*, 1967, p. 126.

[3] Ernest Hemingway, *A Farewell to Arms*, 1929, chapter XVIII.

[4] Edmund Stillman, "Frederick II: The Wonder of the World," (*Horizon*, Autumn 1968, p. 85).

[5] *The Works of George Berkeley, Bishop of Cloyne*, 1955, vol. VII, p. 235.

[6] *Ibid.*, p. 273.

[7] *Ibid.*, p. 274.

[8] Sitwell, *op. cit.*, p. 125.

[9] Leone Battista Alberti, *De Re Aedificatoria*, 1485, Book IV, Chap. V.

[10] Nathaniel Hawthorne, *The French and Italian Note-Books*, 1876, Vol. I, p. 246.

[11] Paul-Henri Chombart de Lauwe, *Des Hommes et des Villes*, 1965, p. 28.

[12] Aytoun Ellis, *Penny Universities*, 1956, p. XV.

[13] "City Easing Rules on Sidewalk Cafes to Encourage Idea," (*The New York Times*, Dec. 5, 1967).

Highway Beauty Awards Competition

Few elements of the urban environment have come in for more bruising criticism than highways. Expressways have been pictured as defilers and defacers of the countryside and highway agencies as callous vandals ruining landscapes and bulldozing architectural treasures. In belated response to such criticism, the federal Bureau of Public Roads initiated an annual good design competition aimed at proving that highways can be aesthetically pleasing and beneficial to the visual environment.

PURPOSE

The Highway Beauty Awards Competition was instituted by the U.S. Department of Transportation in 1968 to emphasize the inter-relationship of today's highways with the beauty of nature. The purpose of this competition is to afford public recognition to those agencies, organizations, and business enterprises which have achieved outstanding results in coordinating the highway location and design with its natural or manmade surroundings, and which have effected en-

vironmental improvement or protection in their treatment. In the second year of the competition—1969—584 pictures were submitted from all parts of the country. First prize and honorable mention awards are given in each of ten categories.

CATEGORIES

I—The Outstanding Section of Highway in its Rural Setting and Environment

II—The Outstanding Section of Highway in its Urban Setting and Environment

III—The Outstanding Bridge, Overpass, Tunnel Approach, Ramp, Interchange Area, or other Highway Structural Feature

IV—The Outstanding Safety Rest Area with Sanitary and other Facilities of Benefit to Highway Users, and may include Information Centers or Sign Plazas

V—The Outstanding Example of Highway-Oriented Private Enterprises, such as Gas Stations, Hotels, Motels, Preserving or Enhancing the Environment

Highway Beauty Awards Competition (continued)

I—The Outstanding Example of Multiple Use of Highway Right-of-Way in Urban or Rural Areas (parks, schools, parking lots, recreation and camping facilities, and parks or buildings under or over highway; etc.)

II—The Outstanding Example of the Preservation of Wildlife or Natural Areas

III—The Outstanding Example of the Preservation of Historic Sites

IV—The Outstanding Example of Landscape Treatment Along Roadsides and Interchanges

V—The Outstanding Example of Screening, Removal, or Disposal of Junked Automobiles adjacent to the Highway Right-of-Way

CRITERIA

Each entry is judged within its own area competition upon the following criteria: (1) excellence of project development; (2) importance to the highway or highway corridor environment; (3) general highway interest; and (4) pictorial quality and composition.

During 1969, all first prizes were awarded while nine of the ten honorable mentions were awarded—no honorable mention was awarded in Category II. Among those entries winning more than one award were:

	First Prize	Honorable Mention
California Transportation Agency	5	1
New York Department of Transportation	1	3
Florida Road Department	—	2

Other entries each receiving one award included: (1) First Prize—Wisconsin Department of Transportation, Mobil Oil Corporation, Chicago Department of Public Works, Vermont Department of Highways; (2) Honorable Mention—Atlantic Richfield, Oregon Highway Commission, and Santa Clara County, California.

The Potrero Hill Wall in San Francisco provides superior structural soundness, plus an interesting landscape treatment.
Photo credit: Federal Highway Administration

A section of Route 17 expressway wins for the New York State Department of Transportation a first place in the annual nationwide contest sponsored by the Federal Highway Administration. It was named the outstanding highway in a rural setting.

Photo credit: Federal Highway Administration

IX

ENVIRONMENTAL MANAGEMENT AND FINANCE

It has become increasingly apparent to government and citizen alike that if we are to preserve a tolerable world for future generations we must accept responsibility for the husbanding of our natural resources. By now, due to a convergence of expanding knowledge, increased sensitivity to environmental conditions and technological capabilities, the general public has been made aware of the potential crisis facing mankind. If our world is to survive, it is imperative that each individual and the institutions of his society abandon traditional patterns of behavior abusive towards the environment. This goal is not a simple undertaking; but it must become one of the highest priorities of government.

The necessity for proper environmental management has been forced into the forefront of public concern because of a growing recognition that government must intervene to protect our fragile life-support system from impairment or destruction. Unfortunately, actions that seem politically wise and economically profitable may be ecologically unsound and vice versa. But the question of how best to utilize our natural resources to meet human needs can no longer be left in the hands of technology working for profit but must be based on social policy operating within a realistic political and economic framework. Survival demands higher priority for ecology.

The environment became an issue of public policy only within the past decade. During the 1960's, the major task of creating the awareness and understanding of the general nature and extent of public responsibility was more or less accomplished. The 1970's should be a time for action, for creating an effective national environmental policy. Achieving this goal requires first of all that numerous and often conflicting environmental concerns be brought together with a new emphasis on implementation, rather than on research, futile hand-wringing and rhetoric.

In the past, the development of environmental programs was characterized by a narrow focus with little effort to consider the broader impact of environmental decisions. A new national environmental policy might be based on the following assumptions:

(1) that a positive public policy to protect the quality of the human environment has now become a practical necessity,
(2) that a maturing science of ecology can provide the informational basis for public environmental policy, and
(3) that the spaceship provides a simplified, dramatic, and persuasive symbol of man's environmental condition.[1]

Analysis of the programs discussed in this book and elsewhere points to several general conclusions which can be drawn regarding the political, governmental and financial problems of pollution control. Some of these points might be summarized as follows:

(1) Although there are still certain technological gaps (e.g., more so in air pollution than in water pollution), there are no insuperable technological obstacles in dealing with pollution problems. The real key to progress in depollution—and the principal unsolved problem —lies in genuine public commitment followed by the development of effective regulatory mechanisms which have the jurisdiction, legal tools, financing and staff to carry out their mandate.

(2) Although the overall costs of depollution still are not clear—due to disputes over standards—it is clear that public commitment as reflected in appropriations rather than verbal assent, falls far short of need. The same observation can be made for the private sector. Despite the ringing speeches, there is a discernible stalling posture on both the public and private side mainly because other priorities seem more important to persons responsible for allocating resources.

(3) Very complicated intergovernmental requirements are involved in the management of most environmental problems. The absence of good regional mechanisms is one serious handicap. Furthermore, existing environmental control agencies, particularly at the state level, seem to reflect the traditions and feeble character of their origins and have not been reinvigorated, nor developed the necessary new directions. Weak enforcement of current regulations (e.g., water, air,

and billboard legislation) suggest that simply passing new laws will not suffice.

(4) Although a carrot-stick incentive-regulation mix may be the right recipe for achieving the various environmental goals, the specific blends (e.g., tax-fee-license arrangements) are still in the experimental and demonstration stages. We simply do not have enough solid experience for clear-cut direction.

(5) There is a serious problem of conflicting priorities, since resources are finite and problems are massive. Health, education and welfare needs, along with other priority issues, are also related to the quality of life, and a good case can certainly be made for increased spending in a number of non-environmental programs.

(6) International dimension: If American companies must absorb additional costs of abatement, some may be priced out of international markets by foreign companies which do not have to meet these expenses. One approach may be to require foreign competition to match United States standards (as in automobile emissions) and to persuade foreign nations to adopt United States standards (e.g., barring the Supersonic Transport).

The preceding sections of this book have concentrated on examples of environmental programs which have achieved some degree of success. The fact that there are not as many examples as one might hope can be attributed to a variety of problems including deficiencies and lags in public understanding and governmental management and financing. This final section of readings focuses on elements in our governmental and social institutions which are the source of some of the most serious obstacles to environmental improvement.

In the first reading, "Environmental Costs and Benefits," Melvin R. Levin disposes of the assumption that most of the enormous dollar cost required for implementing large scale environmental improvements will be unrecoverable. Levin holds that this assumption is false, primarily because the cost of pollution control will be offset by substantial reductions in illness, health costs, and other environmentally related physical and social problems. Furthermore, environmental upgrading will itself represent a major industry, generating substantial profits and employment. Each area of the environmental crisis covered in separate sections of this book is analyzed on a cost-benefit basis to determine the economic, as well as social, feasibility of pollution control programs. The article concludes that while cost-

benefit analysis does not offer precise guidelines, it can be a powerful educational tool. We have sufficient technology to take at least minimal steps toward control of our environmental problems but accomplishments depend on federal leadership, on new kinds of rewards and on a clear understanding of how environmental control can create profits. Finally, it is important for politicians and public alike to see the evidence of quick visible results.

"Pollution Control: Perspectives on the Government Role" examines several aspects of government's role in pollution control programs, including federal and state programs to aid in pollution control, the amount of money provided under these programs, problems of standard setting, different forms—tax devices, subsidies and grants —that government aid can take, forms of government regulation, and the estimated costs of pollution control in the future. This article, a remarkably objective one for an industry-related organization—the Rockefeller-supported Tax Foundation—points up difficulties in several aspects of the pollution problem, including standard setting, costs of pollution control, types of regulations and the form in which government aid should be designated. Although it is impossible to answer many of these questions, it is important to try to understand some of the dimensions of the problem and to realize, as the article concludes, that all of us will at some point or other bear the cost of cleaning up the environment.

[1] Lynton Keith Caldwell, *Environment: A Challenge to Modern Society* (Garden City, New York: The Natural History Press, 1970), p. 1.

24. Environmental Costs and Benefits

MELVIN R. LEVIN

INTRODUCTION

One of the major impediments to implementing large scale environmental improvements is the false assumption that most of the enormous dollar cost required for this purpose will be unrecoverable. This idea is erroneous for two reasons:

(1) Although precise data is unavailable, there will undoubtedly be substantial reductions in public health problems and other environmentally related physical and social problems which will compensate for much or all of the program cost; environmental programs will generate sizable industrial development and payrolls which will recycle much of the expenditure; and the change to a reclamation/reuse economy will open up new entrepreneurial and job opportunities.

(2) Much of the pressure on discovering new and usually more costly natural resources will be relieved if, for example, resources now in use were recycled for future use while resources such as our water bodies were reclaimed or maintained at usable and attractive levels of purification.

The cost-benefit approach to governmental participation in programs such as environmental control has been under almost continuous attack on the grounds of agency bias, manipulation of calculations and tendencies toward overemphasis on quantifiable data at the expense of highly significant social factors. There is an unfortunate tendency to oversell it or to use it to validate and legitimize previously arrived at conclusions. Nevertheless, the task of reaching reasonable decisions is helped by the use of cost-benefit analysis.

In practical terms, cost-benefit calculations can serve as powerful persuaders, and defensive outworks, particularly for those already leaning in the right direction. It may be argued that *all* decisions involve some form of cost-benefit calculation since any allocation of time and money involves a choice between alternatives. Cost-benefit in the sense in which it is used here is an attempt to convert a crude and usually intuitive process into a systematic and rigorous method of assessing alternative options on the basis of comparable data. Unfortunately, completely valid supportive data is often hard to unearth and, for this reason, it must also be understood that cost-benefit arguments are usually most compelling in the absence of competing figures marshalled by skilled opponents.

Each step of the process from definition of project parameters through assumptions of imputed values, interest rates and returns can be fraught with controversy. One is often uncertain, for example, that a given impact was solely or even directly related to any particular program. Studies aimed at measuring the impact of manpower programs and economic development demonstrate clearly the difficulties encountered in isolating the consequences associated with completion of training from those attributable to general economic conditions, particularly the situation in the local job market. Frequently, the impact may be the result of a mix of factors and programs and assessing the importance of any one ingredient may be a fearsome chore for the serious researcher. Another obstacle is the poor quality of much of the data. In the area of air pollution, for example, costs are currently being estimated by statistical manipulation based on limited data for one city dating back to 1913. Lead emission estimates can vary widely depending on whether one uses regular or high test gas.

Given all of these reservations, why then should we pay any attention to such a dubious technique in designing environmental programs? The answer seems to lie in the area of public education, i.e. to present convincing evidence that benefits from environmental programs equal or exceed the costs.

The common property resources—air and water—do not fully enter into the market exchange. They are progressively degraded because they are used as free "dumps" for consumption and production residuals. But such dumping, in fact, exacts positive social costs. It comes at a high price to society—in degraded air and water, impaired health, loss of fish and wildlife, loss of recreational opportunities and esthetic values, and added costs of treatment necessary for downstream water users. Yet these social costs are not to be found in the credit and debit ledgers of dischargers.

Excessive pollution and degradation of the environment are thereby encouraged. Indeed, little else should seriously be expected. Environmental problems stem largely from this fundamental failure of the economic system to take account of environmental costs.[1]

While there have been periodic attempts at measuring economic benefits, most of the discussion in the environmental area has focused on costs alone—$500 billion to remove the billboards, tens of billions for air and water pollution, etc.[2] One of the most recent estimates of pollution costs has been provided by the Environmental Protection Agency on page 448.

POLLUTION ABATEMENT COST SUMMARY

It's not surprising that both the taxpayer and the legislator are absolutely certain that environmental programs will be costly but that benefits remain visionary and speculative. The basic problem is that in an era of tight public and private budgets, there is not going to be firm and consistent support for very large scale programs unless there is a reasonable consensus that we can afford them, partly because such programs will produce measurable payoffs commensurate with their costs.

Another factor affecting the attitude of the public towards governmental involvement in the environmental field is that many poor persons and members of minority groups are concerned that priorities may be awry if protection of wildlife is given precedence over job creating plants and if limited government funds are allocated to open space instead of to housing of low income families. There is some feeling that the threats to baby seals seem to arouse deeper emotions than dangers to baby Negroes, that in fact the environmental movement represents a middle class cop-out from intransigent and controversial human and institutional problems into the consensual sunshine of pure waters, clean air and suburban greenery. For this reason, it is crucial to make it clear that environmental action means new jobs and better living conditions for the poor.

Critical Assumptions

Rearranging public views concerning environmental programs requires basic understanding, if not complete acceptance of a number of key propositions.

(1) *The Defense Plant Analogy.* One of the strangest phenomena

Table I / Pollution Abatement Cost Summary [1]
(in billions of dollars)

Pollutant/ medium	1970 Capital investment Cumulative [2]	An-nual	An-nual-ized costs	1975 Capital Investment Cumulative [3]	An-nual	An-nual-ized costs	Cumulative requirements 1970–75 Capi-tal invest-ment	Total oper-ating costs	Total expendi-tures
Air pollution									
Public [4]	$ 0.2	$0.1	$0.2	$ 0.5	$0.1	$ 0.2	$ 0.4	$ 1.2	$ 1.6
Private									
Mobile	.1	.1	—.2	4.3	2.9	1.5	5.4	.6	6.0
Stationary	1.0	.7	.5	7.7	1.8	3.0	8.0	8.1	16.1
Total	1.3	.9	.5	12.5	4.8	4.7	13.8	9.9	23.7
Water pollution									
Public									
Federal [5]	NA	NA	.2	.3	.1	.3	.3	1.3	1.6
State and local									
Treatment systems	13.7	1.2	1.6	24.2	1.5	3.3	13.6	9.3	22.9
Collecting sewers [6]	(12.0)	NA	NA	(12.0)	NA	NA	(3.6)	NA	(3.6)
Combined sewers [7]	NA	NA	NA	NA	NA	NA	(15.0–48.0)	NA	(15.0–48.0)
Private									
Manufacturing	3.9	.8	1.1	7.1	.6	1.9	4.8	7.2	12.0
Other	.9	.3	.2	1.1	.1	.3	.5	1.0	1.5
Total	18.5	2.3	3.1	32.7	2.3	5.8	19.2	18.8	38.0
Solid Waste [8]									
Municipal									
Public	NA	.1	2.1 ⎫						
Private	NA	NA	2.3 ⎬ NA	.3	7.8 ⎫⎬	1.5	42.0	43.5
Industrial	NA	NA	1.3 ⎭		⎭			
Total	NA	.1	5.7	NA	.3	7.8	1.5	42.0	43.5
Grand Total	NA	3.3	9.3	NA	7.4	18.3	34.5	70.7	105.2

[1] For major air, water, and solid waste pollution control expenditures.
[2] Total capital in place as of the end of 1970.
[3] Total capital in place as of the end of 1975 is net of depreciation for the period.
[4] For construction and operation of Federal facilities only.
[5] For construction and operation of Federal facilities only. Does not include the Federal construction grant funds, which are included under State and local.
[6] Collecting sewers are shown as a non-add item due to lack of data.
[7] Combined sewers shown as a non-add item because of lack of data.
[8] Annualized costs exclude depreciation and interest because of lack of data.
Source: Based on Environmental Protection Agency data.

"We create it, we clean it up—business couldn't be better."

in popular economics is the contrast between the keen awareness of the employment benefits from spending in defense plants and the insensitivity to the payoff from health, welfare or environmental programs. It is almost as if there is a conviction that most civilian-oriented spending pours money into some magic disposal apparatus where it is shredded, pulverized and incinerated. Only in hard pressed slums and other distressed areas is there a realization that welfare money, for example, is high velocity spending—none of it saved—which keeps retail merchandise moving and apartments rented.

In the environmental area, the only segments of the business com-

munity wholly alert to this potential are firms with a direct stake in selling antipollution equipment and brokerage houses attempting to market stock in such companies. The recognition that large scale expenditures for construction will generate first round benefits of construction jobs, employment in equipment manufacturing plants and a substantial increase in monitoring, planning and other types of government personnel has not yet fully penetrated. There are also second and third round benefits: environmental businesses and staff spend their money on subcontracts and on housing, in retail stores and for personal services. Billions for the military are seen, quite accurately, as a bonanza for favored firms and this manipulation of contracts and payrolls has been a powerful influence in assuring continued support for defense spending. Billions for the environment should be viewed in the same way. Environmental programs are not simply a drain on the economy but a generator of enormous payrolls and contracts and sizable profits yielding sizable economic and political rewards.

One obvious source of manpower for the performance of neglected ecological tasks is the unemployed of which there was an ample supply in the early 1970's. Some states, notably New York and California, have made an effort to secure useful work from able bodied persons on the welfare rolls up to the limits of their public

'. . . BUT THE ECONOMY MIGHT SUFFER!'

Fri., June 10, 1966

ST. LOUIS POST-DISPATCH

assistance grants. Significantly lacking, however, are the sophisticated approaches toward mobilizing the millions of unemployed and underemployed workers of the nation on the scale reminiscent of the Great Depression. In the 1930's substantial impact on environmental problems was made by the Civilian Conservation Corps, the Public Works Administration and Works Progress Administration. The military establishment's successful use of casual labor in undertaking sizable construction endeavors coupled with effective utilization of more advanced skills on the Peace Corps and Vista models points to the possibility of enlisting much or most of the nation's surplus manpower resources on a massive attack on neglected ecological problems.

(2) *Redirecting an Ongoing Stream* One of the frightening aspects of many environment proposals is the implication that all action is remedial and corrective and hence involves costly redevelopment and/or reconstruction programs which will necessarily involve very sizable additions over and above current expenditure patterns. This assumption is, of course, erroneous. Much future action (e.g., new towns, cluster zoning, undergrounding utility lines in new subdivisions) represents not new spending but a careful redirection of expenditures which would be made in any event. Grouping housing to preserve open space may in fact be less expensive than attempting to serve widely dispersed units with sewers, water lines, schools and other public and private functions. Similarly, placing utility power lines underground when a subdivision is being constructed may cost more initially—$100 to $500 more per house—but the cost is always recaptured over a period of time since it usually prevents further costs from tree damage to utility wires.[3]

Whatever is done about the environment, many tens of billions will have to be spent to house, rehouse and service a growing, increasingly affluent and migratory population. Allocations to conserve and improve the existing environment should be visualized as incremental expenditures over and above this massive investment stream.[4] In effect, environmental programs represent insurance to protect this future investment.

(3) *Prevention Easier than Cure* The amounts needed for extensive environmental programs can be substantially reduced through timely action. Preventive restrictions on new products (e.g., detergents) are far less expensive than subsequent programs to clean and restock waterways. Often only a modest one-time changeover cost is all that is involved. In fact, at present there is no remedy at any cost for DDT and mercury pollution, along with other dangerous heavy metals. Moreover, costs to some industries may be balanced by gains

in others. For example, fishing fleets may have a brighter future when water pollution is sharply reduced. Pricing and administrative policies can be established to fine polluters heavily, make product reclamation and re-use (e.g., bottles) economically worthwhile as well as mandatory, ensure adequate reserves of open space in new residential subdivisions and keep billboards off highways. All this is much less expensive than correcting mistakes: preventing billboards from going up may cost nothing; removing them once constructed is a slow and expensive process.

Prevention also makes a good deal of sense from the viewpoint of the individual firm. For example, water heavily polluted with salt wears out equipment five times faster than water free from large quantities of salt water intrusion. The popular notion that industry is simply a generator rather than a victim of pollution is obviously false although like much in the cost-benefit field, the supportive data is fragmentary.[5]

(4) *The Bogey of "No Growth"* Some of the more fearful authorities in the environmental field have been pressing hard for a firm national commitment to no growth goals like zero population growth and ceilings (or cutbacks) on the number of automobiles and other consumer and capital goods. Profligate Americans, we are warned, use 50 or 100 times as much natural resources per capita as the average Indian or African and nothing short of acceptance of an immediate national growth ceiling will save the world from early ruin.

Although most proponents of the no growth concept are ecologists and others drawn from the physical and life sciences, their ranks are beginning to include respected economists. Those who are wary of ecological programs on the grounds that excessive worry over the environment will stifle creation of new jobs and higher profits must be reassured: upgrading the quality of the environment should result in improved living standards, particularly better health. Furthermore a redirection of the economy need not choke off further growth. Higher costs are probably inevitable in any event as wages rise and raw materials become scarce. Factoring in environmental considerations represents an incremental and absorbable charge.

A deliberate decision to adopt and adhere to a no growth policy would clearly entail serious consequences, and from a realistic political standpoint, this kind of reasoning is likely to attract little support. If the alternatives are presented as a choice between environmental protection or higher incomes, ecology will surely be the loser. Yet the question arises as to whether the choice is really that simple. With population growth already slowing, with population levels in some economically flourishing parts of the nation increasing at minimal rates, surely the road to further affluence and strength lies in qualitative improvement. We can grow richer by upgrading skills; we can conserve resources by reclamation and recycling; and we can remain strong enough to protect ourselves with technology, not massed cannon fodder.

(5) *Substantial Measureable Payoffs* The most compelling argument for the use of cost-benefit analysis in formulating public policies is that it provides data directly analogous to the balance sheets which serve as guide posts in the business world. It is not that decision-makers are unsympathetic to discussions of beauty, quality of life, historic values and community morale, but that this line of reasoning is "artistic" and cloudy and hence unconvincing when measured against solid realities like dollars and number of users. Only if such sentiment is translated into pressure, particularly campaign contributions and votes, does it assume a tangible form. But most of the time, assessments of programs and proposals tend to be fairly technical, concerned with bickering over mundane statistics rather than clashing philosophic values. Naturally, values underly opinions, but the point is that to a great extent philosophy is armored in statistics because figures help to convince and provide supportive validation for men who like to think of themselves as hard headed pragmatists. For this reason environmentalists would do well to attempt to translate as many proposals as possible into plausible cost and benefit ratios.

ENVIRONMENTAL PROBLEMS AND COST-BENEFIT

It is useful to consider each of the seven arbitrarily defined environmental components separately in evaluating costs and benefits. Although there is obviously a good deal of overlapping—highways may pollute the land, create air pollution, noise pollution, esthetic and even water pollution problems—it is necessary to establish some system of categorization to unscramble costs and benefits. Subsequently, costs and benefits can be aggregated in appropriate combinations. The seven selected areas of concern are population, air pollution, water pollution, noise pollution, land use, solid wastes and esthetics. Each has more than environmental implications, but this discussion is limited to a single question: *To what extent can we identify the benefits as well as the costs of environmental programs in each of these areas?*

(1) *Population* Of the factors bearing on the environment, population is probably the most crucial since it pervades every aspect of environmental pollution. Population control involves two key issues: (1) limiting the overall size of the population, and (2) ensuring a manageable population distribution.

The United States seems well on its way toward achieving the first objective. By 1970, birth rates had dropped below depression levels and zero population growth seemed a strong possibility after the end of the present century. Nevertheless, the present and potential effect of America's population size on the nation's natural resources is so tremendous—with about 6 percent of the world's population the United States currently uses more than 40 percent of the world's scarce or nonreplaceable resources—that the question of population control is as relevant a concern in the United States as it is in other less developed countries.[6] One major problem lies in providing adequately for what may be the last great surge in population growth, another 40 million people by the year 2000.[7]

Among current population programs, family planning—not actually synonomous with population control—has been credited with the largest payoff in cost-benefit terms. Arguments to the effect that the nation can, with proper planning, support several times its present population should carry little weight since the necessary rationalization of planning effort and resources seem a long way off. By age 18 each child may cost upward of $50,000 in public and private rearing costs and may consume tens of thousands of pounds in raw materials before he reaches maturity. It is alleged, however, that man is a producer as well as a consumer and consequently a well reared youngster can return far more in a working lifetime than was expended in his upbringing. Considered on a small scale, this theory has much to commend it. The difficulty arises in the case of the massive 100 million increase in the United States population over the next half century that demographers have been predicting.[8] A low rate of population growth coupled with a heavy emphasis on child care and manpower utilization seems to be the surest road to upgrading the quality of life for nations and families.

Still to be dealt with, however, is the special difficulty of making adequate arrangements for children of the poor in order to provide a higher standard of living for this group and thus break the cycle of poverty, which is closely linked with large often unwanted families: it is estimated that at least one in four children is unwanted. Among low income families large numbers of children may lock the family into poverty and, through parental and governmental neglect, may condemn a large proportion of the poor to existence in a generational poverty cycle. The answer lies in providing mothers of low income families with free access to contraception and abortion information currently available to middle and upper income women.[9] This is the goal of the Family Planning Services and Population Research Act (November, 1970) supported by the Nixon Administration. There is no doubt that the costs are very small but the benefits from this type of effort can be enormous from the standpoint of the welfare mother, her (fewer) children and the nation.

Of the various types of environmental action, family planning is likely to have one of the most favorable cost-benefit ratios. The Planned Parenthood Federation, for example, states that $10 million can fund a family planning program reaching 500,000 women at $20 per capita. The Federation estimates that this will provide a saving of $250 million in reduced expenditures for maternal and child health care, aid to dependent children, care of retardates, etc. This set of figures yields a cost-benefit ratio of 25:1.[10]

(2) *Air Pollution: Health Menace* Air pollution, more than any other form of environmental pollution, can be proven to have harmful effects if allowed to reach extreme levels. Well documented cases include the Meuse Valley in Belgium, where in 1930, a hundred persons were made ill and sixty-three died. A similar situation occurred in this country in 1947, when fog and a low-level temperature inversion covered the horseshoe-shaped valley of the Monongahela River in Pennsylvania. Here, in the valley area around the town of Donora, nearly half the population became ill and twenty people died. In London during two weeks of December 1952, an estimated 4,000 deaths were recorded beyond those normal for the period.[11]

The Environmental Protection Agency (EPA) estimates that the economic cost of human mortality and morbidity from all air pollution is in the neighborhood of $6 billion annually. However, these estimated health costs relate only to medical care and work loss. If the costs of discomfort, frustration, and anxiety were included, these estimates would be greatly increased.

The annual toll of air pollution on health, vegetation, materials and property values has been estimated by EPA at more than $16 billion annually—over $80 for each person in the United States.[12]

Although these extremes have occurred only a relatively few times in the past, it appears that the most serious effects of air pollution can result from extensive exposure over long periods of time to less extreme levels of pollution. This fact should be of great concern to a large share of the American population because at least 6,000 American communities, according to a Public Health Service survey, have varying degrees of air pollution.[13]

Although total costs of air pollution in the United States cannot be precisely calculated, they amount to billions of dollars a year. Some aspects of the total cost include:

To paint steel structures damaged by air pollution runs an estimated $100 million a year. Commercial laundering, cleaning, and dyeing of fabrics soiled by air pollution costs about $240 million. Damage to agricultural crops and livestock is put at $500 million a year or more. Adverse effects of air pollution on air travel cost from $40 to $80 million a year.[14]

Other, more difficult to assess, costs include damage, soiling and added maintenance to homes and furnishings, effects on property values, medical costs and time lost from work because of air pollution or the fall in productivity of business and industry. Because of the difficulty in measuring the effects of air pollution, recent studies concluded that only the impact of sulfur trioxide on property values could be determined with any degree of accuracy.[15] When and if the air becomes unbreathable, as it already does from time to time in some cities, corrective action is indicated regardless of the lack of 100 percent certainty that air pollution is mainly or solely to blame for respiratory ailments. The best analogy is cigarettes: when the evidence mounted concerning the dangers of internal air pollution, action was taken. Certainly there seems to be at least as much foundation for similar programs on the external pollution—beginning with the warning that residing in Los Angeles may be hazardous to the health.

(3) *Water Pollution: Investment and Survival* Of all aspects of the environment, water pollution has probably received the greatest amount of attention. This is a question of assuring human survival by preventing the rest of the Great Lakes, the oceans and the rivers from following the example of Lake Erie, now ten years dead. But the headlong rush to destruction seems to be decelerating. In any event, unlike many foreign nations, most Americans can count on potable water from the tap far into the future. While occasional oil

spills, mercury scares and fish kills serve to remind us of underlying peril, water pollution is regarded, on the whole, as one of the more expensive problems which is likely to provide only a small tangible immediate return.

The fact is, however, that the future of the oceans and other water bodies is crucial to human survival. The menace to the balance of nature posed by continued water pollution raises a threat to the continuation of the species. Jacques-Yves Cousteau, who has been studying the earth's oceans and the life within for many years, reports that since 1950, pollution and overfishing have killed 40 percent of the oceans' marine life.[16] On this ground, costly programs can be justified without the necessity of attempting to prove that there will be major savings from depolluting Lake Erie by reducing the need for swimming pools in Buffalo, or travel to distant areas for other types of recreation. Quite probably raising the quality of the Hudson to drinkable standards will be too costly but making the river swimmable may be feasible at a bearable cost.[17]

Recent attempts to put a price tag on the costs of clean water estimate that over the next five years municipal waste treatment plants will need $10 billion to meet water quality standards—about $2 billion a year. In addition, operating charges are estimated to rise from $410 million a year in 1969 to $710 million in 1974. And the problem of separating sewer and storm overflows has been estimated to cost between $15 and $48 billion.[18] These can only be considered very rough estimates at best. Depending on the alternative solution chosen, widely differing costs will be encountered. Nevertheless, it is possible to conclude that water treatment will be extremely costly, especially in terms of initial capital investment, and this cost, which must be borne by government, industry and the individual citizen, can be justified if only because without it life may become impossible. It is far less expensive to pursue a policy of water husbandry, recycling nearby water supplies instead rather than engaging in schemes which have been suggested for the parched western states, e.g. building aqueducts to the Canadian Rockies.

(4) *Noise Pollution: The Long Road to Quiet* It is generally agreed that prolonged exposure to excessive noise levels (over 85 decibels) can result in serious physical and mental harm. The problem is recognized in industrial safety regulations which call for suppression measures and, where these are not feasible, require wearing of earmuffs in such extreme situations as ground crews in proximity of jet planes during landings and takeoffs. Loss of hearing can occur in far more prosaic environments including subjection to high volume

rock bands, construction, heavy traffic and even household appliances.

The adverse effects of noise are not yet well understood. Some of the more generally recognized effects include hearing loss, disruption of normal activity (classes in school buildings located near airports are often interrupted while a plane on takeoff or landing passes close overhead), and general annoyance. Loud noises, such as the sonic boom, can even cause physical damage to structures. The most common and best understood physiological effect of noise is permanent hearing impairment. Temporary physiological changes can be produced by noise including the constriction of the smaller arteries resulting in increased pulse and respiration rates. Nevertheless, much more research is needed to fully understand this phenomenon. The task is made more difficult because individuals vary widely in their sensitivity to noise—what is annoying to one person may not be so to another. As a quick guide to determining the safety of noise, Aram Glorig, a noted researcher in this field, estimates that when a person is in the presence of noise loud enough to require that person to raise his voice in order to be heard, that noise is at a potentially harmful level.

Simple preventive measures like *not* proceeding with the SST and requiring effective mufflers on motor bikes would be helpful. However, two other lines of action are indicated, introducing stronger regulations in manufacturing and construction and a combination of public education and legislation to make life styles quieter. The task of both regulation and administration would be far easier if there were more accurate information on noise damage. At present, the data offer speculative insights rather than firm totals. For example, the same source estimates that some 6 to 16 million workers may be exposed to unsafe noise conditions—a difference of 10 million.[19] The potential compensation for industrial hearing loss, for example, is estimated at $450 million, a figure which assumes that only 10 percent of workers eligible for such compensation will file claims and that the average award per claim is $1,000.[20]

If the further assumption is made that properly organized, ordinary citizens exposed to high levels of airport, traffic or home noises, file suits on a systematic basis against manufacturers and other targets, the bill for potential damages could be staggering. Certainly it might be large enough to stimulate large scale testing of materials, machinery and people. We also need intensive research and appropriate implementing action, particularly federal standards and federal subsidies to private industry, to lower the noise level.

(5) *Land Use* The mangled urbanization of our environment is partly associated with the expansion and distribution of the population. Enormous messes can develop, however, even where there are very few people. A number of industries are prime land polluters. Coal mining in West Virginia and Pennsylvania demonstrates one of the worst examples of industrial pollution in the nation, but there are also countless junkyards, chemical plants, fertilizer factories and pulp mills which blight the landscape—and often the air and water—for entire areas. The blight, moreover, seems to be creeping inexorably over the countryside. Even outlying resort areas have been marred by shacks and decaying mobile homes. The costs of providing public services for scattered housing is relatively high, the homeowner often finds himself stuck with a wasting capital investment and the upshot is expensive remedial action to clean up the growing slum problem in outlying areas.

The movement is not all downhill. Some tendency to efficient and attractive use of land is observable in a number of industrial parks and shopping centers as well as residential developments. One difficulty is that many of the mistakes of the past can only be rectified at enormous cost. The price tag on cleaning up slum housing alone is likely to exceed a trillion dollars, much of which may have to be provided by government agencies. Other depolluting efforts to remove and regroup inefficient and often dangerous commercial strip development, substandard resort housing, deteriorating waterfront areas and the blight which afflicts open as well as urban areas may run into hundreds of millions of dollars at the very least.

But there are compensations in the form of higher valuations and taxes, increased equity, more efficient provision of services (e.g., replacing fire-traps with fire resistant buildings) and more attractive surroundings.

A 1968 report of the Open Space Action Institute, *Challenge of the Land*, discusses at some length the economic advantages of a strong open space policy. Developers and home builders have learned that it pays to create or preserve a pleasant living environment. The National Association of Home Builders (NAHB) reported that:

> Today's [1968] home buyer is looking for features beyond the confines of the house and lot. Proximity to school, park and community recreation is high on his list of looked-for items. This statement may not impress the newcomer in the building and subdivision field who has not experienced the competition of a buyer's market. The experienced developer, however, knows that the presence of these features enhances desirability, which is translated directly into buyer demand and sales value. In the

vicinity of park and recreation areas, enhanced values of building sites up 15 to 20%, with a high level of sustained value over the years, are not uncommon experiences.[21]

Further evidence of this fact is provided by Carl Norcross in his study of open space:

if a developer "creates an outstanding environment, saves the trees, has a good street pattern, and then adds a pool and a modest recreation area, he might easily get $500 or $1,000 more per house than he would for the same house in an ordinary subdivision." This is, of course, a $500 or $1,000 that shows up on the tax roles, too.[22]

The major unsolved land use problem involves the poor, specifically slum areas. Despite occasional optimistic reports—some by respected scholars—decaying and abandoned slum areas seem to be growing like fungi in a number of large cities and spores appear to be emerging in some suburban communities. Housing in many areas of central cities is being overtaken by physical deterioration.

Over the years, research studies have repeatedly demonstrated that slums are deficit areas, absorbing more in taxes than they return in revenues. However, simplistic solutions aimed at eliminating blighted areas via construction of new or rehabilitated housing have yielded only limited results. It was learned the hard way that new surroundings are not necessarily ennobling, particularly if tenants and landlords are enmeshed in the same old problems and institutional constraints. One especially noteworthy example is the Pruitt-Igoe project in St. Louis. Once heralded as a remarkable advance in housing design, the project has become a jungle of crime and decay.

History suggests that motivation and life styles are as critical in cleaning up slums as changes in the physical setting. In effect, this poses two alternatives in dealing with decaying urban areas:

(a) The first is to adopt a suburban strategy, concentrating programmatic efforts in the areas where most of the new urban development is taking place. The effect of the move to the suburbs is the continual devouring of open space for housing, shopping centers, highways, airports and light industry, often sacrificing recreation and park needs. Such a policy would in effect write off the inner city slums as beyond redemption. The high cost of slum maintenance would be viewed as a given, an inescapable component of modern budgeting, and certainly much less costly than more expensive floundering around trying to reconstruct blighted low income areas. This line of reasoning sometimes calls for corollary efforts aimed at dispersion, a kind of quota system under which suburban communities would be required to set aside some land for construction of housing for low income families.

An important aspect of such a strategy is a new towns policy which will direct and control the development of new suburban communities. European experience in this area—much greater than our own—has several examples worth examining. The most notable is Finland's Tapiola.

(b) An alternative (or corollary) approach might be massive head-on intervention to rebuild the slums, quite possibly with a greater emphasis on home and apartment ownership. This would necessarily have to be accompanied by large scale supportive services to ensure that vandalism, neglect, litter and other human problems do not create instant slums out of new buildings.

Whatever alternative or combination of policies is adopted, it is clear that allocating large amounts of government funds to building housing and neighborhoods for low income families will represent a very large injection of money into the construction industry. In particular, reconstruction can offer substantial employment opportunities for unemployed and underemployed persons in slum areas. Since joblessness is always chronically high in the slums—depression rates of 10 percent or more are endemic—this kind of program could serve to sop up underutilized human resources rather than diverting labor from other pursuits. In addition, in this particular instance, significant second round benefits would be realized. It has been suggested that calculations alleging the creation of second round benefits are sheer fantasy under conditions of full employment: Investing in any particular project requires taking resources away and foregoing gains from other, alternative projects. If, however, many of the poor, jobless and underemployed, can be mobilized to remove the slums and improve the neighborhoods in which they live, the diversion argument does not apply. They are giving up nothing but their relief payments. Furthermore, as indicated earlier, money for low income groups has very high velocity since savings are minimal and purchases absorb virtually all the paycheck.

(6) *Solid Wastes* Rubbish disposal has been a municipal responsibility almost from the dawn of recorded history and solid waste disposal is traditionally an area in which the public has been prepared to pay necessary (even if minimal) costs. Although collection and disposal have been regarded as a problem from a cost-benefit standpoint, in earlier times the value of compost and fill more than outweighed the costs of assembling and eliminating solid waste products.

Modern society, on the other hand, remains relatively unaware of the potential benefits accruing from re-use of solid waste products.

There are some who fear that America will be suffocated in a rising ocean of solid wastes. This euphemism for refuse trash or rubbish covers a vast range of throwaway materials of which paper, metals, rubber and glass are the most prominent. At an estimated one ton annually per capita, the nation now generates about 200 million tons of solid wastes a year in urban areas which are disposed of at a cost of over $4 billion a year. This works out to $21.50 per capita per year for disposing of almost a ton of publicly collected solid waste per capita per year.[23] The various methods of disposal cost somewhat differently, as shown below:

> Landfill costs amount to only one to three dollars per ton, compared for example to incineration, where costs run from about three to ten dollars per ton, depending on the size of the installation and whether some use is made of the heat generated. Increasingly sophisticated stack gas cleaning equipment, dictated by stricter air pollution standards, can be expected to raise these costs still further. Large-scale composting, in the few places where it is done in the U.S., has a comparable price tag, about five to ten dollars per ton, minus whatever credit can be obtained from the sale of compost and other reclaimed materials.[24]

The daily confrontation with masses of material, much of it apparently re-usable, has led to many municipal efforts to develop ways of offsetting collection and disposal costs. The aim of current recycling programs is to return wastes to the economy in some form that will be useful. One of the most common is re-use of completed landfills as parks, playgrounds, parking areas or for residential, commercial or industrial development. Depending on local conditions, the reclaimed land can be a major asset in community development. Many areas, however, including the city of San Francisco, are running out of land suitable for traditional sanitary fill operations and forced to turn to other, more costly means of disposal.

The principal method of disposing of solid wastes is incineration. New central incinerators in the planning or construction stage can handle 1,000–3,000 tons of solid wastes a day. A major problem is the heavy capital cost—$12,000 per ton of installed capacity with operating costs of about $7 a ton.[25] The cost of four proposed mammoth incinerators for New York City was estimated at $1.3 billion. It is not surprising that the city's legislative officials tabled the recommendation in the hope that a less expensive alternative could be discovered. Nevertheless, incineration is an attractive method because it can reduce trash between 10 and 20 percent of the original volume.

The use of incinerators in residential units is being discouraged because of their contribution to pollution. The elaborate and expensive recovery and protective devices suitable for large central incinerators are totally unavailable for small units. Consequently, in New York City as elsewhere, the trend is toward regulations prohibiting indoor and outdoor burning of solid wastes.

At present, less than half a dozen municipal composting plants are in operation in the United States, most of them small, i.e., 50 tons a day. There are plants in Altoona, Pennsylvania; Gainesville, Florida; San Juan, Houston, and Mobile. Since farmers normally spend $20 to $25 a ton for a cover crop used as organic compost, in theory this could offer a considerable source of revenues for a municipality.

Moreover, the use of compost reduces the need for chemical fertilizers by as much as 40 percent and slows the leaching of the rest into streams where it may add to pollutants. Up until fairly recently proponents of organic farming who warned of the dangers of overuse of chemical fertilizers were widely viewed as eccentric screwballs, hopelessly out of touch with modern times. Within the past decade, however, evidence has been mounting concerning the hazards of soil depletion and losses in food values resulting from organic matter with chemical additives.

This review of costs and benefits suggests several conclusions. First, the trend toward production of commodities which are difficult and/or dangerous to dispose of should be halted and reversed. Action has been taken to deal with nerve gases, nuclear wastes, mercury and lead. It seems clear that synthetic materials and metal alloys, among other products, should be designed so as to be biodegradable or better, easily recoverable. The cost-benefit ratio would be far more favorable if preventive steps were taken at the production level. This should include the production of materials from virgin sources as well as from wastes.

> Thus we need, among other things, new attitudes about producing materials which will be reused, rather than discarded after a single pass through the economy. But we need just as badly some new technology for salvaging these materials from wastes. This will cost money, and it will take time. It is at this point that the need for federal government activity becomes visible.[26]

Second, strictures concerning the high cost of U.S. manpower which militate against intensive collection and separation of solid wastes do not apply if the unemployed and underemployed are taken into account. While few would desire a society in which the poor were converted into outcaste scavengers, there are less objectionable ways in which underutilized labor can be used for socially desirable functions.

Finally, the existence of an enormous outpouring of solid waste might well stimulate useful research. It is conceivable that the example of Chicago's Mount Trashmore might be replicated not only to provide flat areas with sorely missed hills for recreation but to affect changes in microclimatology. The United States has not been blessed with east-west mountain ranges like the Alps and Carpathians but instead has north-south ridges like the Rockies and Appalachians which do little to interfere with the icy northern winds. Some communities might consider the possibility of constructing sizable compressed trash windbreaks, Warhol walls, (which can also be used for recreation) to improve local climatological conditions. In any event, many years of carefully recorded experience have not eliminated the need for further innovative research to convert solid wastes from an almost unrelieved municipal headache into a significant opportunity.

(7) *Esthetics* No more than a generation ago there was a widespread feeling in the United States that esthetic appreciation was a feminine preoccupation, its occurrence in males raising serious questions concerning their masculinity. Part of this attitude reflected a holdover associated with both the frontier and the early industrial revolution, the linkage between much and money characteristic of the gloomy English midland cities. To a considerable extent ugliness was not permitted to diminish civic pride. In the author's personal experience in the mid-1950's, an outraged foreigner who described a declining New England textile city as a "rubbish heap" was soon thereafter invited to quit the city's employ. Moreover, some cities and neighborhoods apparently engendered a reverse sentimentality in which males gloried in the tough character building aspects of the stench and filth. Some were rhapsodic about New York's East Side, others praised Boston's West End or South Boston, Philadelphia's Kensington or Chicago's North Side as places which may have appeared brutally unattractive to outsiders but which throbbed with neighborliness and charm for the insider.[27]

Another reason for the lack of concern with a city's appearance was the attitude that smoke stacks belching great clouds of pollutants into the air were actually a sign of progress and economic prosperity. People were happy to have the pay checks which resulted from this prosperity. Only much later, when the standard of living had gone beyond the subsistence level, were people able to concern themselves with the esthetics of their communities as well as their economic condition.

It is particularly striking that this growing sensitivity to the environment is not confined solely to middle and upper income groups. The environment, conservation, parks and civic appearance were once thought of as primarily luxuries for the rich, since the poor were almost exclusively concerned with jobs and other issues relating to sheer survival. But times apparently have changed. The poor are increasingly aware that they live in old, gray, dark shabby neighborhoods which contrast with newness, cleanliness and greenery in the areas inhabited by upper income groups. While they do not feel strongly about the need to combat water pollution or to develop metropolitan green belts ringing the city, low income families seem to be sensitive to the exterior as well as the interiors of their neighborhood. Their focus appears limited to a narrow environmental envelope; they are conscious of being second class citizens living amid uncollected dirt and trash, inadequate street lighting, crumbling siding, and, in general, to the smells and appearance of untended age. Much of this alarm is focused on social indices which tend to get lumped together with the physical decline of the neighborhoods: crime, Negroes, gangs, pornography, hippies, disrespectful children. This may be a special kind of environmental interest, a seething frustration at neighborhood squalor and city hall neglect, but it is nonetheless real.

Given this growing interest in environmental esthetics, what is being done about it? An objective observer would have to concede, not very much. The quality of some institutional architecture seems to be improving: office buildings, churches, city halls, airport terminals, even some residential structures have undoubtedly been upgraded in the past two decades. The least progress seems to be evident in low and middle income housing. All too often housing seems to be constructed without an architect or at best with a low priced hack who enlarges his net profit by using time worn drawings from the files. First rate architects are fully aware that every substantial building is a public monument, good for a century or more in which it either blights or enhances its environment. Amortized over 50 to 100 years, even a sizable architect's fee and an additional 10 percent added to construction costs seems rather modest.

There are various sources of pressure militating in favor of improved design. The urban renewal program is operated in part by frustrated architects who actively harass developers to secure higher esthetic standards. HUD and its annual good design awards and the American Institute of Architects (AIA) annual prizes have been influential. Urban renewal in such cities as Boston and Hartford has had a higher proportion of hits than misses. Probably even more important is corporate rivalry. Banks and insurance companies have clobbered each other with big name architects as well as height and general sumptuousness. Certain fields like the airlines and the churches and a number of shopping center and industrial park developers seem to have developed a tradition of good architecture. Universities, on the other hand, seem to be a mixed bag, high quality in some contrasting with structures resembling gloomy warehouses or Chicago Gothic in others.

One of the chief difficulties in turning the country around on this issue is that there is no easy way to put environmental beauty in the cash register. It is often less expensive to avert one's eyes and reserve environmental appreciation for trips to the country or European junkets, than to spend the money to ensure a good urban environment. Only slowly have the political decision-makers and the businessmen become dimly aware that a high quality environment offers a priceless competitive advantage. In an earlier era this was perhaps less important. The jobs were in Scranton, Duluth, Pittsburgh, Gary, Cleveland and Buffalo because that was where resources were processed. In an age of footloose industry and mobile executives, the urban area which offers attractive living conditions for the sophisticated has a distinct advantage. Advertising in business magazines place heavy stress on environmental amenities. Firms located in San Francisco, Boston, Atlanta, Denver, Madison or Ann Arbor find it easier to attract first rate professional, scientific and academic talent and these areas find it easier to attract technologically advanced industries because of that fact. It is known, for example, that there is keen competition for openings in favored areas while the worst of the grimy urban Siberias often find it troublesome to persuade established talent that their city possesses significant cultural attractions and enticing physical amenities and is unjustly suffering from an undeserved reputation.

In short, relative livability is a powerful weapon in economic development. Surely, some of New York's current difficulties are directly related to the fact that the city is widely believed to offer an unwholesome, even dangerous environment. Thus on a large canvas, economic development is following the precedent of the shrewd real estate salesmen who have been marketing neighborhood amenities (near good schools, churches and parks) to selective buyers for many years. Real estate agents are fully capable of placing a price tag on environmental amenities. Apartments enjoying a good view, located far above the noise and odors of the street may rent for 20 percent or more above flats with identical layouts close to street levels. Similarly, houses located on dead end streets, adjacent to lakes, parks or golf courses, may command substantial premiums.

The national investment in amenities could make a modest contribution to the national balance of payments problem by encouraging more Americans to stay in their own country and more foreigners to visit America. This objective might be particularly attainable if some attractive technological innovations could be developed (climate control? domed cities? underground Bohemias?) representing a breakthrough for the urban environment. But the difficulty remains: translating amenity into dollars is not a simple process. The temptation to sell off the parks for new tax base, to skimp on architects and materials and to continue to give carte blanche to the outdoor advertisers are all hard to resist. But the comparative economic development approach may be helpful in persuading communities that civic ugliness and a flourishing urban economy may be increasingly incompatible as we move toward the end of the century. Certainly rising levels of affluence and education may provide a more receptive audience for both economic and non-economic arguments in favor of urban amenity with pragmatic quantification perhaps used to validate and protect the sense of outrage, frustration, pride and envy which provide the real foundation for action.

SOME CONCLUDING OBSERVATIONS

Technological Breakthroughs: Waiting for Godot?

Prominent among the devices employed to delay action toward radical environmental improvement is the allegation that we are on the verge of major technological advances which will render the heavy investment in current technology obsolete in short order. A forward looking variation on this theme is a call for new research to develop such innovative technology, particularly in such fields as waste disposal.

While one should not always be wary of the assertion that a much better way lies just around the corner, there is ample room for suspicion that the search for perfection may delay the feasible. The national economy is rich enough to afford a considerable amount of slippage, duplication and obsolescence. If we fall into the habit of continually postponing action, launching conferences and pipsqueak programs while waiting for technology to come up with painless, cheaper solutions, the odds are that the nation will fall into the slough described by Robert Wood as it chases after one new priority after another and fails to act on any of them.[28] In fact, waiting for major breakthroughs may be particularly self defeating if the job can be done with current technology.

Need for Federal Leadership

Regardless of revenue sharing arrangements and antipollution spending by private industry, there is no doubt that the primary source of funds in implementing most environmental programs is the Federal Government. Moreover, federal standards as well as funds are needed because of the facts of competitive life. Stringent state or municipal action can usually be aborted by corporations who claim that imposition of added costs will place them at a disadvantage and, hence, they will be forced to close down because of a loss of business or else will relocate their payrolls and tax revenues to a more accommodating jurisdiction.

A few major industries account for most industrial water use and most industrial water pollution. They will bear a much bigger share of the total burden, in most cases their water pollution control costs will probably fall substantially below one percent of the value of their products shipped.[29]

Pollution control requirements will hasten the closing of some older, inefficient plants which have continued to operate because of capital expenditures already invested, tradition, and community ties—especially where the plant provides the principal payroll on which the area is dependent. Eventually nearly all will be closed for a combination of reasons. Companies often will close one or several marginal plants, making up production losses by building a larger, new plant. Some companies, indeed, can use pollution control as an excuse to shut down a plant they have long wanted to close.[30]

The costs of pollution control will be high overall but not great when compared with the gross national product, value of shipments by industry, or even total investment in capital facilities by industry. In general, U.S. business and industry will adjust to these costs just as they have adjusted to other changes in the cost of doing business. The most difficult adjustments will be to solve the temporary dislocation of workers made jobless by plant closings.[31]

There is only one escape from the legal jungle—uniform federal standards to avoid the argument that antipollution measures place a community at a competitive disadvantage. The plain fact is that the goal, or indeed the necessity, of achieving substantial improvement in industrial pollution may create a direct confrontation between health and payrolls. Attempts to arrive at a fair sharing of costs are usually unwelcome because so many interests are convinced that it would be financially harmful. This would be amusing if it were not such an obstacle to action.

Need for Quick, Visible Results: Pointing With Pride

By their very nature many environmental programs resemble an endless guerilla war requiring continual monitoring, policing, regulating and maintenance. Moreover, some improvements tend to be either invisible (e.g., preventing further mercury contamination in water bodies) or long range (e.g., depolluting Lake Erie). Under the circumstances, it is easy for the citizen to be vulnerable to discouragement and for the politician to conclude that, while there may be votes in talking up the quality of life in bold, ringing speeches, there is little benefit in passing and enforcing costly, abrasive legislation.

These facts of life pose special problems in political costs and benefits. It may be concluded that costly environmental programs should always include short term visible gains, tangible measurable benefits which legislators serving two year terms can point to with pride. This can include new jobs in construction or in plants producing environmental equipment, removal of offensive billboards and utility lines, cleaning up smaller bodies of water, suppression of noise pollution and the reduction of air pollution on the part of conspicuous offenders, etc. The hidden dimension in cost-benefit calculations is the personal advantages accruing to the political decisionmaker and his constituencies. Benefits must be tangible and susceptible to conversion into currency for forthcoming campaigns if the environment is to be more than a subject for pious exhortation.

Need for a Timetable

The use of target dates to inspire quick action have long been known. Real or fictitious deadlines have been effective in galvanizing military, civilian and even academic organizations since time immemorial on the principle that time usually slips away without much being accomplished unless there is a firm cutoff date. There may be room for argument over whether 1975 or 1980 is a more realistic date for major reductions in automobile exhausts but there is absolutely no room for dispute concerning the need for setting goals for a target year and sticking to it as closely as possible. A careful line must be drawn between setting standards high primarily as goals to be met at some distant date and setting them low so as to make them achievable in the near future. But this is a matter of selecting the best tactical road to early, substantive progress. The alternative is endless delay, more worrying over intricate technicalities and a tender concern for existing institutional and property relationships which slows reform to a walk.

The Environmental Christmas Tree

There is considerable reason to believe that environmental programs can be made as popular with most of the business community as they are with student and suburban activists. The secret, of course, lies in rewards and incentives. Building profits into recycling, reclamation and the environmental cleanup, meanwhile providing adequate if not lavish salve in the form of compensation for business injured by new standards will remove most of the barriers to rapid progress. Needless to say, more than passing attention should be given to the job creating and real estate enhancing aspects of environmental programs—over and above civic beautification. This process of co-option will guarantee in effect that last ditch holdouts against reform will be a small minority of soreheads.

Given the basic receptivity of the newer breed of businessmen, particularly their growing sensitivity to charges of social and environmental callousness and neglect, an approach which combines profit with reform should meet with an excellent response. Moreover, the stubbornness of business in resisting reform has certainly been real but it should not be overstated. Business can and does adjust rapidly to changing circumstances, particularly when it has to. Furthermore, the prospect for management to simultaneously please stockholders and the public and private consciences should be extremely attractive.

Cross-hairs on a Few Targets

It has become fashionable to suggest that the environment is not only everyone's responsibility but everyone's culpability. In a sense, the situation is analogous to the defeated military who deflect the blame to the politicians, to the public, to their allies—to everyone but themselves. The fact is that there are a limited number of pressure points —three automobile manufacturers, and perhaps another dozen or so industries—which create the most serious pollutants. Furthermore, pollution has far out-stripped population growth, suggesting that in the United States, at least, uncontrolled technology rather than fertility is the chief menace.

The point of this discussion is that a limited number of targets, be they ever so powerful, makes the task of remedial action manageable. We stand a good chance of controlling a baker's dozen industries, but virtually no chance at all of reaching every one of 205 million individual potential polluters.[32]

The Environment as Employer of Last Resort

From time to time, but especially during recessions, there is open wonder at the waste of manpower we permit in unemployment and the various forms of subemployment. We owe much to an earlier generation which put idle men and boys to work on conservation and public works projects. While the Civilian Conservation Corps and the Works Progress Administration had their faults, many of their problems related to the improvised manner in which they were designed and operated on the theory that in Harry Hopkins' phrase "people eat every day," speed was more important than perfect long range solutions.

A substantial amount of unemployment, especially among teenagers, seems to be a permanent part of the economic landscape. The total number of persons out-of-work averaged between three and five million in the late 1960's and early 1970's with perhaps an equal number of subemployed potentially available for adequate employment. There would appear to be every reason why a large proportion of this enormous total—a minimum ten to twenty percent—could profitably be employed on projects of environmental interest. These could range from reforestation to construction, from simple urban and rural clean up campaigns to more complex operations in land, water and air pollution programs.

Some highly necessary action would require virtually no occupational training while varying amounts of classroom and practical training would be required for more advanced tasks. The National Guard model could be followed: There could well be part time, year 'round training and activity to provide both supplementary income and training in a second occupation. For younger people an environmental Vista program could prove an attractive proposition. Mature members of the labor force could find the environmental field attractive from a more practical standpoint. It could offer many a modest increment to wages when they are fully employed and a viable, immediate alternative when they lost their regular job.

From an economic point of view it is clear that the use of some of the unemployed and underemployed to perform tasks useful to society represents an impressive net gain. The alternatives—welfare, unemployment compensation and greater vulnerability to various forms of social pathology—may be far more costly than paying wages for work on the environment. A number of public services including the health, education, and welfare complex, the postal system, parks and recreation and the police could profitably absorb large numbers of aides, paraprofessionals and other auxiliary personnel. There is no earthly reason why anyone in need of a part-time or full-time job should not be placed within a matter of weeks, enrolling if necessary in a combined work-training program. Second, with proper planning and cadres of special supervisors, it should be quite feasible to secure modest output standards from casual labor. The military, construction and automobile industries can teach valuable lessons on the rapid conversion of unskilled recruits into productive personnel. Useful work is possible even for the near-retarded. Naturally, this approach assumes the presence of the requisite motivation and work discipline.

Restructuring the System

Radical critics of the capitalist system have long charged that destruction of the landscape and other environmental problems are the outgrowth of a profit-oriented economy in which human and environmental values have only tertiary priority. Recent experience suggests that the correlation is not quite that simple; even in the absence of large numbers of automobiles and consumer geared economy, Soviet Russia and East Germany are experiencing serious problems in air and water pollution. Apparently communist societies are as prone as capitalist economies to concentrate on narrow production goals to the exclusion of environmental considerations. Some of the most impressive examples of environmental protection are apparent in mixed economies like Scandinavia. In fact, the treatment of the environmental issue in modern nations seems to turn on national sentiments, life styles and priorities rather than resting on the question of public or private ownership of the means of production.

Looking ahead to a future which excludes the kind of conflagration which may consume much of the nation's human and physical resources, questions arise concerning the capability of the existing system to protect and enhance the quality of life. Certainly, most of the approaches discussed in this paper call for only incremental changes in structures and institutions. Their thrust, in fact, is toward redirecting the existing system to achieve new goals and objectives. It is assumed that irreparable disaster is not yet inescapable, that the present system can be made responsive to meeting environmental needs and that a combination of pressures, regulations and incentives will result in substantial, perceptible progress. Hopefully, through a restructuring of the current system of psychic and monetary rewards, we can leave behind the wasteful, destructive throwaway society in favor of an environmental society. Recycling, reclamation, salvage, tidiness and durability become highly rewarded and highly regarded virtues. Waste and environmental degradation become loathsome acts subject to public censure and heavy legal penalties. What this implies is a series of changes in public education and in public policies.

Does all this necessarily mean that everything will become more expensive and inconvenient, e.g., higher priced non-polluting automobiles, no more non-returnable bottles? The answer to this question must be qualified. Certainly control of various forms of pollution will result in impressive savings from reduction of illness, reduction of stress and less erosion of machinery and clothing among other benefits. But obviously, gains and losses will not be evenly distributed. New York may be made more livable but the little town in Maine which depends on a pulp mill for its economic sustenance may be hard hit unless care is taken to set aside sufficient funds to compensate or subsidize the unfortunates who lean on polluters for a living. But on the whole, even in strict profit and loss bookkeeping terms, winners will outnumber and outgain the losers by a very large plurality.

To a degree this conclusion represents an *ex cathedra* observation since we simply do not have the cost-benefit data to develop a definitive balance sheet. Nevertheless, precise figures are probably irrelevant to the main issue. At this point in time it suffices that spending to improve the environment is not purely a desperate and unavoidable deployment of funds in the manner of a military campaign where specialized equipment is left to rot in the jungle. Instead it offers a wide range of highly tangible as well as intangible financial rewards to most of the society while creating losses for a minority small enough to make compensation a feasible proposition.

In Hans Landsberg's words:

When we can compare meaningfully the costs to society—which are, as we have tried to show, the producer's private costs plus costs to others that are not part of his calculus—with the many-sided benefits that are the counterpart of those costs, we shall have taken a long stride toward evolving a workable policy of preserving the quality of the environment without sacrificing the beneficial effects of advancing technology. Only then will we be able to appraise the present and future adequacy of quality of the resources as we have appraised that of quantity. If this means having the best of two worlds, then the time may be at hand to cease calling economics the dismal science. Until then, the economist will have to insist that the frontiers of cost and benefit measurement be vigorously extended—not necessarily to dictate action but to allow it to be shaped in the presence of the newly gained knowledge.[33]

NOTES

[1] U.S., Council on Environmental Quality, *Environmental Quality*, The Second Annual Report (Washington, D.C.: Government Printing Office, 1971), p. 102.

[2] Edmund K. Faltermayer, "We Can Afford A Better America," *Fortune* (March, 1969), pp. 90—91. For additional estimates, see Nelson A. Rockefeller, *Our Environment Can Be Saved* (New York: Doubleday, 1970), p. 151; and U.S., Department of the Interior, Federal Water Pollution Control Administration, *The Cost of Clean Water: Economic Impact on Affected Units of Government* (Washington, D.C.: Government Printing Office, 1967), p. 20.

[3] See "Underground Costs and Charges at Salem Electric," Jere Overs, Assistant Manager, Salem Electric Company, Salem, Oregon, Interdepartmental Report, November 10, 1966.

[4] Faltermayer estimates the amount needed through the year 2000 to accommodate population growth and to replace worn out urban facilities at $2 to $3 trillion. See *Redoing America* (New York: Harper and Row, 1968), pp. 206—7.

[5] See Edward J. Cleary, "Economic Implications of Waste Control," *Public Works*, Vol. 94, No. 2 (February, 1963). Cleary quotes a transcript of hearings on pollution in the Delaware River contrasting experience with tube corrosion failure of heat exchange condensers under stream conditions of 100 ppm of salt vs. 1,000 ppm.

[6] U.S., Council on Environmental Quality, *First Annual Report* (Washington, D.C.: Government Printing Office, 1970), p. 14.

[7] This projection assumes that the rate of increase in the U. S. population will continue to decrease as it has since World War II. If the rate of growth continues at present levels, however, America's total population will reach the 300 million mark by the year 2000, an increase of nearly 100 million.

[8] Such projections are made by Paul R. and Anne H. Ehrlich, *Population, Resources, Environment, Issues in Human Ecology* (San Francisco: W. H. Freeman and Company, 1970), pp. 41—49. Also, Gladwin Hill, "A Hidden Cost of Hard-Won Progress is Pollution," *The New York Times*, April 20, 1970, p. 33.

[9] See Jane E. Brody, "Poor Said to Lack Family Planning," *The New York Times*, May 9, 1971, p. 25.

[10] Stephen Enke, "Fewer Births—More Welfare," in Anthony H. Pascal (ed.), *Contributions to the Analysis of Urban Problems*, A Selection of

Papers from the RAND Workshop on Urban Programs, December 18, 1967–
January 12, 1968 (Rand Corporation, August, 1968), p. 115.

[11] Orris C. Herfindahl and Allen V. Kneese, *Quality of Environment: An
Economic Approach to Some Problems in Using Land, Water, and Air*
(Washington, D.C.: Resources for the Future, 1965), p. 24.

[12] *Environmental Quality, op. cit.,* p. 102.

[13] *Quality of the Environment: An Economic Approach to Some Problems
in Using Land, Water, and Air, op. cit.,* p. 24.

[14] *Ibid.,* p. 72.

[15] "Is There an Economic Solution to the Air Pollution Problem?" News-
letter published by the Bureau of Community Planning, University of Illinois, Vol. 9.

[16] "Issue of the Year: The Environment," *Time,* Vol. 97, No. 1, January 4,
1961, p. 21.

[17] It is assumed that prompt remedial action will continue to be taken as a
matter of course when an obvious water-related health problem emerges as
in the case of typhoid or cholera. Such action may be indicated to deal with
infectious hepatitis. See Paul R. and Ann H. Ehrlich, *op. cit.,* pp. 126–217.

[18] *Environmental Quality, op. cit.,* pp. 42–32.

[19] U.S., Council for Science and Technology, Committee on Environmental
Quality, *Noise—Sound Without Value* (Washington, D.C.: Government
Printing Office, 1968), p. 32.

[20] *Ibid.,* p. 34.

[21] Charles E. Little, *Challenge of the Land,* An Open Space Action Institute
Report for municipal officials and civic leaders. (New York: Open Space
Institute, 1968), p. 85.

[22] *Ibid.,* pp. 84–85.

[23] American Public Works Association, *Municipal Refuse Disposal* (Dan-
ville, Illinois: Interstate Publishers, 1970), p. 10. The APWA estimates that
the actual per capita figure is 10 pounds a day but only about half is collected by public agencies. (See also p. 25.)

[24] Robert R. Grinstead, "The New Resource," *Environment,* Vol. 12, No.
10 (December, 1970), p. 4.

[25] *Municipal Refuse Disposal, op. cit.,* pp. 153–154.

[26] Robert R. Grinstead, *op. cit.,* p. 15.

[27] For an eloquent exposition of this view, see Jane Jacobs, *The Death and
Life of Great American Cities* (New York: Random House, 1961).

[28] Robert Wood, "Housing and Environmental Escapism," *Journal of the
American Institute of Planners,* Vol. XXXVI, No. 6 (November, 1960), pp.
423–425.

[29] For a discussion of the impact of pollution control on industries both
for waste water treatment costs and air pollution control costs see *Environmental Quality, op. cit.,* pp. 123–126. The report states that, in the case of
water pollution, control costs would probably fall considerably below one
percent of the value of the industries' products shipped.

[30] *Ibid.,* p. 128.

[31] *Ibid.*, p. 144.

[32] See Barry Commoner, Michael Corrand, and Paul Stamler, "The Causes of Pollution," *Environment*, Vol. 12, No. 3, April, 1972.

[33] Hans S. Landsberg, "The U.S. Resource Outlook: Quantity and Quality," *Daedalus*, Vol. 96, No. 4 (Fall, 1967), p. 1056.

States Need More Federal Funds to Combat Pollution

The states raced to make up for lost time in the antipollution campaign of 1970, but blamed the Federal Government for not giving them enough money to do the job.

Maryland Gov. Marvin Mandel (D) warned Congress that the states were becoming "fed up with billion-dollar talk and million-dollar action" from the Federal Government.

Other politically attuned state and local government leaders have vied for center-stage to show their concern.

Pollution problems exist in different forms in their cities and states and often are difficult to confine within geographical boundaries. Polluted rivers pass through a number of states and air pollution drifts from one city into another.

But localities and legislatures are enacting laws to halt pollution practices over which they have some control. Progress is slow, however, and enforcement still is sketchy.

Local governments charged that the Federal Government is pushing them to move faster but not giving them the flexibility and funds they need through Federal programs.

Crisis Stage Reached

State officials admitted that pollution problems have reached the crisis stage because of lack of public and official concern in the past.

But as states try to make up for past indifference, they need more help from the Federal Government. States which adopted antipollution measures earl while other states were doing little o nothing are bitter about what they clain are unkept Federal promises to pay then back for their efforts.

New York Gov. Nelson A. Rockefelle (R) said the Federal Government owe the state about $400 million for construc tion of waste treatment plants under th Clean Waters Restoration Act of 196￼ Maryland's Gov. Mandel threatened a one point to go to court to compel th Federal Government to pay the stat about $92 million for new water pollu tion control facilities.

Under the 1966 legislation, the Federa Government was to contribute up to 5 percent of the cost of a treatment plan but the Federal share generally ha amounted to less. On the basis of a 55 percent share, the Federal Governmen owes 19 states a total of about $800 mil lion.

For fiscal 1968 and 1969, Congres authorized a total of $1.15 billion t build sewage treatment plants, but ap propriated only $417 million for actua spending.

The fight between the Federal Goverr ment and the states over money for wast treatment plants intensified in 1969 afte the Nixon Administration requested onl $214 million in appropriations for th fiscal 1970 program. Under the Clea Waters Restoration Act, $1 billion wa authorized for the program, but the Ac

tates Need More Federal Funds to Combat Pollution (continued)

inistration said the cut should be made s part of the battle against inflation.

The $214 million was less than one-nth of the amount they needed, the :ates and cities claimed. Under pressure 'om local governments which had geared 1eir plans to the $1-billion level, Con-ress appropriated $800 million.

The fiscal 1971 authorization is $1.25 illion. On June 24 the House passed a ublic works appropriation bill which icluded $1 billion for waste treatment lants.

rogress Is Slow

tates have to adopt water quality stan-ards under the terms of the Federal law. hey are responsible for seeing to it that ate and local governmental agencies 1d private operators meet those stan-ards within prescribed time limits.

The states complained that their prog-ss is slowed by lack of money. Bonded debtedness is as high as it can go, mu-icipal officers insisted. States and cities e aware of the squeeze on the national udget, Mandel told a Senate committee 1969. But state budgets are under simi-r pressures, he added.

It is unwise to defer construction of ater pollution control facilities, Mandel id, "unless we can defer pollution, too."

An affiliate of the Council on State overnments is the Interstate Conference 1 Water Problems. Made up of water source officials in the states, the Con-rence provides for an exchange of in-rmation among the states on their mu-al water problems.

According to Dean Conrad, staff assis-

tant to the Council of State Govern-ments, the Conference gathered a com-pendium of information on the water pol-lution needs of the states to counter the Administration claim that an $800-mil-lion appropriation was not needed for the water pollution control program. The Conference did not "lobby," Conrad said. "It was simply a question of pro-viding factual data."

"Federal programs that are unreliable are a disaster," said Conrad. Such is the nature of capital investment, he added, that state and local governments have to have a predictable source of funds.

At the current rate of Federal funding for water pollution control, few persons expect the states to be able to meet the deadlines for water quality standards. A November 1969 Government Account-ing Office report said that at the present rate of Federal support, the number of cities awaiting funds was increasing con-stantly.

Don Alexander of the National League of Cities said cities are spending $1.2 bil-lion to $1.5 billion each year in construc-tion costs for treatment plants. As far as municipalities are concerned, Alexander said, the level of funding proposed by the President is "totally inadequate."

The National League has proposed that the water pollution program be op-erated on contract authority as is the mass transit program. When Congress authorizes a Federal agency to enter into contracts up to a certain ceiling, it is obli-gated to provide the money for those contracts when payments become due. When Congress merely authorizes funds,

States Need More Federal Funds to Combat Pollution (continued)

it need not appropriate as much money as was authorized.

Cities also want a change in the matching formula, Alexander said, so that the Federal and local shares each are 50 percent. Many cities are cut out of the water pollution control program, Alexander said, because they do not have sufficient matching funds and because of the tight credit market.

The cities strongly support national regulations on pollution control, Alexander said, to avoid economic competition. If one city passes strict antipollution ordinances and enforces them, it wants some assurance it will not los economically as a result.

Cities agree with the states, Alexande added, that national standards should in clude a "nonpre-emption clause" leavin local governments free to adopt stronge statutes than the Federal Governmen The water pollution control program nov has this kind of provision, Alexande said, but there are still problems.

He said a Federal agency can establis a facility in a state, say the facility ha met certain Federal standards for contr of a pollutant and insist that those star dards should prevail over state standard

25. Pollution Control: Perspectives on the Government Role

TAX FOUNDATION, INC.

GOVERNMENT ROLE IN AIDING POLLUTION CONTROL

Government activity in connection with pollution control involves several major dimensions. Government units have acted as regulators, establishing law, setting standards, monitoring and supervising compliance. Government also has offered a helping hand by providing special tax assistance and subsidies, and by underwriting or directly engaging in appropriate research. In addition, certain operations require government to turn attention to ways of coping with its own harmful byproducts.

Federal Legislation

Federal action dates back as far as the turn of the century, when the Refuse Act of 1899 prohibited the discharge of waste material into navigable waters. A 1912 act assigned responsibility for pollution, previously under the Secretary of the Army, to the Public Health Service. The Oil Pollution Act of 1924 forbade discharge of oil into coastal waters.

In 1948 Senators Barkley and Taft sponsored the Water Pollution Control Act of 1948. Asserting that pollution problems are better handled at the local level, the act nonetheless authorized the Public Health Service to coordinate research, provide technical information, and, on request from the states involved, provide limited enforcement over interstate waterways. Congress's failure to make suitable appropriations rendered largely ineffective a provision for individual project loans (up to $250,000 at 2 percent interest). The appropriations reached a high of $3 million in 1950 and declined to less than $1 million by 1955.

The Water Pollution Control Act of 1956, along with amendments in 1961, 1965, 1966 and 1970, considerably extended Federal involvement, both regulatory and financial, in water pollution control. The Water Quality Act of 1965 created the Water Pollution Control Administration. Almost as soon as this body was set up, it was transferred to the Department of the Interior. Responsibility for air pollution, however, remained with the Department of Health, Education, and Welfare.

Federal laws concerned with air pollution were instituted in 1955, when Congress authorized technical assistance to states and localities, as well as a research program. In 1963, the Clean Air Act established direct grants to states and localities for the purpose of developing, establishing, or improving control programs, as well as Federal enforcement action in interstate pollution cases. The 1963 act also provided for expanded Federal research, particularly in connection with pollution from motor vehicles and from the burning of coal and fuel oil, called for development of data on the effects of air pollution on both health and property, and emphasized the need for controlling pollution from facilities operated by the Federal government. A 1965 amendment authorized Federal regulation of motor vehicles, through standards to become effective in the 1968 model year. In 1966, another amendment expanded the Federal aid program, making grants available for maintenance of state and local control programs.

The Air Quality Act of 1967 directed HEW to delineate broad atmospheric areas for the entire country, as well as air quality control regions.[1] The 1967 act continued and strengthened most of the provisions of the earlier legislation, and provided for special studies of jet aircraft emissions, the need for national emission standards, and manpower and training problems. The 1967 law also established the Presidential Air Quality Advisory Board.

The Clean Air Act of 1970 requires that by 1975 new cars be virtually pollution-free, specifying that emissions of hydrocarbons and carbon monoxide gases must be 90 percent less than levels permissible in 1970. The Act requires manufacturers to provide a 50,000-mile warranty on auto emission control devices. It also establishes strict standards for fuel additives and permits a ban on the sale or manufacture of fuels containing additives deemed dangerous to health.

The 1970 act also provides for national standards for air pollution, with the states required to establish and enforce programs which meet national standards within the next four to six years. Wilful polluters will be subject to fines of up to $50,000 a day and jail sentences of up to two years. The Act gives all citizens and groups the right to sue in Federal court to force polluters, the U.S. government included, to cease and desist. The act also authorizes $1.1 billion for state agencies to use over the next three years for air pollution research, establishes a one-year study of noise pollution, and sets up a Federal Office of Noise Abatement and Control.

The National Environmental Policy Act of 1970 created a permanent Council on Environmental Quality, consisting of three members and a small professional staff, whose functions are to advise and assist the President in environmental matters. The act also requires all Federal agencies to consider the environmental effect of all contemplated actions.

Legislators introduced more than 600 proposals related to pollution problems during the 91st Congress, and of these a dozen or so, mostly concerned with relatively limited matters (such as the extension of particular research programs, effluents from navigable vessels, etc.), have been passed.

State Legislation

States have enacted air and water pollution control regulations at an accelerated pace in recent years. Virtually all states now have enacted legislation which establishes a legal basis for control of sources of pollution. Much of this legislation, particularly in the case of air pollution, has appeared very recently. For instance, 23 states enacted their initial law concerned with air pollution during 1967–1968, and by 1968 only 30 states had adopted air pollution regulations.

Many states now offer financial assistance in the construction and operation of local waste treatment plants; 21 of the 31 states which have authorized assistance programs have funded their programs. A few states (for instance, Nebraska, New Hampshire, and New York) underwrite local bond issues for local treatment plants. Ohio has authorized the Ohio Water Development Authority, with power to construct, operate, and assess charges for treatment plants within the state. Maryland has established a Waste Acceptance Service with similar functions.

States also have improved supervision of local waste disposal operations by expanding monitoring and inspection of plants, and upgrading operators' qualifications and skills through mandatory certifications requirements and training programs. At present, some 46 states require permits for industrial and municipal discharges; in six states plants are inspected monthly, in five quarterly, and in 13 annually. Certification of waste plant operators is mandatory in 16 states, and monthly operating reports must be submitted in 43 states. Unfortunately, it is reported that in many states these regulations do not work as well as they might.

Control of Pollution from Federal Facilities

As a consequence of the provisions in the Air Quality Act and the Clean Air Act, considerable action has taken place to abate pollution from Federal facilities. During fiscal 1968, remedial steps were taken at 387 installations located throughout the nation. In 126 cases, open burning or poor incineration was discontinued, and in 140 cases the Federal facility switched to fuel oil or coal with a lower sulfur content or converted to gas. Chemical or vapor emissions were reduced at 31 installations. Other action included installation of new or upgraded incinerators, replacement or improvement of heating plants, installation of improved particulate collectors, and introduction of monitor systems.

In 90 cases, however, "action" consisted merely of studies, project cost estimates, and the like. Moreover, a number of important exemptions were granted, primarily on grounds that the large capital expenditures required would make it impossible to meet Federal regulations established for its own facilities. Exceptions included installations of the Department of Defense in New York City and Philadelphia, Atomic Energy Commission in New York and Chicago, Department of Transportation in New York, and Department of Agriculture in New York.[2]

Tax Devices

Increasingly in recent years, Federal and state governments have turned to the use of tax and fiscal devices to encourage the introduction of pollution control facilities. These have taken the form of subsidies under the Federal grant-in-aid program and a variety of tax credits and exemptions in 31 states.

The Federal government offers some inducement to investment in pollution control equipment by allowing accelerated depreciation of such equipment. A profitable company thus gets whatever advantage

Table I / Special Tax Provisions for Installation of Pollution Control
Facilities, by State, June 1970

State	Property tax exemption	Sales and use tax exemption	Income tax credit	Rapid amortization
Alabama	x			
Arizona				x
Arkansas		x		
California				x
Connecticut	x	x	x	
Florida [a]	x			
Georgia	x	x		
Hawaii	x			x
Idaho	x			
Illinois	x	x		
Indiana	x			
Maine		x		
Massachusetts	x			
Michigan	x	x		
Minnesota	x		x	
Missouri		x		
Montana	x			
New Hampshire	x			
New Jersey	x			
New York	x		x	
North Carolina	x			x
Ohio [b]	x	x		
Oklahoma			x	
Oregon	x		x	
Pennsylvania		x		
Rhode Island	x	x		x
South Carolina	x			
Tennessee	x			
Vermont	x			
Virginia				x
Washington		x		
West Virginia		x	x	
Wisconsin	x			x
Wyoming	x			

[a] Sales tax exemption repealed at time property tax exemption introduced, in July 1969.

[b] Also provides pollution facilities not to be considered assets in determining value of stock on which Ohio's franchise tax is levied.

Source: Based on data from Commerce Clearing House and state pollution control laws.

there is from early as against later deduction in computing taxable income.[3] Seven states also provide for rapid amortization—in all cases, over a 60-month period—of new pollution control facilities (Table 1) on page 485.

At the state level, however, the most favored tax approach appears to be an exemption of pollution control facilities from the property tax, with 24 states specifying such exemption in 1970. In many states, the exemption is carefully restricted to that portion of a facility which can be demonstrated to be utilized in pollution control, with any portion producing a marketable byproduct subject to tax.

Twelve states specifically exempt pollution control equipment from sales and use taxes. Six states provide income tax credits. Connecticut, Minnesota, and Oregon allow a credit amounting to 5 percent of outlay for qualified equipment (restricted in Minnesota to $50,000 annually with provisions for carryback and carryover); Oklahoma permits a 20 percent credit. In New York, the taxpayer has the option of taking either the usual 1 percent tax credit allowed for new equipment of any kind, or deducting the entire cost of the pollution control equipment from taxable income.

In Louisiana, plants which utilize principally waste materials in their production processes are valued for property tax purposes at only 25 percent. The law mentions specifically such waste materials as water hyacinths, rice hulls and straws, sugar cane stalks, bagasse, waste rags and clippings, waste paper, oyster shells, and other items, but does not appear to confine the exemption to the materials listed.

Subsidies and Other Direct Expenditures

Federal expenditures for air pollution control began in 1956, when less than $1 million was spent on a research program in the Public Health Service and technical assistance to state and local agencies. Expenditures have risen steadily since that time, totaling more than $4 million in 1959 and more than $67 million in 1969 (Table 2). Federal expenditures have been divided among a number of functions. Direct operations include such activities as abatement and control, manpower training, various management services, research, development, and demonstration projects. The grant program, begun in 1961, has expanded rapidly, from an initial outlay of $1.9 million up to $27.4 million in the latest year for which details are available, 1968.

Fairly substantial portions of these grants have gone to state and local governments directly since 1965. The amounts have varied considerably from state to state, both in terms of totals and per capita

Table II / Federal Expenditures for Air Pollution Control
Selected Fiscal Years, 1959–1971 (Millions of dollars)

Year	Total expenditures	Direct operations	Grants
1971	$111.0[a]	NA	NA
1969	67.6	NA	NA
1968	49.6	22.2	27.4
1967	32.9	15.3	17.6
1966	25.4	11.6	13.8
1965	20.6	9.8	10.8
1964	12.8	8.0	4.8
1963	10.4	7.0	3.4
1962	8.4	6.3	2.1
1961	7.0	5.1	1.9
1960	5.2	NA	NA
1959	4.4	NA	NA

[a] Estimate by Bureau of the Budget.
Source: Bureau of the Budget.

amounts (Table 3). Five states (Alaska, Delaware, Maine, South Dakota, and Vermont) received no grants for air pollution control at all during 1965–1968, while four others (California, Illinois, New Jersey, and Pennsylvania) each received a cumulative total in excess of $1 million over that same period. At first glance it would seem that population explains the variance among states, since the zero-grant group consists of generally small states, while those getting most have large populations. But per capita figures suggest otherwise. Per capita grants range from zero to 27 cents; the five highest states on a per capita basis (Kentucky, Connecticut, Colorado, Arizona, and Washington, in that order) seem to have no relevant traits in common, such as population density, geographic location, prevalence of large metropolitan centers, or unusual pollution problems.

Very little information is available with respect to state and local expenditures for air pollution control. HEW estimates that 85 local air pollution control agencies operated with total expenditures of about $8 million, and 17 state agencies with total outlay of about $2 million, for a state and local total of approximately $10 million in 1961. By contrast, in 1969 an estimated 142 local agencies spent $29.7 million and agencies in nearly all the states spent $17.6 million, for a state and local total of $47.5—close to a fivefold increase over the 1961 total.[4]

Table III / Federal Grants to State and Local Governments for Air and Water Pollution Control, by State Fiscal 1965–1968 and 1968

State	Grants for air pollution control, 1965–1968		Grants for water pollution control, 1968	
	Total (millions)	Per capita	Total (millions)	Per capita
TOTAL	$13.8	$.07	$264.9	$1.33
Alabama	.3	.07	4.4	1.24
Alaska	—	—	.6	2.18
Arizona	.3	.16	3.9	2.36
Arkansas	(a)	.02	6.3	3.11
California	1.2	.06	21.6	1.12
Colorado	.4	.19	4.5	2.22
Connecticut	.6	.20	3.1	1.05
Delaware	—	—	1.8	3.37
Florida	.2	.03	9.9	1.61
Georgia	.2	.05	6.9	1.51
Hawaii	(a)	.05	2.3	3.02
Idaho	(a)	.02	2.4	3.42
Illinois	1.4	.12	11.4	1.04
Indiana	.3	.06	5.9	1.16
Iowa	(a)	.01	4.6	1.68
Kansas	(a)	.01	5.5	2.40
Kentucky	.9	.27	3.3	1.03
Louisiana	.1	.03	3.9	1.04
Maine	—	—	3.0	3.02
Maryland	.6	.15	5.0	1.32
Massachusetts	.3	.06	2.6	.49
Michigan	.4	.05	8.6	.99
Minnesota	.1	.04	5.9	1.62
Mississippi	(a)	(b)	3.4	1.45
Missouri	.3	.06	6.3	1.35
Montana	.1	.11	1.6	2.36
Nebraska	(a)	.01	2.1	1.49
Nevada	(a)	.06	4.6	10.11
New Hampshire	(a)	.08	1.4	2.00
New Jersey	1.0	.14	6.8	.96
New Mexico	.1	.12	3.3	3.23
New York	.9	.05	16.3	.90
North Carolina	.2	.04	7.9	1.55
North Dakota	(a)	.04	1.6	2.63
Ohio	.3	.02	10.7	1.01
Oklahoma	.1	.02	2.9	1.15

Table III / Federal Grants to State and Local Governments for Air
and Water Pollution Control, by State
Fiscal 1965–1968 and 1968 (continued)

State	Grants for air pollution control, 1965–1968		Grants for water pollution control, 1968	
	Total (millions)	Per capita	Total (millions)	Per capita
Oregon	.2	.13	2.8	1.42
Pennsylvania	1.2	.10	9.1	.77
Rhode Island	.1	.06	1.7	1.87
South Carolina	.1	.03	3.6	1.32
South Dakota	—	—	2.4	3.71
Tennessee	.1	.03	5.8	1.46
Texas	.6	.05	12.2	1.11
Utah	.1	.06	1.8	1.77
Vermont	—	—	2.6	6.10
Virginia	.1	.02	6.6	1.43
Washington	.5	.16	6.0	1.83
West Virginia	.1	.05	3.6	2.01
Wisconsin	(a)	.01	6.9	1.63
Wyoming	(a)	.01	.7	2.19

ᵃ Less than 0.1 million.
ᵇ Less than 1 cent.
Source: Computations based on data from U.S. Treasury.

The U.S. Budget for 1971 provides information on Federal expenditures for water pollution control in urban areas, giving some impression of the rapid expansion in such programs. In 1961 water pollution control outlays came to $24 million, and by 1969 had increased fourfold, to $104 million. Expenditures for water and sewer facilities also had increased, from $36 million in 1964 (the earliest year data are available) to $52 million in 1969.

Federal grants to state and local governmental units for water pollution problems fall under many different categories and agencies, and consequently are quite difficult to identify in total. While air pollution has been in the domain of the Department of Health, Education and Welfare throughout, an assortment of departments and agencies concern themselves with water. These include a program in the Department of Agriculture concerned with rural water and waste disposal; in the Department of Housing and Urban Development concerned with water and sewer facilities; several programs in the Department of Interior dealing with such problems as waste treatment works construction, water resources research, and pollution control directly.

The Federal government expends considerably more on water pollution than on air pollution, if judgments may be made from the comparative size of grants-in-aid to state and local units for the two purposes. In 1968, for example, total grants for air pollution amounted to $13.8 million, whereas all the grants concerned with water pollution in that year totaled $264.9 million. Per capita amounts to states in 1968 ranged from $10.11 in Nevada down to 49 cents in Massachusetts (Table 3).

Regulation and Fees

Late in 1970, President Nixon announced a mandatory industrial waste permit system, to be administered by the Army Corps of Engineers under the 1899 Refuse Act. An estimated 40,000 industrial dischargers into navigable waters or their tributaries have until July 1, 1971, to submit an application for a permit, but the President has warned that violators of standards will not be exempt from legal action during the period preceding the permit deadline. The Environmental Protection Agency is developing guidelines for 22 industrial groups. The Refuse Act provides criminal and injunctive measures against noncompliance, and the administration has stated these will be actively utilized. The Refuse Act, because it specifically exempts refuse flowing from streets and sewers, generally does not apply to municipalities, but the President has indicated he will seek other regulatory devices to reduce municipal water pollution.

Some states take a straightforward regulatory approach, with no financial concessions offered. One such, Mississippi, levies annual inspection fees ranging from $50 to $200 for firms, depending on their employee-size, and from $50 to $1,000 for municipalities, depending on population.

Vermont has embarked upon a new approach which will require every individual or firm discharging waste into a watercourse to obtain a permit from the state. Fees will be charged for permits, the amounts presumably so designed as to induce polluters to install suitable processing equipment. The law, which was passed in mid-1970 and becomes effective July 1971, provides broad scope to the Department of Water Resources in establishing fee levels, which must be set by the beginning of 1971. An economic-engineering study will provide the basis on which fees will be determined.

PROBLEMS OF SETTING STANDARDS

The need to set standards raises some of the most serious problems which must be faced in connection with pollution control. In the process of establishing standards, legislators and administrators must render judgments on many levels, and the difficult fact is that not only are subjective choices involved, but, in many cases, the core of information on which decisions should be based is piteously thin and sometimes totally lacking.

Technical and Political Problems

Authorities must solve excruciating technical and political problems —problems which intertwine endlessly. The political chore, defining an acceptable level of pollution, hangs on at least some knowledge of what kind of damage various foreign substances might do, as well as a policy decision on the purposes for which the cleaned-up air or water might be used. For instance, to take the more simple case of water (simple, only because it has been an object of concern for a longer period and hence more definitive research has been accomplished), purity standards might be established which would make the water adequate for navigation only, for commercial fishing, for swimming, for drinking, etc. Each added function generally requires more stringent standards: one can swim with impunity in some water that would create severe problems as a beverage. Politicians would have to obtain technical guidance on precisely what substances in water interfere with the various uses, the source of these substances, how costly it might prove to withhold them, and whether, in fact, it even is possible to withhold them. All this information then must be balanced against the question of just how desirable the contemplated uses of the water might be. For instance, perhaps the benefits to be derived from purifying the Hudson River enough so that New Yorkers might swim in it simply do not amount to enough to justify all the costly adjustments which would have to be made to bring the river to such condition; building public swimming pools might prove more expedient and economical.

Far more difficult questions must be confronted in establishing standards for air quality, partly because many technical matters remain subject to controversy. Authorities do not agree on the amount and kind of damage which will ensue from a specified level of many airborne substances, such as sulfur oxides and particulates; in some instances, scientists do not even agree on whether or not some substances, such as organic carcinogens, should be matters for concern.

Furthermore, as in the case of water, decisions involve choices as to the degree of purity for which to aim. Without question, air quality should be above that level which would prove lethal over a period of, say, a few days or even a few years, but a whole spectrum of effects lies beyond this point. Suppose the air merely smarts the eyes? or damages paint? or worsens asthma? or makes a town look ugly? Policymakers must answer such questions as these. Technical information provides guidance only on possibilities and some costs, not on whether such effects matter enough to justify the cost of control.

Reliable technical information, however, should underlie any attempts to regulate pollution. When the regulatory approach is used, there always exists a grave danger that goals will be set which are unrealistic in terms of the state of technology or costs, establishing standards which for all practical purposes are impossible, or which require exorbitant expenditures relative to the improvements that might be gained. The danger of regulations which outpace the growth of scientific knowledge seem particularly acute in a period of great emotional concern about pollution.

Costs Compared with Benefits

Often there runs through discussions of pollution control the naive implication that the "best" level of pollution control is that level which most nearly approaches perfection. In fact, the gains derived from a specified level of control do not appear magically without price, and when gains are balanced against costs they may not seem particularly inviting at the higher levels.

Chart 1 gives a visual impression of this point—a simple point, but one all too often overlooked. The figures, of course, are theoretical, but in line with the general principles which seem likely to operate (general principles which do in fact operate in many situations in which it is possible to measure both costs and benefits with considerable accuracy). The black area in the bars on the chart represents the cost of the damage resulting from pollution, the shaded area the cost of control, and the entire bar, the total cost society will incur at each of the levels of control depicted. Total costs, the chart shows, reach the largest amounts at two points, at the very lowest amount of pollution abatement and at 100 percent abatement. Under the set of figures presumed in Chart 1, lowest total costs occur at the level of 50 percent control; someplace around the midpoint may indeed be a realistic guess.

Many economists and others urge that a cost-benefit analysis precede the introduction of any regulatory scheme. While a great deal

Chart 1
Cost to Society from Pollution Damage and for Pollution Control

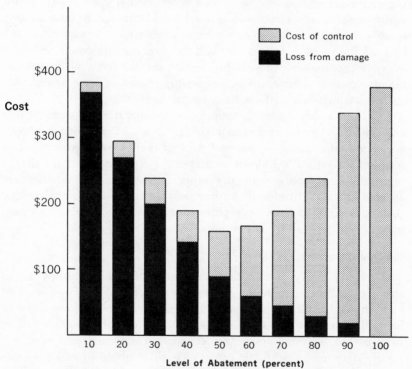

Source: Based on Azriel Teller, "Air Pollution Abatement: Economic Rationality and Reality," Daedalus, Fall 1967, p. 1085.

can be said for such proposals, their efficacy can easily be overrated. Perhaps even more than in other areas where cost-benefit analysis has been recommended, pollution cost can be very difficult to measure, and at present benefits are even more elusive. Benefits in the case of pollution are a somewhat inverted concept, consisting for the most part of negative damage. Thus to measure benefits the investigator must discover and impute dollar values to all additional costs brought on by pollutants.[5] As usual, the intangibles can create real headaches. What is the dollar value of lost recreation when it becomes unsafe to fish and swim in a river? What does it cost a firm which loses a key employee, warned by his doctor to find an area more compatible with is respiratory weakness? In measuring the cost of damaged exteriors, should the investigator count only the expense incurred by those who repaint on the basis of preventive maintenance or their aesthetic judgment, or add in some amount for surfaces which should be refinished but are not?

One researcher, who attempted a comparatively sophisticated analysis of the value of pollution control in a St. Louis neighborhood, suggests that reliance on political policymakers may provide the best solution for setting standards at present. He points out that "elected representatives, more than any other segment of our society, are attuned to the attitudes that form psychic costs, and since psychic costs are likely to be a large portion of total costs, their assessment may not be too far from the mark."[6]

Local Variations

The wide diversity in conditions from one locality to the next raises another complication in the setting of standards. The problems of Los Angeles differ from those in Pittsburgh and even from those in Santa Barbara, only 90 miles distant. Matters of typical weather, form of the surrounding terrain, economic conditions, and even culturally determined aesthetic preference all combine to make the degree and kind of pollution control optimum for one region differ from that for another. For example, in predominantly Mormon Salt Lake City, where presumably the use of tobacco is lower than in otherwise comparable cities, less importance may attach to low levels of benzpyrene, a byproduct of both cigarette smoking and coal burning which may have some causal relationship with lung cancer. To establish nationwide standards appropriate to, say, New York City, might work needless hardship on cities in Utah. In view of the temper of the times, however, the tendency of the electorate may be to ask for national standards, especially for air.

Fortunately, the groundwork has been laid for nationwide standards which take some note of varying conditions, at least on a large scale. The Air Quality Act of 1967 established a system requiring the designation of "air quality control regions"—regions in which two or more communities, not necessarily in the same state, have a common air pollution problem. Congress recognized the twofold nature of pollution problems—that the problem rarely confines itself to a given political boundary, but at the same time differs from one part of the country to another. The National Air Pollution Control Administration has identified eight atmospheric areas for the United States; these are large areas over which the average meteorological conditions affecting transport and diffusion of air pollution are quite similar. But superimposed on the atmospheric area concept, air quality control regions have been designated on the basis of such factors as location and quantity of pollution emissions, social and governmental factors, etc.

Yet other difficulties arise in setting pollution standards. One very obvious factor, seasonal variation, exerts an important effect on pollution levels but often is forgotten. For instance, summer can bring much more serious water pollution problems, and a drought can turn a level of industrial municipal effluents which would be harmless in normal times into a serious mess, by reducing the amount of water which can act as a purifier. Winter can increase the use of coal in many areas and thus intensify air pollution.

Local economic conditions may present another variable which creates difficulties in the setting of standards. When an area is underdeveloped and most of its residents earn low incomes, those who set standards confront a subtle ethical question. Perhaps poor health characterizes the inhabitants of such an area, and hence the marginal effect of bad air or water may be felt even more severely than in another locale. On the other hand, the imposition of high and rigid standards might inhibit the attracting of new industries which would give needed employment and thus improve average incomes and health. Then it might be unjust to insist such an area adhere to the same standards as elsewhere, even if the economically depressed area is part of an atmospheric area or a water basin which might be adversely affected by any exceptions granted. At the same time, authorities must consider that privileges once granted are not lightly relinquished; once the deprived area achieves the desired economic status, it might be extremely difficult to force it to meet higher pollution standards.

Yet another problem relates to the stage of development of the science of ecology. Only the most naive would assume that ecologists or any other specialists can predict the effect of all substances in use today. For instance, no one anticipated, nor could have been expected to anticipate, the alarming longrun effects of widespread use of DDT; in fact, when it was first introduced all but dyed-in-the-wool organic farmers greeted it with enthusiasm as one more victory over nature's hardships. Similarly, only recently has the potential damage from thermal pollution or mercury discharges become evident.

The time period over which standards should be implemented also raises difficult issues. Ordinarily, the sooner an improvement becomes operative, the better. But pollution control facilities can cost a great deal of money, and raising the necessary funds may be extremely difficult even over a long time span. But when standards must be met very quickly, the capital requirements can become prohibitive, with the result that at least some firms, who might have managed over a longer period, will give up the struggle and go out of business. Consequently, a certain amount of the economy's productive capacity will be irretrievably lost. When a new plant begins to operate, on the other hand, there would be no waste of resources should authorities insist high standards be adhered to from the outset. Thus dual time schedules, with older plants allowed deadlines which would take into account the realities of the capital market, might prove wisest over the long run.

GOVERNMENT AID THROUGH TAX DEVICES, SUBSIDIES, AND GRANTS

Many people, once they concede that autonomous control provides a weak reed to lean upon and that some special form of government assistance may prove requisite, probably think first of tax and other financial devices as an appropriate method. In fact, many municipalities, states, and the Federal government have offered both industry and communities various types of financial inducements to reduce the level of pollutants they impose on their surroundings, as outlined in Section III.

A number of compelling arguments can be drawn up in favor of the tax approach. An important part of the burden of cleaning up water and air, the argument runs, will fall on industry and will cost a great deal; these expenses will affect a firm's competitive position by increasing the average cost of its product. Since any abatement of pollution serves the general good, and is of value to the producer primarily in his role as a private citizen, when he installs antipollution equipment he is providing a social benefit, the expense of which should be shared by society through government. The hard fact of life about pollution control equipment lies in its cost. The dredging up of sufficient investment funds for any capital equipment almost always presents a problem, and the problem is made more acute in the special case of pollution equipment, when often no tangible return can be expected. Hence in some cases tax help can make just enough difference to change the investment from a hardship, or even an impossibility, to something manageable.[7] Moreover, there exists a considerable precedent for using tax laws to encourage various types of behavior deemed to be socially useful: deductions for charitable contributions and certain education expenses, outlays for child care, etc. Finally, fairness dictates that when a firm undertakes the responsibility of improving the world we live in, with little or no hope of tangible gain for itself, tax credits provide at least a token of society's appreciation for the effort and sacrifice.

Tax devices, however, represent a far from perfect method for the reduction of pollution. For one thing, at best they have relevance for only a partial segment of the polluters. Municipalities, a very important source of pollution, do not modify behavior on the basis of the type of incentive which can be created through tax advantages, since they are not subject to taxes. But even business firms respond imperfectly to tax devices. For one thing, income tax credits or exemptions mean almost nothing to the marginal firm, which may have little or no income tax liability, simply because its profits are small or even negative. Unfortunately, the marginal firm may be the worst pollution offender of all, operating frequently with outmoded plant and equipment, cutting costs wherever this is even remotely possible. If the marginal firm can obtain capital funds for investment, business sense usually will dictate that investment in equipment to improve its profit position makes far better sense than pollution abatement devices.

Tax preferences, it must be remembered, by no means offset the full cost of an investment; the taxpayer is always out of pocket for at least a portion of the outlay. The actual money value of a tax credit can represent quite a small portion of the cost of equipment, especially when that credit is offered at the state or local level. When a state allows a tax concession, at least part of that concession is offset by the resulting higher Federal tax. For example, suppose a hypothetical firm, My Brother's Keeper Chemicals, Inc., installs a precipitator which under state laws entitles it to a reduction in state income tax liabilities amounting to $5,000. MBK Chemicals will find that when it prepares its Federal tax returns, the income base upon which tax is computed is now $5,000 higher than otherwise, since for Federal purposes state taxes *after* credits, not before, are deductible. MBK, as a medium-sized firm with earnings over $25,000, will be subject to Federal corporation income tax rates, and thus Federal taxes reduce the state's tax concession by about half.

The use of tax provisions to reduce pollution can lead to inflexible and possibly inefficient technology in pollution control. Tax credits inevitably must relate to installation of specific types of equipment, with measurable price tags. For at least some industries and individual firms, a radical, or perhaps partial, change in the production process may provide a far more efficient approach to pollution control. But how to grant tax concessions for modifications in the manufacturing process?—particularly if such changes increase the firm's productivity at the same time they reduce pollution? From the point of view of the general welfare, the second approach has far more merit than the installation of some type of device which merely processes wastes. Both may add to the cost of the product, but there will be times when changes in methodology add less. If, however, the government underwrites part of the costs of a particular kind of abatement equipment, then that which is more expensive to society at large will be less expensive from the point of view of the firm, the one who will make the choice. In such circumstances, the revenue code could act as a barrier to the most effective technological development, since more research funds inevitably would be channeled into directions most like to qualify for tax preferences.

Critics of tax credits for pollution control also assert that this approach distorts production in favor of products whose manufacture creates severe pollution. Polluters, it is argued, should be forced to pay the cost of cleaning up wastes, passing on the additional expense to consumers of their products. If government subsidizes the cost of cleanup through tax advantages, at the expense of taxpayers who may or may not care for the product, pollution-creating products are provided at a price cheaper than normal. Consequently even more of the offending product may be sold, perhaps competing with substitutes whose production would not bring so high a social cost.

In seeking economic incentives, government need not confine itself to tax assistance. Outright subsidies, analogous to the type of payment made to farmers for planting cover crops which enrich the earth, might bypass one of the major shortcomings of other tax-oriented approaches, the fact that they are ineffective with respect to marginal and/or loss firms, which can be the worst polluters.

Direct and open subsidies could be set at any percentage of the cost of facilities which policymakers or the electorate might prefer, or to reduce administrative problems they might take the form of some flat-fee bounty. A subsidy slightly exceeding the typical *immediate* cash outlay (not the total price) required for purchase of control facilities might prove quite effective, and not much more costly than complex tax incentives. Also, this type of aid far better fits the case of the nonindustrial polluter, and has the advantage that more explicit goals can be achieved. For instance, the Federal government can specify that a project thus supported must be part of a regional effort, or designated for a particular direction in research. If well designed and administered, such direct subsidies might have potential for achieving a given level of pollution control at a much lower cost than would a program of broad tax incentives. On the other hand, the use of subsidies might only introduce a new set of complex rules administered by an added, and untried, bureaucracy.

One final objection to tax preferences and various types of subsidies—i.e., all reward-based approaches to control—comes to light if the method is taken in a simple aspect: payment for not scattering pollutants. Several troublesome questions become immediately apparent when subsidies are viewed in this way. Suppose that such a program is introduced at a time when the hypothetical firm MBK Chemicals already has built, at considerable cost, a new plant which reduces its pollutants to a very low level. Its competitor, Cain Agrochemicals, Inc., for various reasons has made no attempt to curb its polluting effluents, but now, in response to government's subsidy offer, decides to install expensive pollution control equipment. Thus Cain Agrochemicals in effect is rewarded for its previous inaction, inefficiency, and pollution, whereas MBK Chemicals receives nothing, in spite of having made a considerable outlay which resulted in social benefit. Similarly, Organic Orchards, Inc., a responsibly operated farm corporation whose product may actually reduce pollution levels by removing carbon dioxide and adding beneficial oxygen to the air, neither expects nor receives governmentally-dispensed rewards.

Punitive taxes, such as those which are from time to time proposed on the sale of products considered harmful to the environment, stand midway between regulation and tax incentives. Such a tax could be used to adjust the comparative price between two products, one of which is more deleterious to the environment than the other, so that the attractiveness of the more harmful one is reduced. A case can be made for a punitive tax in the special and unusual situation in which some consumers could not use product B in substitution for product A without extreme inconvenience, whereas for most consumers the two products are such close substitutes that price determines which one is selected. Outright prohibition of the production of A might work severe hardship on the first category of consumers. A tax on product A, not necessarily very high, would deflect the second category of consumer to product B, keeping the use of product A down to acceptable levels.

But even under these special circumstances many objections arise. The use of such a tax implies precise knowledge of the characteristics of the two groups of users, of the ecological damage resulting from the use of the products, and of the consequences of the tax on the industries involved.

GOVERNMENT USE OF REGULATION

Many Americans automatically oppose more government control than they think absolutely essential. Ordinarily, such citizens hesitate to trade reduced independence of individual action for possible increased efficiency in the economy's operation, unless the trade-off will bring marked gains. Businessmen in particular may deplore and oppose any hint of further regulation, cramped as they are today by a multitude of laws, codes, ordinances, and the like. And yet some companies are beginning to consider the possibility that, given the desirability of achieving improved levels of pollution control, the goals may be impossible of achievement without at least some government supervision. Moreover, President Nixon's recent decision to invoke the Refuse Act of 1899 gives new importance to regulation.

Those who advocate a regulatory approach to pollution problems reason that when polluters expel their unwanted wastes into the air or water, they are imposing a cost on society; they abuse common ownership rights in what is ordinarily regarded as a free resource. Regulationists point out that in the case of common property, as with private property, ownership bestows merely a body of rights, both positive and negative, with respect to the item. Generally, ownership includes the right to use of the object, but almost always this use is subject to certain social constraints—some so obvious they ordinarily are not even considered restrictions. Restrictions take on more significance with certain kinds of property, i.e., firearms, radioactive material, even automobiles. Regulationists contend that tacit restrictions exist in the common ownership and use of air and water and that if these restrictions were respected, pollution would drop to substantially minimal. When restrictions are ignored, violaters should be subject to penalty, just as in the case of private property.

If one takes the viewpoint that those who pollute air and water do not have the right to use common property in an abusive way, then a tantalizing question arises. Both air and water possess an enormous capacity for self-cleansing, and can accommodate substantial amounts of foreign substances without permanent damage. While some substances can never be discarded with impunity, many residential, municipal, and industrial wastes do no harm in "reasonable" quantities; they become troublesome only when large amounts are exuded into limited areas. Fundamentally, then, only those who put "too much" waste into the water or air can be said to misuse the common resource. If everyone were prohibited from using water and air as a disposal medium, then to the extent that natural forces could have processed waste, misallocation of the economy's resources would follow, because other means would have to be employed. The person who says, "My bit of pollution doesn't hurt," does have a point, since it is not waste substances *per se*, but the amount of the aggregate above some level which does the damage.

Is there any solution to this dilemma? An ingenious possibility, often misunderstood, has been proposed from time to time. The underlying notion, which unfortunately is rarely made explicit, is that while air and water may be commonly owned by all, the right to use them as a medium for waste disposal represents a *scarce resource* under today's population and consumption conditions. Thus, some say, that aspect of air and water ownership—that property right—which has to do with waste disposal no longer can be considered a free good in most areas; it ought not be treated as if it were, even though those related property rights which have to do with obtaining oxygen for one's lungs, etc., may continue to be considered common property.

How, then, might air and water waste disposal rights be "sold"? Various schemes have been proposed, ranging in sophistication from a simple fee levied on all industries and municipalities discharging effluents, up through elaborate schemes that would establish a price system to ration the use of water and air.

A precursor of the air and water price rationing system for waste disposal operates in many states through laws, some very early in origin, governing the use of water for irrigation. Water laws differ considerably in provision and underlying philosophy, but they generally attempt to mitigate uncertainties which would result in an unregulated situation. Obviously, with no regulation the greatest advantage goes to that operation located the farthest upstream; those downstream would be subject to uncertainties which would induce firms and individuals to locate much farther upstream than other factors—such as accessibility to raw materials and to markets—might dictate, with resulting losses for the economy as a whole.

Where state law clearly defines certain water rights as a form of property, these rights in time become a "commodity" of sorts, with definite price tags attached. For instance, in California where irrigation is essential for agriculture, first rights to water use are attached to certain parcels of land, secondary rights to others, and so on. Thus in years of abundant rain and full rivers, all farmers have access to sufficient water; in other years, farmers with first rights generally have plenty of water but other farmers either must see their crops parch or must install expensive equipment for pumping up ground water. Inevitably, when a farm with first rights appears on the market, its owner receives a considerably higher price than does the owner of an otherwise equivalent farm with lesser rights, although no explicit, separate price tag is attached to the water right.

Some writers have suggested formalizing this type of arrangement, with government selling property rights, not for the irrigation function of water but rather for the purifying function of both air and water.[8] Generally, the mechanism would operate as follows: First, a technical survey would determine approximately how much waste matter the air and water in a given region could accommodate without deleterious effects.[9] Certificates entitling the holder to utilize the purifying capacities of the river for a specified number of standardized units of waste material would be issued and sold, up to a total fully utilizing the natural resource. Only holders of certificates would be entitled to discharge waste; all others would be required to process wastes to render them harmless, meeting standards to be established by the certificate-issuing board, before releasing them. Advocates brush over a rather large problem, that the initial price must be determined by estimates. The crucial point, however, is that ownership of the certificates must include the right to resale through a government-operated control board. Resale rights permit ordinary market processes to establish an efficient equilibrium between the price of using the common resource for waste disposal (the price as reflected in resale value of certificates) and the cost of installing in-plant pollution control facilities. Two results should follow. Maximum efficiency in the use of the natural resource could be achieved as the certificate issuing board, through experience, finally sets the exact level of effluent which the total community may release into the environment. At the same time, because the certificates would be relatively scarce, incentive would be created to develop more and more efficient in-plant pollution processing methods.

The rules under which waste disposal certificates are sold would permit anyone to buy them, even with no plan or facility to use them. Under such an arrangement, conservationist groups could, if they wished a higher standard of purity than established by the administering board, buy blocks of certificates which would withhold any amount of effluent from the water they could afford.

Many disadvantages can be found in the regulatory approach. Regulations can hamper opportunities for investment and change. Regulations go hand in hand with bureacracy and all the attendant delays and red tape. Some regulatory methods—for instance, the use of zoning to reduce pollution—could be abused as monopoly-creating devices.

Even the most devoted advocate of the regulatory approach to pollution control must concede that problems of policing and administration represent an important impediment to success. The technical problems of measuring offending effluents can be extremely difficult, particularly in the case of air. Effective regulation would require more or less continuous monitoring; thus measurement techniques which are costly, or which can be performed only by highly trained specialists, would raise costs of administration. Inexpensive, simple methods for measuring many pollutants have yet to be developed.

In general, the difficulty of administration depends on the reasonableness of the regulations, costs of compliance, and penalties for evasion. This principle will apply in pollution regulation just as in any other case. Thus problems of administration will depend in large part on the particular form any regulatory legislation may take.

Higher levels of government also can render help to municipalities with relatively little outlay by setting up the framework for inter-municipal or interstate cooperation, establishing certain standards which all must meet.[10]

THE COST OF POLLUTION CONTROL IN THE FUTURE

Relatively few have attempted careful study to answer the important question: how much will it cost to restore the environment to a desirable condition, and maintain it at that level?

Any attempt to deal with the question quickly reveals why there has been so much hesitancy about making cost estimates. First of all, much of the technology is new—some, indeed, has not yet evolved—so the basic engineering costs are subject to many uncertainties. Moreover, it is difficult to obtain a broad perspective on how much remains to be done; some plants and cities very effectively process their wastes, while others do virtually nothing at all. Estimating what proportions fall into each category requires bold guesswork. Then the further problem remains—*whose* cost should be measured? government's? industry's? consumers'? And the related question: costs under which method of control, since the amount borne by the various segments will hang to some degree on whether control is a matter of autonomous action, response to incentives, or regulation.

The really significant variable in costs, however, relates to the goal, or level of environmental purity desired. Under present technology, in many situations costs shoot up rapidly as the degree of control approaches perfection. Table 4, which is based on engineering estimates, illustrates how both investment and operating costs skyrocket as control (in this case, of particulate matter) is increased from an 80 percent level to the maximum level possible. Eighty percent control of particulates resulting from the provision of industrial heat and power, for instance, requires an investment of $13,000 per unit plant, whereas maximum control costs $66,000, or more than five times as much, for not more than one fourth more accomplishment. While industrial heat and power represent the most extreme example, other pollution sources listed in Table 4 show similar patterns. Similarly, annual costs for maximum versus 80 percent control are drastically higher for most industries.

Air Pollution Control Costs

One attempt to estimate the cost of air pollution control assumes standards calling for a 60 to 75 percent reduction of sulfur oxides and particulates from the typical levels prevailing in 1967. Simulation techniques yielded an estimate for such reduction in a hypothetical city of 2 million inhabitants; these figures were then extrapolated for the entire United States. The resulting estimate: annual capital costs of $160 million and operation and maintenance costs of $1.1 billion, for a total of $1.3 billion in 1967 (Table 5).

A more recent estimate of the cost of air pollution control, pre-

Table IV / Estimated Unit Plant Costs for Controlling Particulate Matter, Selected Levels of Control, by Industry Source (Dollars in thousands)

Source	Investment costs				Annual costs			
	80% control	90% control	Maximum control	Maximum as multiple of 80% control	80% control	90% control	Maximum control	Maximum as multiple of 80% control
Steam-electric power plants	$317	$488	$812	2.6	$225	$245	$389	1.7
Industrial heat and power	13	48	66	5.1	4	9	13	3.2
Steel industry								
Open-hearth furnace	90	90	142	1.6	52	65	97	1.9
Basic oxygen furnace	338	338	534	1.6	100	243	365	3.6
Electric furnace	72	72	114	1.6	37	47	68	1.8
Sintering plant	246	707	861	3.5	169	262	288	1.7
Hydraulic cement industry								
Wet process	47	108	158	3.4	16	20	32	2.0
Dry process	107	206	354	3.3	36	40	71	2.0
Gray iron foundry	20	34	42	2.1	4	6	7	1.8
Sulfate pulp industry	209	352	509	2.4	43	68	98	2.3
Petroleum refining	—	70	137	2.0[a]	—	14	25	1.8[a]
Sulfuric acid industry	—	31	62	2.0[a]	—	5	10	2.0[a]

[a] Maximum as multiple of 90% control.

Source: Department of Health, Education, and Welfare, based on industry sources.

Table V / Estimated Cost of Achieving Hypothetical Standard by Reducing Human Exposure to Sulfur Oxides and Particulates by 60–75 Percent in a "Typical City" of 2 Million Persons and in the United States, 1967—(Millions)

Type of cost	Typical city		United States	
	Least cost [a]	Proportional reduction [b]	Least cost [a]	Proportional reduction [b]
Capital cost	$ 1.2	$ 2.3	$ 81.9	$ 160.3
Operations and maintenance	9.8	15.8	686.7	1,104.6
Total	$11.0	$18.1	$768.6	$1,264.9

[a] Only those discharging harmful waste loads and technically able to reduce waste loads were required to abate in the simulation.
[b] All waste-load emitters must reduce discharges by the same proportion.
Source: Adapted from Robert N. Grosse. Some Problems in Economic Analysis of Environmental Policy Choices. In U.S. Department of Health, Education, and Welfare. Public Health Service. Consumer Protection and Environmental Health Service. *Proceedings of Symposium on Human Ecology* (Public Health Service Publication No. 1929. Washington, D.C.: Government Printing Office, 1969), p. 48.

pared by the Department of Health, Education and Welfare, takes a different approach. Costs were estimated for 21 types of sources which fall under several broad categories: waste disposal (open burning and incineration), fuel combustion (powerplant, industrial and commercial uses, and residential heating), and industrial processing (manufacturing, refining, etc.). Then specific estimates were made for each of 100 metropolitan areas on the basis of the actual situation in the area, such as the number and type of installations currently controlling pollution, their efficiency, the location and capacity of polluting sources, and similar data. The areas include 57 which either have been or definitely will be designated air quality control regions under the provisions of the Clean Air Act, plus an additional 43 arbitrarily selected; the 100 areas taken together represent about 60 percent of total U.S. population or nearly 90 percent of the population in standard metropolitan areas. Thus estimates for pollution control in the 100 metropolitan areas should come close to costs for the entire nation, since air pollution problems are generally most acute in large population centers, and outlays elsewhere would not be large relative to those of the large cities. The estimates represent the prospective costs of implementing provisions of the Clean Air Act, as amended in November, 1967. The figures thus derived appear in Table 6, which gives U.S. totals for both investment and annual costs, broken down by the three major sources, for fiscal years 1971 through 1975.

Table VI / *Estimated Costs for Controlling Air Pollution in 100 Metropolitan Areas* [a]
Fiscal Years 1971–1975—(Millions)

Source of pollution	1971	1972	1973	1974	1975	Total 1971– 1975
Investment costs						
Solid waste disposal	$ 17	$ 56	$ 80	$ 50	$ 18	$ 221
Fuel combustion	82	291	443	331	142	1,289
Industrial processes	78	261	410	278	104	1,131
Total investment costs	177	608	933	659	264	2,641
Annual costs						
Solid waste disposal	8	35	74	98	107	322
Fuel combustion	107	445	912	1,200	1,330	3,994
Industrial processes	37	147	303	404	443	1,334
Total annual costs	152	627	1,290	1,710	1,880	5,659

[a] Based on requirements under the Clean Air Act as amended in 1967.
Source: Department of Health, Education, and Welfare.

Comparing the estimates with those in Table 5, at first glance the figures appear to diverge widely. Table 6 gives first year investment costs of $177 million, compared with $160 million in Table 5. But investment outlays are projected to increase sharply over the following three years such that they total $2,641 million over the five-year period. Annual costs are put much higher in Table 5, $1,105 million compared with $152 million in the first year. But annual costs also are projected to increase, totaling $5,659 million over the five-year period. If Table 5 is taken as representing a "typical" year, then total costs over five such years would equal $5,523 million operating costs, plus roughly half the capital costs for depreciation allowance (included in annual costs in Table 6) for a total of $5,603 million— almost identical to the Table 6 total.

A relatively small number of very large metropolitan areas account for the major part of costs, as shown in Table 7. This table gives prospective total costs over the five-year period for the 50 cities with the largest annual costs. Total annual costs for Chicago alone are projected at $801 million, or 14 percent of the figure for all 100 metropolitan areas. Chicago plus New York and Pittsburgh will have estimated costs of $1.4 billion, or one-fourth of the costs for all 100 areas. The addition of Detroit, St. Louis, Cleveland, Philadelphia, the Steubenville region, Cincinnati, and Buffalo—all told, 10 areas—accounts for half of the 100-city costs.

Table VII / Estimated Air Quality Control Annual and Investment Costs for 50 Metropolitan Areas Total, Fiscal Years 1971–1975—(Millions)

Area	Annual costs	Investment outlay [a]
Chicago	$801	$228
New York	338	130
Pittsburgh	288	117
Detroit	264	82
St. Louis	258	76
Cleveland	210	89
Philadelphia	199	94
Steubenville/Wierton/Wheeling	167	46
Cincinnati	163	57
Buffalo	129	75
Louisville	115	26
Milwaukee/Kenosha/Racine	110	56
Washington	99	48
Birmingham	95	26
Baltimore	84	43
Denver	67	15
Minneapolis/St. Paul	58	34
Boston	46	31
Indianapolis	46	25
Toledo	46	13
Youngstown/Warren [b]	46	34
Hartford	44	19
Allentown/Bethlehem/Easton [b]	43	33
Los Angeles	42	19
Dayton	42	18
Saginaw/Bay City	42	16
Grand Rapids, Michigan [b]	41	10
Houston	38	51
Atlanta	35	11

[a] Includes charge for investment on annualized basis.
[b] Assumes designation as AQCR after June, 1969; i.e., no expenditures in fiscal 1971 or 1972.
Source: Department of Health, Education, and Welfare.

Table VII / Estimated Air Quality Control Annual and Investment
Costs for 50 Metropolitan Areas
Total, Fiscal Years 1971–1975—(Millions)

Area	Annual costs	Investment outlay [a]
—continued		
Scranton [b]	31	80
Kansas City	29	14
Tampa [b]	28	10
Charleston, West Virginia [b]	26	7
Peoria	25	17
New Orleans	23	35
Portland	23	22
San Francisco	18	9
South Bend [b]	18	15
Providence/Pawtucket/Fall River	17	9
Seattle/Everett/Tacoma	17	17
Salt Lake City	17	19
Harrisburg [b]	17	25
Rochester	17	11
Dallas/Ft. Worth	16	18
Omaha	16	16
Mobile [b]	15	11
Knoxville [b]	14	20
York [b]	14	8
Albany/Schenectady/Troy [b]	12	9
Norfolk [b]	11	19

In addition to the expenditures shown in Table 6, note must be taken of government expenditures. Table 8 shows estimates of expenditures by Federal, state, and local governments combined for research and control programs plus abatement of pollution from Federal facilities.[11] The estimates assume that government programs will increase by about 30 percent annually. Since there is no meaningful historical period on which to base an estimate about future government spending for pollution control, it is difficult to assess the validity of the assumption. Should it be correct, then by 1975 the Federal government will be spending $490 million annually on iar pollution control, with about 40 percent of the total on research and development.

Government costs are not confined to the type of activity covered by Table 8, however. It could happen that costs in the form of fore-

510 · ENVIRONMENTAL MANAGEMENT AND FINANCE

Table VIII / Estimated Federal, State and Local Expenditures for
Air Pollution Control [a]
Fiscal 1970–1975—(Millions)

Year	Research and development [b]	Abatement and control	Total
1970	$ 50	$ 82	$ 132
1971	65	107	132
1972	84	139	223
1973	110	180	290
1974	143	234	377
1975	186	305	491
Total	$638	$1,047	$1,685

[a] Based on requirements under the Clean Air Act as amended in 1967.
[b] Excludes outlays by Federal agencies other than National Air Pollution Control Administration.
Source: Department of Health, Education, and Welfare.

gone tax collections will represent substantial amounts. Table 9 gives some impression of what various forms of Federal assistance might cost.[12] For instance, allowance of 3-year accelerated depreciation, a not unreasonable possibility, could lead to the reduction of Federal taxes by $382 million dollars over the period 1971–1975. If 3-year depreciation were combined with a 14 percent tax credit, the Federal cost would approach three-quarters of a billion dollars over the five-year period. Another possibility, low interest loans, could cost $312 million for 3 percent loans or $156 million for 6 percent loans.

One further aspect of air pollution costs, not taken into account in the two preceding tables, must be considered: the cost of controlling pollutants produced by motor vehicles. Table 10 presents one estimate, taken from the point of view of the investment costs that have been or will be passed on to new car buyers (not necessarily equivalent to additional production costs). On the basis of Federal law extant in 1969, industry sources estimated annual buyer costs of $18 million in 1968 and 1969, $36 million in 1970, and $58 million in the years thereafter, for a cumulative total of $304 million over the period 1968–1974. It should be noted, however, that even if these estimates were accurate at the time they were made, they now are vastly understated as a consequence of the stringent standards set forth in the Clean Air Act of 1970.[13]

Table IX / *Comparative Gains by Industry through Alternative Forms of*
Federal Assistance for Capital Investment in Air Pollution
Control, and Estimated Federal Cost 1971–1975

Type of assistance	Percent-age	Per $1 billion capital investment (in millions)	Estimated Federal cost 1971–1975 [a] (millions)
Accelerated depreciation			
5 years	8.5	$ 85	$221
3 years	14.7	147	382
1 year	18.3	183	476
Tax credits [b]			
7 percent (existing before 1969)	7.0	70	182
14 percent	14.0	140	364
20 percent	20.0	200	520
Accelerated depreciation and tax credit combined			
14 percent credit, 3-year depreciation	28.7	287	746
20 percent credit, 1-year depreciation	38.3	383	996
Reduced interest loans [c]			
6 percent	6.0	60	156
3 percent	12.0	120	312

[a] Assumes capital investment of $2.6 billion (see Table 6).
[b] Assumes 48 percent effective tax rate, 15-year functional life (straight line), 9 percent discount rate, and accelerated depreciation available in tax laws effective in 1965.
[c] Straight reduction loan, 15 years.
Source: Adapted from Allen V. Kneese and Blair T. Bower, *Managing Water Quality: Economics, Technology, Institutions*, Baltimore, Johns Hopkins Press for Resources for the Future, 1969, p. 176.

Water Pollution Control Costs

Estimates of water pollution control costs come in fragmented form and have generated some dispute. Difficulties stem from the fact that water pollution originates from many sources—municipalities, industry, agriculture, mining, etc.—and relatively firm background data are available only for municipalities. Estimates made thus far, therefore, must be regarded as greatly understating costs, since no estimates take into account the cost of cleanup from any sources other than the municipal and industrial.

Table X / Estimated Cost to New Car Buyers of Motor Vehicle
Emission Control Systems, 1968–1974—(Millions)

| Year | Capital investment [a] | | Annual costs | |
	Annual	Cumulative	Annual	Cumulative
1968	$180		$18	
1969	180	$ 360	18	$ 36
1970	360	720	36	72
1971	480	1,200	58	130
1972	480	1,680	58	188
1973	480	2,160	58	246
1974	480	2,640	58	304

[a] Based on costs passed on to new car buyers, not necessarily equal to costs of production (which have not been published). Assumes sale of average of 10 million new cars annually.
Source: Department of Health, Education, and Welfare, based on industry sources.

Table 11 presents estimates, prepared by the Federal Water Quality Administration, for the costs of control of water pollution from industry and municipalities over the period 1965–1974. Industrial outlays for water pollution control over the five-year period up to 1974 will total an estimated $3.3 billion for investment plus an additional $3.2 billion for operating expenses. Moreover, these estimates do not include the costs of preventing thermal pollution, expected to require an additional $2 billion over the five-year period.

Municipal control costs will run even higher than those for industry. Investment needs for waste treatment plants are estimated at $10 billion over the five-year period, and operating charges at an additional $3 billion. In addition, cities must contend with the problems of combined sewer overflows, not taken into account in Table 11; the solution of this problem has been estimated (by the American Public Works Association) to call for an outlay of between $15 and $48 billion.

It should be noted, moreover, the FWQA estimates have been challenged by the cities as too low. The National League of Cities and the U.S. Conference of Mayors have announced an estimate, based on the results of a special survey of cities, counties, and special districts, of $33 to $37 billion over the period 1970–1976.

Summary

On the basis of the preceding tables and discussion, what can be said about the cost of controlling pollution?

Table XI / *Annual Outlays for Water Pollution Control, 1965–1974*
(Millions)

Year	Industrial outlays		Municipal outlays			Total annual outlays
	Investment	Operating charges	Investment		Operating charges	
			Treatment works	Collection		
1965	$640	$200	$476	$355	$270	$1,940
1966	780	270	520	400	295	2,215
1967	565	365	550	505	320	2,306
1968	530	430	655	500	350	2,465
1969	740	515	880	450	410	2,995
1970 [a]	655	555	2,000	[b]	470 [c]	3,680+
1971	655	595	2,000	[b]	530	3,780+
1972	655	635	2,000	[b]	590	3,880+
1973	655	675	2,000	[b]	650	3,980+
1974	655	715	2,000	[b]	710	4,080+

[a] 1970–74 expenditures represent those associated with an investment level that will achieve controls required by water quality standards within the period.
[b] No estimates available.
[c] No estimate of incremental collection operating and maintenance costs.
Source: Federal Water Quality Administration.

A summary of the estimates presented here for air and water control costs appears below. The data generally speaking apply to the first half of the 1970's.

	Five-year total costs (billions)
Air Pollution	
Total annual costs in 100 metropolitan areas (industry and municipalities)	$5.6
Tri-level government outlays for research, development, abatement, and control	1.7
Consumer outlays—amounts to be passed on to new car buyers (under 1969 Federal standards):	
Capital investment	2.3
Annual costs	.3

Water Pollution
Municipal outlays:

Waste treatment plants	13.0+
Sewer overflows	15.0-48.0[14]

Industry outlays:

Industrial abatement costs	6.4
Thermal pollution	2.0

As has been shown, numerous limitation apply to any set of estimates of the costs of pollution control, including those presented here. One factor of importance is the practical problem of isolating the amounts which are incremental to those now being spent. It has been estimated that total spending for pollution control in the United States—from government and private funds—now ranges between $20 and $40 billion.[15] Although it would be exceedingly difficult to back up any single estimate, it is certain that a great deal of money is already being spent to control pollution.

Another limiting factor in projecting costs into the future is that estimates must be based on some assumed level of standards and will be under or overstated to the degree that actuality happens to correspond with the assumptions. Experience to date suggests underestimates will be more likely than the reverse, since standards are rapidly becoming more stringent, and costs rise sharply as 100 percent control is approached.

The estimates presented in this chapter, it should be noted, apply only to air and water pollution. They do not take into account the costs of coping with pollution from feedlot wastes, fertilizers and pesticides, sediment and erosion, mine drainage, oil spills, watercraft wastes, and various other sources. Moreover, there presumably will be expenditures for control of other kinds of pollution—for instance, noise and radiation. So little is known at present about the effects and possibilities for control of such pollutants, no estimates of costs can possibly be attempted.

The question of the costs of pollution control would not be complete without taking note of the existence of various types of costs which cannot be quantified. These include, for instance, the dislocations which ensue if, as happens sometimes, a firm discovers it cannot meet pollution control standards while continuing to operate one or more plants at a profit. When such a firm faces reality by closing its doors forever, the resulting unemployment can lead to serious but unmeasurable human costs. The demand for pollution control equipment will put even more stress on already strained capital markets. Because many commodities will cost more to produce, international competitiveness may be weakened or even destroyed, and consumers will find they can buy less with a given amount of income. Possibly such price increases as have already resulted from the costs of pollution control may have been a significant factor aggravating general inflationary pressures. For some areas and some industries with special problems, the hardships may prove substantial for some years to come. Ultimately, however, everyone will bear the brunt of the cost of pollution control, either through higher prices or higher taxes.

NOTES

[1] See p. 495 for description of areas and regions.

[2] Secretary of Health, Education, and Welfare. *Air Pollution Abatement by Federal Facilities* (Sen. Doc. 91-10, 91st Congress, 1st Session.), Government Printing Office: March 1969, 27 pp.

[3] Under provisions of the Tax Reform Act of 1969, a 60-month write-off is allowed for pollution control equipment added to plants which were in operation before January 1, 1969, if the equipment is placed in service before January 1, 1975.

[4] U.S. Secretary of Health, Education and Welfare. *The Cost of Clean Air* (91st Congress, 1st sess. Sen. Doc. No. 91-40; Washington, D.C.; Government Printing Office, 1969), p. 11.

[5] Some researchers have attempted to make such measurements for specific areas. See Ronald G. Ridker, *Economic Costs of Air Pollution,* New York: Praeger, 1967, pp. 141–151; Richard D. Wilson and David W. Minotte, "A Cost-Benefit Approach to Air Pollution Control," *Journal of the Air Pollution Control Association,* May 1969, pp. 303–308.

[6] Ridker, *op. cit.,* p. 231. For St. Louis survey, see Ridker and J. A. Henning, "The Determinants of Residential Property Values with Special Reference to Air Pollution," *Review of Economics and Statistics,* May 1967, pp. 246–257.

[7] The financing of pollution control raises many difficult problems for a firm. See, for instance, W. James Lopp, "Alternative Methods of Financing Waste Treatment Facilities," *Journal Water Pollution Control Federation,* February 1970, pp. 291–297; *The Economic Impact of the Capital Outlays Required to Attain the Water Quality Standards of the Federal Water Pollution Control Act,* prepared by Eastman Dillon, Union Securities and Co. for U.S. Department of the Interior, 1968, 227 pp.

[8] For one extremely detailed proposal and analysis, see J. H. Dales, *Pollution, Property and Prices,* Toronto, University of Toronto Press, 1968, pp. 77–100.

[9] See Section IV for discussion of problems encountered in setting stan-

dards. Under presnt knowledge and technology, this first step may be extremely difficult and even impossible.

[10] The Ohio River Valley Water Sanitation Commission (ORSANCO), with two decades of highly successful interstate cooperation, illustrates the results which can be achieved through regional regulatory activity. The Ohio River and its 19 major tributaries pass through a heavily populated, highly industrialized area covering 155,000 square miles in 14 states. As the Ohio Valley developed, untreated sewage and industrial wastes brought the Ohio drainage basin to an acute condition. Severe droughts in 1930 and 1934, by reducing water supply, made both aesthetic and public health dangers so visible that in 1936 Congress yielded to increasing public demand for interstate action by authorizing negotiation of a compact. A commission agreed on terms of a compact in 1938, and by 1940 six of the affected states had accepted the compact and Congress had approved it. Other states accepted later; in mid-1948, the compact became effective. The cooperating states agreed to join in the abatement of existing pollution and the control of future pollution, pledging to enact any necessary legislation to achieve the goals. The compact authorizes ORSANCO to obtain compliance with its standards through various appropriate forms of legal action. In practice, ORSANCO rarely has used this power—only six times during its first two decades of operation—usually eliciting compliance through education and persuasion.

[11] Expenditures for research and development by Federal agencies other than the National Air Pollution Control Administration are not included.

[12] Present Federal law permits 5-year amortization of pollution control facilities, plus retention of the first year additional 20 percent depreciation available for other categories of property.

[13] See page 482.

[14] Estimated total costs, depending on the alternatives chosen.

[15] Senator James B. Pearson, "Are Nixon Administration Moves to Date a Sound Response to Problems of Pollution?" *Congressional Digest*, Vol. 49, No. 8–9 (August-September, 1970), p. 208.

CONCLUSION

THE ROLE OF THE CITIZEN IN THE ENVIRONMENTAL CRISIS

The preceding readings have covered a variety of solutions including a wide range of environmental problems from population to aesthetics. One important aspect of the environmental crisis which has received little attention in the readings concerns the role of the citizen in upgrading the environment. It is the author's intention at this point to suggest ways in which the reader can bring about an improved environment by (1) altering his life style to a limited extent and (2) bringing to bear his influence on government and the private sector.

No serious attempt has been made to produce a comprehensive, detailed guide for citizen action including all the dos and don'ts, the hows and whys. Each person will have to decide what programs and projects are most critical in his particular area. Hopefully, this material will serve as a quick guide and stimulus to indicate some of the ways the public can bring about changes in his immediate environment as well as in the nation's environmental programs and policies.[1]

Some Changes in Personal Life Style

Probably the hardest and yet a most important method of demonstrating deep commitment to an improved environment is to follow a way of life that contributes as little as possible to the already overwhelming amount of pollution. It is easy to become confused and frustrated when trying to alter accepted life patterns in favor of a life style contrary to the established model. Yet in small, seemingly insignificant ways individuals can have an immense, cumulative impact by reducing their contribution to the pollution problem. In the sections which follow, each aspect of the environmental crisis dealt with in the preceding chapters is examined with a view to pointing out some of the ways by which this goal can be achieved.

I. *Population:* Population control involves one of the most critical questions facing the individual. Increasingly, couples are deciding that they want to limit the size of their families, enabling them to combine more personal freedom with higher standards for fewer children. A small but rapidly increasing number of parents—male more than female—are undergoing sterilization, usually after the birth of their second or third child. Many more are relying on effective birth control methods to prevent unwanted pregnancies. Unfortunately, too many families are waiting until they have had three or four children before adopting birth control measures. Since it has been shown that even with two-child families population in the United States will continue to grow at alarming speed through the early decades of the next century, parents committed to preserving the environment and our natural resources will take it upon themselves to have no more than two offspring; those who want larger families can adopt additional children.

II. *Air Pollution:* The individual's primary impact in this area can be in reducing the amount of pollution from automobiles, which generally account for over 50 percent of air pollutants. First, alternatives to the automobile should be considered: walking, bicycle riding and public transportation. Second, maximum use should be made of motor vehicles when there is no alternative; use car pools. Third, the automobile's pollution power should be kept as low as possible: cars serviced regularly and driven at moderate speeds only; air conditioners and leaded gas avoided; engines not allowed to idle for extended periods of time; emission control devices added and kept in good working order; small cars preferred to large cars. In general, private automobiles ought to be used as little as is reasonably possible.

Because the fuel-powered generating plant constitutes a major source of air pollution, it is important to evaluate ways in which electricity is used in the home so that power can be conserved wherever possible. It is useful to keep in mind the wattage rating of each home appliance per hour of use. Accurate records on how often and how long appliances are used may suggest ways to reduce their use —and cut electric bills. Secondly, marginally useful appliances such as electric can openers might be avoided; when purchasing new appliances preference might be given to those that require no power or less power. Finally, reducing use of electricity during the peak consumption periods in the early evening (5 to 7 p.m.) is important. To meet peak demands at that time of day, new power plants are built which otherwise would not be needed.

III. *Water Pollution:* Decreasing consumption of electricity is just as important in preserving the quality of our water systems as it is in attacking air pollution. Heating and lighting usage (and costs) in the home can be reduced by: (1) keeping thermostats low, insulating

Electricity Consumption

Appliance	Typical Wattage	Appliance	Typical Wattage
Air Conditioner (Room)	800–2700	Lawn Mower	250
Blanket, electric	200	Range	8000–16000
Broiler-Rotisserie	1320–1650	Built-in Oven	4800
Can Opener	200	Sewing Machine	75
Coffee Maker or Percolator	440–1000	Television (B&W)	90–175
Clothes Dryer	4500–9000	Television (Color)	195–360
Dishwasher-Waste Disposer	1500	Toaster	up to 1150
Food Blender	230–250	Waffle Iron	up to 1100
Freezer	350	Washing Machine (Automatic)	700
Heater	1000–1500	Waste Disposer	500
Iron (Hand)	1000	Water Heater	2000–4500

Source: *Ecology At Home*, pp. 12–13.

houses to keep the heat in, heating only rooms in current use; and (2) making use of fewer lights, natural light and lower wattage bulbs.

Hand washing of small amounts of dishes and laundry is preferable to machine washing because it requires less water (and no power); a washing machine should be fully loaded; and water should not be allowed to run unnecessarily. Water heaters should be turned down low not only to save water but because heaters consume substantial amounts of power.

Another major problem in curing water pollution is detergents. Americans are obsessed with cleanliness and, as a result, there is considerable competition to manufacture increasingly powerful detergents to cope with the daily accumulation of soil and dirt. The major source of the problem focuses on the phosphates used in many detergents. These may rid our clothes of dirt and grime, but they also have an unpleasant effect on our water systems by rapidly increasing the process of eutrophication. As a result, many manufacturers are quickly developing new detergents which will hopefully clean as effectively as phosphates but do not destroy our natural water resources.

Detergents present a very complex problem to the consumer who wants to contribute as little to the pollution problem as he can. Many new detergents intended to replace the phosphates are advertised as biodegradable but they can still contain phosphates or other harmful chemicals.[2] Thus, as a general guide, it is safer to use soap instead of detergents; avoid all use of presoaks and water softeners and use liquid dishwashing detergents (although these present another problem since they are marketed in a plastic, non-biodegradable bottle). For all around cleaning purposes one of the most effective cleaners is ammonia and water. Washing soda and water is another good, non-polluting cleaner.

Pesticides and insecticides provide another source of water pollution just as perplexing as the detergent problem. Much debate has been heard in the past few years over the potentially harmful effects of such long lived pesticides as DDT and other hydrocarbons. It has been difficult to demonstrate the effect of these poisons on man, although a number of fish and birds have clearly shown damage to their systems due to the intake of pesticides. Other pesticides are increasingly being substituted wherever possible, although as new methods are tried new problems seem to arise. At a 1971 meeting of the American Medical Association, for example, a toxicologist reported that second-generation pesticides which are replacing DDT and related poisons are capable of interacting in the body with such common drugs as tranquilizers and antihistamines, with potentially fatal results.[3] The best approach is to use as little of these pesticides as possible. In addition, experiment with natural methods of controlling insects: birds, toads, lizards, spiders and most snakes are harmless and helpful in the garden, happily and greedily devouring insects; herbs are excellent insect repellents, besides adding beauty to gardens and flavor to food; certain flowers (marigolds and other members of the chrysanthemum family, for example) protect the garden because they are insect free and help to protect nearby plants. Beyond nature's way, hope rests with the development of new non-polluting chemical techniques of dealing with the insect problem.

Also, with respect to gardens and lawns, it is important to avoid use, as much as possible, of artificial fertilizers. These are also composed of phosphates and other chemicals which produce harmful effects when drained into water systems.

One alternative to chemical fertilization is the compost heap. Compost heaps can be used for fertilizing both gardens and lawns. There are many methods of constructing a compost heap and since such a project requires space, time and effort, one can purchase compost or natural fertilizers from nurseries. Compost techniques can be applied directly to the garden: pet dogs can be invaluable—their droppings can be buried to enrich the soil and keep flies from breeding; coffee grounds or grass cuttings can be spread as mulch, or can be worked into the soil.

IV. *Noise Pollution:* Many of the noise problems encountered in everyday life are produced by machines purchased to make life easier or more entertaining and levels inside or outside the home are too often uncomfortably and unnecessarily high. Use of a hand mower instead of a gasoline powered mower would contribute less noise—and no air or water pollution—in addition to reducing waist lines. Turning down the volume on television sets, radios and phonographs contributes to the art of conversation, family harmony, good hearing and good neighbors.

The other major source of noise is the automobile and other motor vehicles. People who cannot do without an automobile (or motor-bike) should make certain that it is equipped with effective mufflers and other devices to control the noise level. Other vehicles, like the motorcycle and snowmobile, whose producers market virility with their decibels, should be avoided like the unsafe plague they are.

Because much of the noise is produced outside the control of the individual and the home environment, it is necessary to resort to methods of preventing noise from intruding into the home. This can be done partly through sound proofing within the house and by strategically placing fences and hedges outside as a kind of perimeter defense.

V. *Land Use:* This is not an area easily influenced by the individual in his daily life style. The only possibility of changing present land use practices is through the negative means of *not* doing certain things: not buying or building houses on erodable hills, wetlands or dunes unsuitable for development; not selling or contributing space for billboards. In some cases, a person might also deed portions of his property (or property easements) for conservation purposes.

VI. *Aesthetics:* This is an area in which the individual can through very simple means have a significant impact on his immediate environment. Probably the easiest project to undertake is that of beautifying the home. Structures should be kept in good repair; flowers, shrubs and trees are always a net gain and also help to counter the air pollution and noise problem. Apartment dwellers in large cities can participate in such activities as well. No landlord would prevent a tenant from helping to improve the appearance of his building and some might even contribute paint and plantings if the tenant would volunteer the time and effort.

VII. *Solid Waste Disposal:* The citizen can have a significant impact on the solid waste problem because he is the one responsible for producing much of it. Much waste is unnecessary: in the frugal New England tradition: 'wear it out, use it up, make it do.'

Before making purchases it is well to consider how the packaging can be used or recycled. First preference should go to those products with no packaging, next to items in reusable or returnable containers, and finally to those in recyclable containers. Purchases of products in non-recyclable and especially non-biodegradable packages should be avoided.

Other ways of cutting down on trash include: carrying personal cloth or canvas shopping bags; using more elegant and non-disposable cloth napkins and towels whenever possible; eliminating use of disposable cups, plates and glasses; reducing use of plastic wrap, wax paper and aluminum foil; returning clothes hangers to cleaning establishments; reworking or donating outgrown or worn clothing to goodwill agencies. In general, it is better to reuse glass jars or tin cans, rather than disposing of them or purchasing other items. It is useful to remember that despite warnings of higher costs and added inconvenience, good ecology can have a salutary effect on the bank account. The counterculture, the whole earth communards, have much to teach us about achieving a low cost harmony between man and his environment.[4]

Citizen Action

A person may feel he is powerless to confront the behemoth organizations of our society in both the public and private sector which seemingly control his life, but in truth the individual can effectively influence the decision-making process of government at all levels and of business and industry. An important rule which cannot be overstated is that by joining with others who share similar concerns it is possible to achieve an impact even on change-resistant systems.

Recent experience in the environmental field indicates that there are a number of methods available for affecting improvements in government and business policies and practices. It is important to remember that no single approach works all of the time; each aspect of the environmental crisis requires a different tactic or combination of tactics. To complicate the situation further, some types of action are effective at one level of government and less potent at another.

Container	Potential for Reuse or Reclamation
Glass Jars & Bottles	Ecologically a good buy. They can be reused in numerous ways around the house or fashioned into other useful objects. Preference should be given to returnable bottles.
Tin Cans	These are also being recycled by metal recovery plants and can be reused in many ways around the house.
Mixed Metal Cans	These have aluminum pop tops and side seams. They are being recycled by the can companies, but the difficulty in separating the metals makes the process more troublesome.
Aluminum	Although aluminum is non-biodegradable, it is being recycled. Remember, the manufacture of aluminum requires six times more electricity than steel, from which tin cans are made. Aluminum foil, pie tins and frozen food containers may be recycled, too. Never throw aluminum away!
Aerosol Cans	These are not being recycled and are extremely dangerous when burned—they explode. Avoid wherever possible!
Uncoated Cardboard & Paper	These are not being recycled and their manufacture consumes vast amounts of paper. Avoid!
Coated Cardboard	These include, for example, milk and cottage cheese cartons. They are covered with a plastic which makes them non-biodegradable. Try to buy milk in returnable glass bottles. If this cannot be done, limit purchases of coated cartons and reuse them wherever possible.
Plastics	These are not ecologically sound from any point of view. Their reuse is limited; they are not being recycled; and they are highly undisposable. Avoid!
Compressed Paper	Such as egg cartons and some meat trays. These are made from recycled newspaper and may be recycled again. Encourage their use, especially in supermarket meat trays instead of plastics.
Excess Packaging	Boxes that contain bottles or tubes and many other forms of excess packaging are wasteful and unnecessary. Avoid buying these products or express your opinion by leaving the excess with your grocer or by mailing it back to the manufacturer.

Source: *Ecology at Home*, pp. 21–22.

And the private sector is a different ball game. Discussion of citizen action, therefore, must focus on each area of the pollution problem to determine tactics which are likely to yield significant results. After discussing these methods separately, an attempt will be made to show how each of these techniques can be applied to the environmental problems examined in this book.

I. *Environmental Organizations:* The simplest and easiest approach is to join forces with other concerned citizens in already established environmental organizations. A number of such groups have been in existence for some time and new ones are constantly springing up. (A list of some of the most prominent organizations can be found at the end of this essay.)

These organizations require little of the individual but continued financial support and occasional visits, telegrams or letters to persons in critical decision-making positions. The organization's professional staff, supported through membership fees and contributions, lobbies in government circles to persuade decision-makers to pass legislation, establish strict control regulations, etc. The effectiveness of such groups is based largely on the fact that legislators (and candidates for public office) are made aware of the size and concern of the organization's membership, whose voting power may be felt when a legislator next goes to the electorate asking to be returned to office. Few legislators care to face the risk of alienating a politically active organization which is obviously working in favor of the public interest.

II. *Creating New Task Forces:* When established organizations do not exist to deal with a specific problem, the individual may want to create a new permanent or ad hoc organization. This type of undertaking requires a great deal of effort and commitment on the part of everyone involved, particularly those who initiate such an operation. Chances are good, however, that the response will be rewarding, especially if the organization focuses on a specific, deeply felt local issue.[5]

A variety of methods can be employed, similar to those of the large established organizations: writing letters and meeting with government officials, enlisting the cooperation of the news media to get important project publicity, conducting campaigns by telephone and mail to encourage others to join the cause and contribute time and money, seeking the assistance of local professionals who might contribute their expertise in preparing publicity materials or background resource information useful in convincing other citizens and public officials of the program's merits. Because of widespread concern over the nation's environmental problems, many people are willing to help on a specific issue when shown how they might participate.

III. *Guerilla Activities:* There are other less conventional ways by which an individual can express his concern over the pollution practices of the private sector. Some have already been tried, without great success to date, and additional methods are constantly being devised.

Ralph Nader and others, for example, have tried to work through the leverage of company stockholders to change harmful practices and policies. Moreover, an employee whose company contributes to pollution must consider his responsibility for 'blowing the whistle' by releasing information available on company operations detrimental to the public interest so that government regulatory agencies or the courts can take appropriate corrective measures.

Another important potential source of influence on business operations are employee unions. Well organized, many of these groups could exert tremendous pressure on business to alter practices that contribute to pollution. As yet, unions have been primarily concerned with pay rates and fringe benefits, but they could assist in creating a better living environment for themselves as well as the rest of the population if they would also manifest concern over the environment they are helping to produce.

IV. *Class Action Suits:* The first three approaches described above are focused largely on the legislative and administrative processes by helping to create new legislation, new programs, etc. Nevertheless, to enforce, reform or change laws already on the books, environmentalists are turning to the legal system as an increasingly effective tool. To enact legislation and establish regulations does not mean automatic compliance by the private sector or even public agencies; the legal system is especially important in forcing polluters to abide by legal standards and regulations. Moreover, as polluters are increasingly forced into compliance, they may serve as encouraging examples to other would-be violators. But there may well be a continuing need for guerilla legal action against public and private polluters.[6] In any event, it is possible for groups of citizens (and in some jurisdictions a single citizen) to initiate effective action against polluters.

A. *Population:* Efforts to control population growth should be concentrated on the state and national governments. To one degree or another, unfortunately, many states prohibit citizens from obtaining and doctors from distributing birth control information. At both levels, the important emphasis is presently to pass legislation which allows the dissemination of birth control and family planning information to everyone wishing to receive it. A network of family planning centers, particularly in urban and rural slum areas is indispensable for the delivery of this vital service.

Liberal abortion laws have been successfully established in only a few states, most notably New York. New York's recent experience with its considerably relaxed abortion law has certainly demonstrated the need for safe, low-cost abortion services. In the author's view the availability of effective means of birth control will almost obviate the need for large numbers of abortions, but abortion services should nevertheless be available as a backstop for the ignorant, the lazy, the forgetful and the mentally retarded.

On the federal level, major emphasis should be placed on supporting research to develop new birth control techniques. There is yet to be developed a birth control method that is simple, low cost, and 100 percent safe and effective. If the United States is going to try to prevent unwanted births as a first step in reducing population growth rates, it is imperative that new techniques be made available. The federal government is best suited to fund this research. In addition, ample federal funds are needed to bring family planning services to urban and rural low income areas.

Citizen action is probably best focused on membership in the Planned Parenthood organization, as well as other local organizations having similar goals, and legal action. The Planned Parenthood organization is active in trying to liberalize abortion and birth control laws and in weakening traditional opposition to such legislation. Through legal action, some attempts have been made to have strict state laws declared unconstitutional. Although this approach has had little success to date, it is worth pursuing.

At the international level, Americans can also influence the rapid increase in population growth rates which many countries, especially the underdeveloped ones, are experiencing. The United Nations offers the best mechanism for making birth control information available to large numbers of people throughout the world as well as assisting in the various national family planning programs. The United States through the programs of the Agency for International Development (A.I.D.) and the Ford Foundation has contributed greatly to many of these programs (See Chapter I) and citizen support of these programs can enhance their effectiveness.

B. *Air Pollution:* Pressure to improve the fight against air pollution can be manifested at the local, state and national levels. The emphasis, however, is somewhat different at each layer of government. At the local level, citizens should be concerned that standards are adequate and regulations are enforced. This means that when evidence of a violation is available, the citizen should assume personal responsibility for making such violations known and if necessary in prodding enforcement officials to take the required steps to force the violator into compliance. If the efforts of a single citizen are not sufficient it would then be important to enlist the assistance of existing citizen groups interested in this problem or if necessary creating a new organization. Notification of the problem to the local news media and publicity given to the violation might embarrass the violator into compliance, particularly if the news release is accompanied by suitably damning photographs.

At the state level, emphasis should be placed on the establishment of strict air pollution control standards. Within the guidelines of the federal legislation, air quality control standards are required to meet only the minimum requirements. It is left to the state to decide whether it wishes to have stricter standards than the federal law stipulates. In this area the public can play an important role. The citizen can join local groups concerned with the problem, including scientists, engineers and lawyers, and lobby elected representatives to establish high standards.

Also at the state level, it is important to establish effective, enforceable regulations. Professionals, lawyers as well as engineers, can play an important role in helping to convince sympathetic legislators that standards will remain ineffective if enforceable regulations are not established and in discouraging or punishing recalcitrant legislators who seem to be overly sensitive to the wishes of polluters.

At the federal level, stress should be placed on increasing allocation of funds for research into pollution control devices. Other problem areas also need to be explored: use of air rights over highways and the possibility of harmful effects, and the difficulty of devising land use controls to reduce or limit the effects of air pollution. Highest priority should be given to developing a replacement for the internal combustion engine, since the automobile is the single largest contributor to air pollution. Only the federal government is in a position to force the entire automotive industry into altering the internal mechanism of motor vehicles to meet stringent standards.

C. *Water Pollution:* At both the state and local level the most important goal of the concerned citizen should be the prompt authorization of the requisite bond issues for the construction of sewage treatment facilities. This is probably the most expensive problem facing the nation in the environmental field. The sooner the public faces up to the costs involved and legislators accept the responsibility for approving funds for treatment facilities and sewers the sooner we will improve the quality of our water systems. Citizens must make it clear to their elected representatives that they are willing to finance the necessary construction programs and attendant maintenance costs.

At the state level also, citizens must be concerned with the enforcement of water pollution control laws. Through legal suits, if such action is necessary, and the efforts of citizen groups, attempts should be made to stop polluters, whether they are corporations or municipalities, and force them to provide the means for cleaning up the effluent before it is released into public waterways.

At the federal level, stronger standards should be established with the support of active citizen group lobbying efforts. It would also be helpful to persuade federal legislators of the need to provide funds for the construction of treatment plant facilities to augment and stimulate efforts of fiscally overburdened state and local governments.

D. *Noise Pollution:* Few effective noise control ordinances are on the books today; most state and local laws are difficult if not impossible to enforce. In this area more than in any other aspect of the environmental field, the citizen-enforcer role is very important. Excessive noise levels from automobiles or other sources are difficult to identify. Thus, the citizen who is annoyed by loud record players, motorcycles or the like must take on the exasperating responsibility of informing the authorities of the nuisance. Nevertheless, major emphasis should be placed on devising more effective noise control ordinances. The California motor vehicle law offers one example.

At the federal level, more research is needed into the effects of noise from various sources and the means for controlling these noises, and the development of products with lower noise levels. Also, major enemies of a quieter environment, such as the manufacturing, construction and aircraft industries, must be persuaded to control excessive noises emitted by their products.

E. *Land Use:* Legislation in this area lags far behind what is needed to cope with a multitude of problems. Some legislation is on the books; it is not well enforced and much can be done simply by improving present enforcement procedures. For example, steps should be taken to see that legislation enacted to control billboards is enforced through state and federal action.

Generally, however, present legislation is inadequate. Additional legislation should be supported by the public to provide new mechanisms, planning powers and funding capability, for controlling development and protecting the nation's land and water resources. One model, described earlier in the book, is the Urban Development Corporation (UDC) of New York. Powers such as those granted the UDC might well be made available to other, similar organizations elsewhere in the nation. Another example of effective land use legislation is Hawaii's statewide land use law.

Whatever the approach, concerned citizens working through their elected officials should try to promote powerful new land use legislation. The assistance of many environmental groups and the legal profession might be enlisted in this cause.

At the federal level, the concern is much the same. The President and the Congress should be persuaded to enact a National Land Use Policy. Although proposals have been advanced to make such a policy a reality, they remain in the rhetoric stage. Support for a national, uniform policy is increasing, however, and additional public pressure will help speed it along to enactment.

F. *Aesthetics:* The emphasis here should be on the state and local levels. At the local level, for example, residents of neighborhoods could join together to establish local parks, cleaning up debris from vacant lots, planting trees and flowers in open areas, establishing playgrounds and in other ways improving the environment in which they live.

At both the state and local levels, efforts might also be directed at preserving areas and structures of historic or cultural importance. The establishment of historic preservation districts within cities is worthy of emulation by all communities which have not yet permitted the complete destruction of their historic and architectural heritage.

Furthermore, standards of excellence in the design of public buildings should be sought. Boston's City Hall, described by Ada Louise Huxtable, is an example of the outstanding architectural achievements of which government is capable. Boston's City Hall was expensive, it is true, but it is the one major new achievement for which the city is renowned throughout the world. Its citizens should be justifiably proud.

At the federal level, citizen action should encourage the allocation of funds to preserve landmarks of value to the nation's history. Additional protection should be given to areas of natural beauty, the national park system, trails, lakes and rivers which might otherwise be sacrificed to the bulldozer. Once lost, these precious resources can never be regained.

Citizens should also be concerned about the attractiveness of the nation's highway system. The U.S. Department of Transportation has made some attempt to encourage highway builders to make highways pleasing to look at and to cause as little disruption to the landscape as is at all possible. These efforts should be praised and the approach adopted by every highway department in the nation.

G. *Solid Waste Disposal:* The trend in this area is toward recycling materials for future use, especially when these products are not easily disposed or cannot be reused. To facilitate the recycling of valuable materials, it is important to establish the necessary procedures for doing so and, as Grinstead has pointed out, alter the present attitudes of our economy from one of use and dispose to that of use and reuse. Many industries, paper, glass, plastic, tin can, etc., have already indicated a willingness to make adjustments to provide reclamation centers where used materials can be brought for recycling. Unfortunately, this has not been done on a large scale and consumers wishing to return used materials must often travel long distances to do so. Pressure from citizen groups would encourage industries to expand their efforts at recycling and merchants might be persuaded to accept used materials for collection and subsequent return to centralized reclamation centers.

The procedures for recycling used materials are not necessarily complicated and many industries have proven that it can be profitable to recycle. Part of the problem is the public: To what extent is the citizen willing to make the extra effort required for recycling? Some merchants are discovering that if people can buy an ecologically sound product they will do so—just so long as there is no added inconvenience or expense. When the public must pay more or expend more effort for the 'good' product, it is apt to purchase the ecologically unsound product instead. If this reflects the extent of the public's commitment to improving the environment, there is no reason for business and industry to promote environmentally sound products. It is up to the citizen to convince the corporate world that it is committed to environmental quality despite added cost and inconvenience. Once this has been accomplished, better products will be forthcoming and expanded recycling programs will be instituted.

At the federal level, pressure should be applied to have the government encourage business to develop new, easily disposable products and incorporate the recycling process into the production process. A combination of legislative and economic incentives from the government and unrelenting pressure from the consumer will prompt the businesses of the United States, and foreign companies as well, to meet environmentally improved standards.

And at all government levels, especially in campaign seasons, the citizen should be alert and energetic, working to support political candidates committed by deed as well as word to the environmental cause. He must also seek by every means available to defeat political allies of the polluters. The ballot is the citizen's heavy artillery and it must be used on target. There has already been some success in picking off some of the most notorious politicians and bureaucrats on the wrong side of pollution issues. The defeat of the SST against heavy administration pressure suggests that the tide is running in the right direction. Hopefully publicity, organization and votes will prove powerful medicine. Tools and allies of the polluters will be pushed into the political graveyard—unless they undergo a timely and miraculous conversion. (The latter alternative has many recent and historic precedents.)

Finally there is the touchy question of extra-legal action. To pose a more-than-hypothetical scenario, when all else fails, it is conceivable that a community, neighborhood or citizen group distinctly unhappy with a state's failure to eliminate offensive billboards and equally unwilling to give localities the right to do so, may be willing to dramatize this glaring failure with the use of a chainsaw. With a little exercise of the imagination other scenarios relating to air and water polluters can be devised. Depending on circumstances and the degree of commitment, civil disobedience, leading to test cases to dramatize ecological problems may serve as an effective last resort.

NOTES

[1] Many of the suggestions included, as well as many other worthwhile recommendations not mentioned here, can be found in *Ecology at Home: How Your Housekeeping Habits Can Help Save Our Environment*, edited by Jacqueline Killeen (San Francisco, California: 101 Productions, 1971).

[2] After extensive publicity about the dangers of phosphates and the subse-

quent development of new detergents containing caustic acid and NTA among other cleansers, the federal government in the fall of 1971 reversed direction and recommended the general public return to the use of phosphate detergents and money be appropriated to clean up the resulting water pollution. Assuming funds will be made available for a greatly expanded program of constructing sewage treatment plants, the phosphate detergents are apparently less potentially harmful to humans. Unfortunately, considering present and past levels of funding, it is unlikely that adequate treatment facilities can be made available in the near future. The result of this discussion is only to confuse and frustrate the consumer and to leave him with little in the way of reasonable solutions to the pollution problems. (*The New York Times*, September 16, 1971, pp. 1, 20.)

[3] Richard A. Knox, "Substitute Pesticides Called Peril," *The Boston Globe*, June 24, 1971, p. 2.

[4] *The Last Whole Earth Catalog: Access to Tools* (Portola Institute, 1971).

[5] Saul D. Alinsky, *Reveille for Radicals* (Chicago: University of Chicago Press, 1945) and "From Citizen Apathy to Participation," Paper presented at Association of Community Councils of Chicago, October, 1957.

[6] An excellent source of information on this approach is Joseph L. Sax's *Defending the Environment: A Strategy for Citizen Action* (New York: Alfred A. Knopf, Inc., 1970).

CONCERNED ORGANIZATIONS

Citizens Committee on Natural Resources
        1346 Connecticut Avenue, N.W.
        Washington, D.C. 20036
(To influence legislation in behalf of conservation. Seeks to inform the public of matters before the Congress and alert the Congress to the thinking of conservation leaders and organizations.)

The Conservation Foundation
        1250 Connecticut Avenue, N.W.
        Washington, D.C. 20036
(Conducts research, education and information programs to develop knowledge, improve techniques, and stimulate public and private decision-making and action to improve the quality of the environment. Carries out environmental studies, demonstration planning programs, and offers a variety of conservation services at home and abroad.)

The Conservation Law Society of America
        1500 Mills Tower
        San Francisco, California 94104

(Nonprofit, tax-exempt organization, providing services of a legal staff on a fee basis to research and accumulate the laws, decisions and other precedents relative to conservation problems; to advise conservation groups on the basis of such research; and to represent these groups in court when necessary.)

Friends of the Earth
    451 Pacific Avenue
    San Francisco, California 94133
(Organization created specifically to fight openly and actively for legislation on behalf of conserving the environment. Joins with other organizations to fight environmentally harmful legislation and to encourage enforcement of protective legislation. Scrutinizes public officials to find out where they stand on conservation issues. Sets up task forces to study environmental problems.)

Keep America Beautiful, Inc.
    99 Park Avenue
    New York, New York 10016
(Nonprofit, public service organization for the prevention of litter and the preservation and improvement of America's scenic and man-made beauty, urban and rural. Conducts a year-round program of public education to stimulate pride in clean surroundings and a feeling of personal responsibility for the proper disposal of litter.)

League of Women Voters of the U.S.
    1200 17th Street, N.W.
    Washington, D.C. 20036
(Nonprofit organization working to promote political responsibility through informed and active participation of citizens in government.)

National Audubon Society
    1130 5th Avenue
    New York, New York 10028
(To advance understanding of the value and need of conservation of wildlife, plants, soil and water, and the relation of their wise use to human progress.)

National Recreation and Park Association
    1700 Pennsylvania Avenue, N.W.
    Washington, D.C. 20006

(A nonprofit service organization, dedicated to wise use of free time, conservation of natural resources, and beautification of the total American environment.)

National Wildlife Federation
    1412 16th Street, N.W.
    Washington, D.C. 20036
(To create and encourage an awareness among the people of this nation of the need for wise use and proper management of those resources of the earth upon which the lives and welfare of men depend: the soils, the waters, the forests, the minerals, the plantlife, and the wildlife.)

Sierra Club
    1050 Mills Tower
    San Francisco, California 94104
(To explore, enjoy, and protect national scenic resources. The Club's nonprofit program includes wilderness outings, whitewater trips, skiing, mountaineering, knapsacking, films, exhibits, conferences, a library and publishing.)

Water Pollution Control Federation
    3900 Wisconsin Avenue, N.W.
    Washington, D.C. 20016
(Devoted to advancement of fundamental and practical knowledge concerning the nature, collection, treatment, and disposal of domestic and industrial waste waters, and the design, construction, operation, and management of facilities for these purposes.)

NOTE: The National Wildlife Federation publishes a "Conservation Directory" which lists all national, international, regional and state organizations and government agencies in the conservation field. It may be obtained by writing to the Federation's national headquarters in Washington for a modest price.

SUGGESTED READINGS

(In addition to Joseph L. Sax's book mentioned in the notes, the following may be of interest to the reader. Editor)

Garett De Bell (ed.), *The Environmental Handbook: Prepared for the First National Environmental Teach-In* (New York: Ballantine Books, 1969).

The 1970's is our last chance for a future that makes ecological sense. This handbook focuses on some of the major problems of our deteriorating environment, explains the nature of ecology and—most importantly—suggests action that can be taken right now in any community, by any individual.

————, *The Voter's Guide to Environmental Politics: Before, During and After the Election* (New York: Ballantine Books, 1970).

What you need to know to bring about change now. A guide to the major environmental issues—what bills are before Congress which will affect the environment, and how your congressman has been voting on them up to now. There's still time to bring about change, and this is the book to show you how.

Norman J. Landau and Paul D. Rheingold, *The Environmental Law Handbook* (New York: Ballantine Books, 1971).

This book explains the legal remedies in existence now to stop government and industry from destroying our environment.

Paul Swatek, *The User's Guide to the Protection of the Environment* (New York: Ballantine Books, 1970).

The User's Guide gives specific information to the reader on the ways in which he must change; the daily decisions he can make that will improve or deteriorate his environment—which household cleansers contribute the most pollution and which the least, what effects excess packaging has, and what products should be done away with completely.

SUGGESTED PERIODICALS

AMERICAN INSTITUTE OF ARCHITECTS JOURNAL
American Institute of Architects
1735 New York Avenue, N.W.
Washington, DC 20006
Monthly: $5.00 to architects, libraries, etc; $10.00 to all others

AMERICAN INSTITUTE OF PLANNERS JOURNAL
American Institute of Planners
917 15th St., N.W.
Washington, DC 20005
Bi-monthly: $10.00

ARCHITECTURAL RECORD
P.O. Box 430
Hightstown, NJ 08520
Monthly plus mid-May issue: $6.60 to architects, engineers,
etc; $20.00 to all others

DESIGN AND ENVIRONMENT
RC Publications, Inc.
527 Madison Avenue
New York, NY 10022
Quarterly: $11.00; $14.00 foreign

ENVIRONMENT
Committee for Environmental Information
Circulation Dept., Environment
P.O. Box 755
Bridgeton, MO 63044
Monthly: $8.50

ENVIRONMENT ACTION BULLETIN
Emmaus, PA 18049
Weekly: $8.00

ENVIRONMENT REPORTER
Five sections covering State and Federal laws, court decisions
and current developments.
Bureau of National Affairs
1231 25th St., N.W.
Washington, DC 20037
Weekly: $280.00

NATION'S CITIES
> National League of Cities
> 1612 K Street, N.W.
> Washington, DC 20006
> Monthly: $6.00

POPULATION BULLETIN
> Population Reference Bureau, Inc.
> 1755 Massachusetts Ave., N.W.
> Washington, DC 20036
> Bi-monthly: $3.00

PROGRESSIVE ARCHITECTURE
> Reinhold Publishing Corporation
> 600 Summer Street
> Stamford, CT 06904
> Monthly: $6.00 to architects, engineers, etc; $12.00 all others

NOTES ON CONTRIBUTORS

Judith Blake is chairman of the Department of Demography, University of California, Berkeley. She is the author of *Family Structure in Jamaica: The Social Context of Reproduction* (1961).

Azriel Teller is assistant professor of economics at the University of Illinois. His dissertation, "Air Pollution Abatement—An Economic Study Into The Cost of Control," is being prepared for publication.

George H. Hagevik is assistant professor of Urban Planning and Policy Development at Livingston College, Rutgers University in New Jersey. He teaches and does research in the area of environmental quality. He is contributor to a number of professional journals.

Allen V. Kneese is a staff member of Resources for the Future, Inc., in Washington, D.C. He is the author of *Managing Water Quality: Economics, Technology, Institutions* (1968).

E. W. Kenworthy is a journalist with *The New York Times* and frequently writes on topics of environmental concern.

Farley Mowat is a Canadian who has written a number of books including *People of the Deer, The Dog Who Wouldn't Be* and *The Grey Seas Under.*

Charles H. W. Foster is Secretary for Environmental Affairs in Massachusetts. At the time the wetlands legislation was being formulated and finally enacted by the state's General Court, he was the Commissioner of Natural Resources.

Claude A. Armour is Commissioner of the Tennessee Department of Safety. At the time this article was written, he was chief of the Memphis Police and Fire departments.

Ross A. Little is an Automotive Equipment Standard Engineer with the California Highway Patrol. He is a contributor to a number of professional journals.

Peter Hall is a lecturer in economic geography at Birkbeck College, London, where he specializes in the economic geography of cities and the geography of planning. He has written two books on London, *The Industries of London* (1962) and *London 2,000* (1963).

Shirley S. Passow is a planner with the Department of City Planning in New York City. She holds a master's degree in Urban Planning from Columbia University. The data for her analysis of the Stockholm land bank were collected during a visit to Sweden.

Shelley M. Mark is director of Hawaii's Department of Planning and Economic Development.

Andrew J. W. Scheffey is a member of the faculty of Amherst College in Massachusetts.

Wolf Von Eckardt is architecture critic for the *Washington Post*. He is also the author of *The Challenge of Megalopolis*, *Life for Dead Spaces* and *A Place to Live*.

Robert R. Grinstead is a research chemist at the Western Division Research Center of The Dow Chemical Company, Walnut Creek, California. He is a member of the Water Pollution Subcommittee of the Northern California Committee for Environmental Information, and also writes a regular column for several local newspapers.

Bertram B. Johansson is a journalist with the *Christian Science Monitor*.

Ada Louise Huxtable is architecture critic of *The New York Times*. She has also served as assistant curator of architecture at the Museum of Modern Art in New York City and is the author of *Classical New York* and *Pier Luigi Nervi*.

Bernard Rudofsky has held professorships at Yale, and Waseda University of Tokyo and has had two exhibitions at the Museum of Modern Art in New York City. He is also the author of several books, including *Behind the Picture Window* and *Architecture Without Architects*.

Melvin R. Levin is professor of Urban Affairs and director of the Division of Urban Studies at Boston University in Massachusetts. He is the author of several books including *Community and Regional Planning* (1969), *Bureaucrats in Collision* (1971) and *Exploring Urban Problems* (1971).